The MS Autobiography Book

**An Anthology
of Autobiographical Prose & Verse
Written by Persons Who Have
Multiple Sclerosis**

**Compiled & Edited by
Eric Smirnow**

The MS Autobiography Book
was composed, typeset, and published by
Specialized Computer Services
P.O. Box 581
Cedaredge, Colorado 81413
U.S.A.

Inquiries regarding custom printing & publishing are welcomed

Acknowledgments

This anthology exists thanks to the many people who helped me create it, and joined me in seeing the project through to completion. Had this assistance not been available and offered, this book would not have become a reality. In particular, I would like to express my appreciation and gratitude to the following:

⊷⊶ ⬧⧫⬧ ⊷⊶

Special thanks to the Colorado Chapter of the National MS Society and Dianne Williams for the initial go-ahead with soliciting writing from potential contributors in the Colorado Chapter's newsletter. Thanks, too, to all the branch and chapter offices of the NMSS in the U. S. A., and MS Societies in other countries everywhere who printed my solicitation for submission of manuscripts. Thanks, also, to others who "spread the word" about this project while it was underway.

Thanks to Colorado Rehabilitation Services and Jim Page, for helping me acquire the computer hardware and software necessary to do this job. This book would not exist were it not for that help.

Thanks to Barbara J. Ettner, for her initial input way back when, sharing her ideas for the book with me, and for her help with the beginning of its creation.

Thanks to all the contributors and others who inquired about the project, whether published or not. Thanks also to everyone who offered ideas and suggestions, and also to those people who offered to help me out with one thing or another as time went on.

Thanks to Sharon Alfaro for her dedicated and invaluable help with the tedious task of proofreading.

Thanks to Vicki Cook, Director of the Western Slope Branch of the NMSSC for her encouragement with the project when I needed it, which was more often than I'd like to admit..

Thanks to Mike Magnuson Photography, Excelsior, Minnesota, for his beautiful photograph of Split Rock Lighthouse which graces the cover of this book.

Thanks to my father, Virgil Smirnow, for his suggestions, comments, constructive criticisms, encouragement, and financial assistance with the printing of my book.

And last, but certainly not least — a *very* special thanks to "S" — for her comments about the various manuscripts, her help with reviewing the first draft of the book, and with initial proofreading. Lastly, and most importantly, I thank her for just being herself, and for being my friend.

— The Editor

Foreword

Multiple sclerosis is nothing if not paradoxical. As random and ruthless as a serial killer, it also cracks open the shells of pretense and reveals gifts of the human spirit and psyche.

The stories in this collection are tender and sad, hideous and gentle, sweet and bitter, enraged and grim, powerful and subtle, funny and outraged, inspirational and messy, emotionally complex. These stories assure us that the quality of life can be measured in the everyday triumphs of baking cookies, making love, going for a run. They remind us of the power of love, laughter, and faith. They offer an unflinchingly honest look at pain and despair. They tell truth.

As a psychotherapist who specializes in journal therapy — the purposeful and intentional use of process or reflective writing to further psychological healing — I believe it can be inherently healing to give voice to the story of an individual life, captured with idiosyncratic wonder in the pages of a notebook. I further believe it can be inherently healing to witness the stories of others, when we are given permission to do so. The reverberation of authenticity and courage echo deep within our own cores, lighting up the dark places and offering a glimpse into our own possibilities.

Journal therapy pioneer Dr. Ira Progoff suggests that reflective writing offers the writer an opportunity to "...savor the beauty and stare straight into the pain." As a simultaneous testament to the fragility and indomitability of the human spirit, this remarkable collection extends the opportunity to you, the reader, as well. May you be enriched and moved by the gift.

Kathleen Adams, M.A.
Director, The Center for Journal Therapy
Author of: Journal to the Self

Introduction

Sometimes the beginning is in fact the end — and conversely. So it is for my introduction to *The MS Autobiography Book.*

When I was writing my own story, a process that would take more than a year to complete, the words almost always came easily, although the memories or present-time events that brought them forth were often ineffably painful and difficult just to acknowledge, let alone confront. To this day, many of these recollections, experiences, and the words I wrote to describe them return to my mind often, sometimes daily. And, the memories are still just as poignant for me as when I first wrote about them.

Writing this short introduction to what is now essentially a *fait accompli,* the book now lacking only its printing and distribution, has in its own way proven to be a more arduous task than the writing of my story. Now that I have actually arrived at the conclusion of the creation of my project, I am, frankly, at a loss for words to express my feelings. But, the time has come when I must close the cover on this very different, interesting chapter in my life, and move on.

At first, I was unsure of what seemed to compel me to describe and chronicle my own descent into chronic disease. In the beginning, I wrote only for myself, feeling that I had been cast adrift in time and space by my own body and the strange disease which had become an unwelcome companion in my day-to-day life. I struggled to try to understand what had happened, why it had happened (if indeed there might be such a thing as a "reason"), and to force myself to face, head-on, what — if anything — might or could happen to me in the future. Do not most of us think that when we are well and undamaged by the passage of time and the consequences of its vagaries, that the misfortunes of life happen to others and not to ourselves?

But, the compulsion to express myself by writing about my MS and its effects on my life — and by doing so to attempt to understand and accept, rather than deny, fight, and rail against something that no one could undo or remedy — continued to be strong within me. In time, the value of this means of expression and its own uniquely curative powers became more and more apparent to me. And thus the concept for a book such as this one was born and nurtured.

As my work progressed, and as I read more and more of the writing of other people whose lives had also been affected in one way or another by MS, it soon became obvious that many of the new challenges I was facing were in fact just part of a much more complex set of circumstances and processes. The feelings others had similarly described in their own way(s) also seemed to reflect and encompass much of the scope of human experience when people are faced with adversity and travail. After reading the writing of other people who also had MS, I found that I felt less isolated and estranged from myself, the rest of humanity, and existence in general, and I realized that I was indeed, not alone. It was clear that these people were dealing with many of the same experiences and issues as was I. Perhaps, as you, too read the stories and poems within this book, you will find that these sentiments will also be true for yourself.

Although it is impossible for me to say anything salubrious about a disease that insidiously and often "invisibly" robs people of their vitality and control over their bodies, it is also true that only because of multiple sclerosis do I have the great honor and privilege of presenting this book, and the authors whose writing is within it to you, the reader.

Eric Smirnow
Cedaredge, Colorado
December, 1992

Dedication

This book is dedicated with love to my mother, Beatrice Smirnow. Herself an MS person for many years, her love of life and personal courage has, and always will serve as a daily inspiration to me.

It is also dedicated to *everyone* who must deal with disabilities, whenever, wherever, or whomever they might be.

Table of Contents

Table of Contents
— continued —

Table of Contents
— continued —

Choices

by: Peter C. Andre
Colonel, U. S. Army (ret.)

"I have MS," I said, looking around the crowded conference room of 70 or 80 seated and standing people. "That's multiple sclerosis, and shortly I'll be medically retired." To watch the stunned faces as the news sunk in was a macabre sort of exhilaration. A weight had been lifted off my back. It had been held in secret for 14 years. *"I have MS!"* And I was smiling! Looking back at that moment it now seems weird.

As commander of an Army Readiness Group, holding a newly acquired cane, wearing a foot brace, and leaning on the podium for support, I moved on to explain what MS is, how I had handled it, and to outline the actions my command would take to maintain continuity until a new commander could be brought on station.

My odyssey of 29 years of military service in the U.S. Army would soon be brought to an abrupt end. As a Special Forces officer, my career included over 18 years of parachute status, three tours in Vietnam, and promotion to the rank of Colonel — all while silently carrying MS.

Over the years my choices had remained the same when "put to the wall" of facing an MS attack; either continue or quit. To continue was always to go down the dark road of uncertainty; the never knowing when next the beast would appear, and having to make the same hard choice again. But once you have crawled out of the belly of the beast after the first time, facing it again isn't as hard the next time. This is not a story of heroics, with the sounds of drums and bugles and brightly colored banners flying. It is a story of choices.

Blame it on The Old Monterey Weather
or The Korean Kimchi
mid–1963 to mid–1964

Looking back, the first signs of MS appeared in late 1963. I was at the Defense Language Institute in Monterey, California studying the Korean language for a year. The Korean language is considered one of the harder languages to master since you must learn a few hundred written Chinese characters in addition to the written and spoken Korean language. The Institute allowed a two-hour lunch break so we could work off some of the daily frustrations.

The year before I had been the assistant operations officer in a Special Forces Group at Fort Bragg, North Carolina. It had been a hectic year of being tied to a desk, and consequently, my own physical fitness suffered. Daily exercises and running were more light stuff rather than hard–charging; enough to stretch the muscles and work up a little sweat. Shortly before departing I had set up a night parachute jump for line units of the Group; they would parachute near a Marine base close to the North Carolina coast. Tied into the jump was a series of four night marches back to Fort Bragg, a total of 102 miles. I decided to go with them. Piece of cake. In 1959 as a lieutenant, I had a Special Forces team called "The Road Runners." The name was given to us because we moved so fast and so far, easily outdistancing other teams. One march was along the Appalachian Trail for over 150 miles. But that was a few years ago, and this present march cut me down to size. After the first night of 25 miles I could hardly move a muscle. Maybe that's what happens when you get promoted to captain and go up to the staff; you just don't maintain the physical edge. Each time we stopped for a rest and then started again it was pure agony for the first 10 or 15 steps. I finished the march along with the rest of the group and silently vowed I would never let my physical conditioning reach a point where I wouldn't be able to parachute from an aircraft, march 100 miles, and still be ready for the job. I departed for Monterey shortly afterwards with a goal of starting in earnest my own physical conditioning program at the Language Institute.

The post was ready–made for runners since it was situated on a hillside overlooking Monterey Bay. Cool sunny days made for good long runs. I took full advantage of that two–hour lunch break. About three months into the Korean language course I started to experience tingling sensations in my legs after my daily runs; these were odd feelings, but I didn't think it warranted going to sick call. Besides, I was too busy studying to take the time. It would pass, I assured myself. In November the Korean instructors had a Korean–style picnic for the students in a nearby park on the windswept hillside. Korean barbe- cued beef, hot kimchi, and chopsticks were the order of the day. Shortly afterwards I came down with a 24–hour virus, followed by loss of sight in my right eye. I checked into the medical section of the Institute and was sent to the hospital at Fort Ord. With no appoint- ment, I had to wait until the very last to be seen. I remember the doctor looking at me sitting there totally engrossed in my Korean study books with just the sight of one eye. The next stop was to Letterman Army Hospital in San Francisco. With nothing else to go on, the doctors determined it to be an eye infection. I would remain there for two weeks, getting a shot in the backside each day of something other than penicillin, since I was allergic to it.

Language training was an intense year, and I didn't want to be dropped from my nine–man section to another one because I wasn't keeping up with the studies. I called Ginnie, my wife, and asked her to contact Mr. Kim, the senior instructor, to explain my situation and to ask him to record on tape the daily lessons. Ginnie and our two sons, Scott and Colin, would come up on the weekend carrying with them the old Army tape recorder we had been issued and a Korean language tape. Even with one eye I could continue my studies; however, as I practiced the dialogues I noted others in the ward were slowly being driven out. The head nurse, after some very vocal complaints, put me into a private room. Not bad for a young captain! I even had a nice view. My eyesight returned after a couple of weeks, and my vision checked out 20/20. After I went back to school, graduation and departure in August to the Special Forces Group on Okinawa followed quickly. The tingling sensations by that time had also disappeared. My only regret was that I was already scheduled to leave for Vietnam two weeks after arriving on the island rather than getting a chance to use my newly acquired language skills in Korea.

An Island of Coral, a Land of Jungle, and Feeling Fine mid–1964 to mid–1967

The Far East was not new to me, having spent 14 months there, with part of it as a rifle company commander on the demilitarized zone (DMZ) in Korea in 1957 and six months with Special Forces in Laos in 1960. During my present assignment I would make 2 six-month tours in Vietnam. The first tour was too hectic for keeping any kind of a regular physical conditioning program. In our location outside of Saigon, running was not in vogue since there was too much terrorist activity in the area; however, once we relocated to a new Special Forces camp outside of Tay Ninh, at least we could play some volleyball and do some regular exercises. On the next tour at another Special Forces camp, when time permitted, I used the noon period for running while our Nungs, one of the northern mountain tribes, took their afternoon rest. My course was inside the camp for most runs and once in a while outside the camp along a nearby rubber plantation was at random times, so as not to set a regular pattern for any skulduggery. Each time I returned to Okinawa there was a full agenda of parachuting, running, and other physical activities. For three years I experienced no symptoms related to MS.

Following George Washington's Trail to Valley Forge
mid–1967 to mid–1970

The beast would make its presence known during the next assignment as an ROTC instructor at Drexel Institute of Technology in Philadelphia. It was a full schedule; besides teaching, having extra duties of organizing a cadet Special Forces company, and night classes at Temple University for a Master's program in history, I also exercised daily and ran inside a gym. Once a week there was an extra–long run around Drexel's football field before the corps of cadets gathered for their drill period. The symptoms of MS would not come all at once but would drag on over a year.

Early in the tour I failed my annual medical examination. It was my eyes. To correct this I visited the nearby Naval Hospital for glasses. The optometrist couldn't understand it. I was having trouble with my distant vision. People my age may need reading glasses, which I didn't require, but not glasses for distant vision. The new glasses corrected the problem as far as the Army was concerned. On another occasion an Engineer officer named Al, a very perceptive guy, asked me if I realized that when I walked I angled toward the right. It was especially noticeable while I was walking in open fields or unenclosed areas. I told him I was never aware of it and forgot about it, which was too bad. Years later it would almost cause a disaster with my military career.

Teaching a class one morning I stumbled. It was strange, almost like losing my balance. Me, a low and high hurdles man in high school and college, stumbling. I must be careful how I "waltzed" around the stage, I thought, or the cadets would think I had a morning hangover!

In the spring of 1968 I took the cadets up to Indiantown Gap Military Reservation for a weekend exercise. That evening the cadets, like normal college students, gathered around campfires talking well into the night. Their laughter woke me. I had been off in the underbrush wrapped up in a poncho. I decided to go over and tell them to get some sleep, for tomorrow would be a full and challenging day. As I got up I fell down. I had been sleeping on a slope and in the dark I had no balance. After a few tries I grabbed hold of a small tree to balance myself. However, attempting to walk in the darkness was just as bad as trying to stand. Yet as the sun broke over the mountain tops the next morning, it was like I had never had a problem with my equilibrium.

At the ROTC Summer Camp in 1968 I started to have a vague feeling of weakness. I still ran every afternoon and it didn't affect me significantly. However, something just didn't seem right. I thought of going to the camp doctor, but how the hell does one explain that feeling. Maybe it was the water, I thought. I had had a constant run of morning diarrhea for two weeks straight. I remembered having the trots for the first three months in Laos, when we had been eating mainly water buffalo, and that did affect me! So probably it was something in the Pennsylvania mountain water. Afterwards, toward the end of summer I took the family camping with a pop–up trailer. It was our first experience camping as a family. We went to the upper part of New York state and into Canada. It was there that I experienced my first bout of losing control of bowels and bladder. Maybe it was a bug I picked up. When I returned to work it seemed to subside; however, I slowly became aware through the fall and winter that the problem was still lingering. It wasn't acute, and so to remedy it I cut down on liquids and insured I had a bowel movement prior to leaving for work each morning. With that regimen, the problem was gone. Then the tingling and numbness in the finger tips appeared. If I reached for my wallet in my back pocket I could not pull it out unless I looked around at what my fingers were doing.

In December another officer and I drove down to Fort Belvoir, Virginia for a weekend refresher course in nuclear weapons deploy-ment required in order to maintain our proficiency. It was during that weekend that I realized I had to see a doctor. The course was full of templates and diagrams, lining up dots with clear plastic rulers and making calculations. A wave of stiffness had come over me. Trying to handle a simple problem was almost impossible. My fingers were not responding properly and the ruler kept slipping off the scales, making it difficult to get exact readings. The final exam was excruciating. I was the last to finish and hand in my paper. I passed by the narrowest of margins. We returned to Philadelphia the next day. I was determined to see a doctor, but having had some hard experiences with missing the holidays with the family, I held off until January 1969.

It seemed like a replay of Monterey five years before. The nearest doctor was at the Defense Supply Agency. I decided to go to sick call. Doing the duties was a civilian doctor. After taking my vital signs he gave me a prescription for cold pills. No improvement. I returned the next week. He gave me a shot, probably some super vitamins, and sent me on my way. No improvement. I returned again the following week. Nothing had changed. He looked me over a little closer, scribbled some lines on a paper with the letters "MS?" being distinguishable, and handed it to me saying go see a neurologist at the nearby Naval Hospital. Again, no appointment. It was well into the late afternoon before I was seen. The neurologist asked questions: "Was I a premature baby?" "Yes, 2½ pounds." "Born where?" "Brooklyn, New York, with most of my childhood in Rhode Island." Then a series of balancing tests. He left the room and came back with another neurologist who asked a few more questions, and then announced "You don't have MS. But we can't handle your case. Go see a neurologist at the Valley Forge Army Hospital." What was it that he said I didn't have — MS? The only thing that came to mind was a picture of a child in a wheelchair. But then he said I *didn't* have MS. The following week I took a day off to drive up to Valley Forge. First it was the sick call route to see a doctor. After showing him the medical report from the Philadelphia gang he got hold of a neurologist who read the report and gave me a few balancing tests. After he finished he said when I had the time, come on up for about a week so he could run some other tests. I told him when I could work out my schedule I would call him.

The neurologist was young and wearing captain bars. All medical doctors come on active duty as captains, and after a year or so get promoted to major. He might even be an intern, I thought. His asking me to come up when I had a chance sounded innocuous enough. No bells clanking. No crisis. But there was something nagging me — hospitals.

I hate hospitals: this feeling has been ingrained in me since childhood. Although I don't remember it, I was in a hospital for double mastoid operations at the age of nine months. At five or six years of age I broke my arm in three places from jumping off a tractor, and was confined to the hospital for weeks. It was hard, just laying there, looking out the hospital window as spring turned the trees green, children played, and I was not able to take part in it. When I was about eight years old I was taken to The Children's Hospital in Boston for another mastoid operation. When I could finally move around the ward I was given slippers, a shirt, and short pants to wear. The boy next to me and I made plans to escape. Daily we would look out the balcony window of the play–room to see a paneled laundry truck parked below. The nurses always stayed out in the ward, never coming into the play–room unless there were screams from kids fighting. We could do it. Out the balcony window, down a fire escape and hide in the truck. Get out after it departed the hospital grounds. I would then take my nickels and call my mother — in Pawtucket, Rhode Island — to come pick me up. Lady Luck smiled down on me. I didn't "escape." Never mind that it cost more than a few nickels to call out of state, and summer short pants were not the normal wear for the biting winds of March, it would have been my parents' reception that I was saved from. In any case, that was my thinking on hospitals. Never get into one and if you are in one, get out fast.

Arrangements made, I headed back to Valley Forge. It was a quiet drive with Ginnie. There were lots of unsaid thoughts. A spinal tap and a host of other exams were pending. At the end of a week the doctor said I could leave, but to stop into his office first.

He started by saying I had MS, but quickly added, "Just like there are many forms of cancer, there are many forms of multiple sclerosis. You have a mild form of MS." I thought to myself — that's like the old joke of "being slightly pregnant." I just as quickly cut in with the big question, "Is it terminal?" "No," was his reply. The captain's prognosis: "Probably nothing more will happen to you, or at the most you may become somewhat weaker as years go by." He added that he didn't recommended I go to a library and do a lot of reading on MS, for "it will make you sick to your stomach." On the upside, the doctor said he would put me on something called steroids and that should correct my problems. Then the zinger came boiling in: "By military regulations you'll have to go before a medical board. I think you can do your job, and I'll be glad to tell the board as much." A medical board! It is made up of one doctor and some line officers who look at the medical reports and ask: "What is your speciality?" Oh, Special Forces. You mean that one where you jump out of airplanes in flight? Go humping a 60 or 70 pound rucksack up and down the hills? No way. That's for the soldier who is totally fit. The medical board is the final step before going out the door and being medically retired from the service. That board could bring a career to an abrupt halt. The doctor said in parting that he would arrange a meeting in about a week to talk to a senior medical officer. I was right. Never get into hospitals!

A minute. No, it was more like a few fleeting seconds. "Why me?" I asked myself as I walked down the corridor and saw an overweight young man about my age walking, no, waddling in my direction. He was a visitor carrying a package for some patient. Why me, who was physically fit? The fleeting seconds passed. I never asked myself that question again. Those are the cards that were dealt to me. It's a lousy hand, but it's the only game in town. No, not in town; in life.

I'm not sure what was harder to explain to Ginnie: what I had, or the possibility of release from the Army. It was a tough drive home. The following weekend, with the boys involved in some recreational activities, Ginnie and I took a ride to Valley Forge Park. We talked of the unknowns; what would happen in the next week; a future without a view. The steroids had already started to have their effect. Walking, balance, everything was swinging back to normal. Here I was in the prime of physical fitness, a major, on the promotion list to lieutenant colonel; selected to attend the Army's Command and General Staff College at Fort Leavenworth, Kansas, this summer. Now I was being told it could all shortly end for something that appeared already "cured." As we walked along the trail looking at a line of old cannons, the snow on the ground was blowing and it was bone-chilling cold. When we came upon one of the revolutionary encampments, I couldn't help but think about our ragtag Continental Army. General George Washington and his troops must have faced the same kind of weather as they huddled around their campfires. I recalled some words from a diary of one of those soldiers: "I am sick, my feet lame, my legs are sore, my body covered with this tormenting itch... and all the reward I shall get, will be... 'Poor Will is dead'."

This was my life and my career. I was not prepared for a pat on the back and a verbal "Poor Pete" as I walked out the door. We both agreed not to go down without a fight. Washington and his troops made it, and so would we.

At the appointed time I was ushered into an office by the neurologist and introduced to a large, overweight medical doctor with the rank of colonel. As he reviewed the medical report he threw out questions to the neurologist. For a better part of the meeting I was just a bystander. I sensed by the questions the colonel was not completely sold on the diagnosis of MS. The young doctor seemed to be defending his conclusions and wasn't doing too good of a job. The colonel finally looked over at me and instead of talking about MS, he talked about my time with Special Forces. Ah! John Wayne had done us good with his movie "Green Berets!" He noted my CIB — the good old Combat Infantryman's Badge, my master parachute wings, and even my ribbons. Now I felt uneasy. Was he trying to soften me up for the "Poor Pete" punch line? I geared myself for it but it never came. He finally ended by saying he was not going to send the medical report to Washington. He said that he would like me to go to a hospital every six months for a checkup. And that was that. I hadn't even had a chance to deliver an impassioned "give me liberty or give me death" speech. Nothing. As I walked out of the room I looked down at my ribbons. A couple of Bronze Stars and a couple of Air Medals. Nice, but not something to rave about. Why? Years later, in reflection on that meeting, I could only surmise the neurologist didn't have enough in his report on this elusive disease to convince that senior medical officer it was MS, so the good colonel had the foresight not to destroy my career on the spot. If it was really MS, it would raise its ugly head soon enough when I was carried into some hospital!

I paid one last visit to the Valley Forge hospital. The doctor, recently promoted to major, checked me over. A–OK. He handed me my records and I was on my way to Fort Leavenworth, Kansas.

We had liked camping so much I had bought a pop–up trailer. The first night was spent in the Adirondacks. By luck that day, we had picked up an *Army Times* newspaper. It carried the information we had been waiting for — promotion. In the glow of the evening campfire, Ginnie, with an official voice, read the date and promotion number while my two sons pinned the lieutenant colonel's silver leaves on the epaulettes of my old French parachute jacket. Washington and his troops, with "Poor Will" among them, had marched out of Valley Forge in the spring and finally to ultimate victory. Now it was our turn.

⋯⋯⋈✦⋈⋯⋯

"Don't Make Yourself a Cripple"
mid-1969 through 1970

After arriving at Fort Leavenworth, one of the first things I did was to sign for a locker at the gym, having previously been told they would be in short supply. The Command and General Staff College was strictly an academic environment. We were organized into sections, each with about forty or fifty officers from all branches of the service as well as personnel from many other countries. The senior officer was the section leader, who in our case was a medical officer — Doc Arbiter. We all liked him. He had his feet on the ground. He would, during that year, give me words to live by. For the most part one's physical fitness was up to the individual. The "jocks," as we were called, had our own regimen. Classes ran 50 minutes with a ten-minute break between them. Lunch was one hour. As the last morning class finished the jocks would make a hasty dash across the street to the gym as the others were moving toward the cafeteria. For me it was a quick change and out to the track, a few warm up exercises, and then a fast mile or so run. Back to the gym, strip down and get 10 minutes in the sauna, shower, dress, grab a coke, get back to the classroom, sit down next to my table mate, and usually I still had five minutes to go before class started; time enough to eat my sandwich. If I was lucky I wouldn't be called upon to get up on the stage and present my homework solution with a bite of my sandwich still in my mouth.

As the hot days turned to cool days and finally cold days, the regimen continued. After Christmas it snowed and became down-right nasty, but the really hard-core jocks were still out there exercising. One day during early February as I rounded the track for the last lap my right leg stopped. I toppled over into a snow bank. After a few minutes I walked back to the gym, not sure what had caused it to stop. It wasn't a pulled muscle, since it wasn't sore. It just stopped. The next day I ran again, and at about the same distance where I "crashed and burned," it happened again. (Okay, I'll rest the leg for a week before hitting the track again.) By chance, one of the section students asked me to join him on an extended run around the post. It was a slower, leisurely pace, but I still staggered as the leg stopped after about the same distance. As we walked back to the gym I was now worried. I talked about my past problems with MS. He recommended I see a doctor. He was right. When all else fails, try common sense.

The next day, before going to the small post hospital, I visited the post chapel and said a prayer. The doctor I saw told me there was no resident neurologist, so he set up a visit to a nearby VA hospital. There the neurologist went through what I had started to call the tap–tap–bang–bang routine with his little hammer. He finished with a few balancing tests and concluded, "You have MS." He talked about a state official who had MS. Every February he would have an attack. Could it be that I would have the same pattern? He said he would normally have a person in my condition lay down and rest for six weeks, but in my case that would be impossible, so he was going to recommend a course of steroids, adding that he really didn't believe in them, but it was the only thing around.

At about the time I was to start the steroids, I was hit with other symptoms: stiffness encapsulating my whole body; no equilibrium; and "klutziness" in my hands to the point where I couldn't handle small items without dropping them. In class we were studying the Army corps in the deliberate river crossing. The section was broken down into staffs and I was selected to be the G–3, the Operations Officer. It's a noble position when all cylinders were functioning. However, in this case, I would have preferred to have been on the sidelines. We went through a map exercise, and at the end of the day were told to prepare the operations order, maps, annexes, etc., to be handed in the next morning; there would also be some special visitors the next day. Since I was responsible for the overall plan, the other staff officers handed me their inputs which I took home to prepare for next morning. It took the better part of an agonizing evening to put the package together. Holding colored pencils to draw boundary lines, routes, etc., on a map overlay and writing the operation order by hand was almost a Gordian task. The next day it was announced that the commanding general and his party would listen to one student staff presentation. Lady Luck was not smiling that day. Through a process of elimination it fell on our staff to make the presentation. I was the main briefer. The stiffness, klutzy hands, and balance all played a part in making a miserable day for me. Frustration set in rapidly once I stepped up to the stage to start my briefing. The very simple tasks of tacking maps up onto a wall, holding a pointer steady, and answering the general's questions almost brought me to chucking the whole thing. One of the colonels, the "joker" of the general's party, commented that I was "having a hard time walking straight and chewing gum at the same time." Everyone laughed; everyone that is, but me. I was the butt of a joke, an oblique insult, being held up to ridicule in front of my peers. I was fuming but all I could do was to stand there hoping not to lose my balance or drop the pointer, while I silently called the "joker" a name saved for those of doubtful parentage. It had not been my finest hour.

That evening I was down in the pits. I thought, "Is this what I am going to be faced with for the rest of my career? Is it time to leave the service?" These were deep, dark thoughts I really didn't want to think about, but I couldn't shake them. Yet, it only takes a few words to cause one to grab hold of his boot straps and pull himself up. That was the night Doc Arbiter came to visit Ginnie and me. Doc was someone you could trust immediately. He was an enlisted man during WW II, then went to medical school, and returned to military service as a pathologist. He had heard of my medical problem, so he came to give some encouragement to Ginnie and me. Over a drink, I gave a chronological picture of my experiences with MS. Doc told me about one of his men in a medical unit who had MS and remained on active duty by taking steroid treatments.

At the time it sounded good, but I wasn't sure if he was just trying to boost my morale. I started to ruminate on what my future in the military would be. If I didn't quit the service maybe I should get off the fast track and get out of the high risk business. After graduation, perhaps I should try to go back to college to complete my Master's degree, and then get a desk job.

Doc Arbiter knew my expertise was in Special Forces, and that's what I really wanted to do. When I had finished speaking he said "Look, don't make yourself a cripple. Go and do the things you want to do; just know your limitations." If there was a benchmark along the trail of my fight against the beast it was that night. I decided if the steroid treatment worked I would stay in the Army doing the things I wanted to do as long as I could do the job properly and didn't endanger others. If I couldn't survive I would raise my hand and "come in from the cold" knowing I had fought the battle as best I could. Ginnie was by my side. She too would know when and if I should raise my hand. Together, we would go down that dark road together.

In early spring there is a day when the administrative personnel place in the assigned mailboxes, located outside in the cloakroom of each section, assignment orders for the next change of station. The anticipation of that day starts building up at least a month before. If the instructor is a good guy he will end the class a little early. If he is sadistic, liking to see the students squirm, he may run over his allotted time by a few minutes. Either way, at the end of class there is a mad scramble out the door to the boxes followed with joyful yells of the next posting. I didn't yell for there was no joy in my orders: Vietnam again.

There were just a few of us selected to go back to Vietnam; we called ourselves "The Chosen Few." It didn't take long for the wives to get together and decide where they would spend that year-in-waiting: Hawaii. There would be some logistical problems and bureaucratic paperwork to overcome, but C & GS graduates were more than a match for them. If there was a bright spot it was the Vietnam R & R and leave policy. One could expect at least three separate weeks for a return to paradise. My other tours in Vietnam had allowed a week R & R, which I took to meet Ginnie in Hong Kong each time. Those were second honeymoons! If I had to go back to Nam then the three trips would again be second honeymoons, only this time in a lush paradise of flowers, green landscape, and beaches of white sand.

As we moved toward graduation I continued light exercises, most of it muscle stretches. I finally had to see if the steroids had done their job. Running inside the gym at a very slow pace I went a full mile. They had worked!

After graduation it was off to another school at Fort Bragg for about five months. During that time I just did easy runs, not really pushing myself. Near the end of the course I obtained an appointment with the neurologist at the military hospital, showed him my records and asked for an exam before I departed for Vietnam. He was taken aback with the request. In fact, he went and got another neurologist to simply look at me. They both were wearing captain bars. Young. It was the tap–tap–bang–bang routine. No problems. I smiled, shook their hands, said thanks, and as I departed they stared at me like I was out of my mind. Going back to Vietnam!

After graduation it was a dash with the family driving cross-country to San Francisco and on to Hawaii by military air. Some of the wives of "The Chosen Few" met us at the airport and helped us get squared away. We moved into an apartment complex outside of Honolulu along with a small shipment of furniture on 24 December. Ginnie took time to go to the local shopping center to buy a small artificial Christmas tree, on sale, at one of the five & dime stores. She placed it on a small table and decorated it with a string of lights that she had carried from Fort Bragg. The presents, which we had carried in our luggage, were placed around the tree. It had been a tiring trip, but we would make it a merry Christmas even with the shadow of departure right after the first of the new year.

Korean Kimchi and Vietnamese Rice Balls Never Tasted Better — 1971

The personnel pipeline for Vietnam could be very impersonal. It was based on "needs," not desires. On my arrival back in "'Nam" I tried to get assigned to Special Forces again, but the big computer had me tagged for something else. Since Korean linguists were a rare commodity in Vietnam, I was to work with the Korean forces, which consisted of over 30,000 troops that were stationed in Vietnam. My assignment would be the Military Assistance Command–Vietnam (MACV) Senior Korea Plans officer, located in the Korean headquarters (ROKV). The title of my position was misleading, for there never was any real planning. My little section (myself and two others) was in the bowels of the ROKV Headquarters in Cholon, on the south side of Saigon. The only window had an air conditioner that was ready for the junk pile and which blocked any light from the outside. I immediately thought of the black hole of Calcutta. I was doomed to sit there for a whole year because I had studied the Korean language.

1971 was a time of drawdown for the U.S. troops. However, the Korean forces were going full steam. To the Korean staff I was just another "me-guk" (American) officer, and we probably all looked the same to Korean eyes. The Koreans came in for assistance on routine matters, but nothing to challenge the imagination. It took time, but finally early one morning the commanding general's special assistant, a lieutenant colonel like myself, came in asking for help. He was between a rock and a hard place trying to get an airplane to take his general to a distant location up–country. Okay, it wasn't the "planning" function, but what the hell; I was also told to help the ROKS anyway I could, and that meant *anything* to me. A few telephone calls and I had Ambassador Bunker's four–engine aircraft on loan for the day! As the General disembarked from that aircraft with his subordinate commanders gathered at planeside, his prestige was enormous. Things changed thereafter; I started to get out of that "black hole." I was being invited not only to the Korean generals' offices to discuss problems and give recommendations over morning coffee or Ginseng tea, but also as a dinner guest at their quarters. I was called to their offices anytime a senior American officer or U.S. diplomat, up to ambassadorial level, paid a visit to their headquarters. I was the "go between." The Korean principal staff officers started visiting me, and my office door became a swinging door. From that point on I had a chance to move around. If I wasn't up–country visiting their Dragoon (marines) Brigade or the Tiger and White Horse (Army) infantry divisions, it would be down to the Delta to assist their medical or small naval units. There was always something to do. I even had a chance to do some traveling out of country. Time sped by.

Like mad dogs and Englishmen, I would take every noon period I could to exercise and run. My body felt good. I still had the bowel and bladder problems, but if I was careful I could keep it under control. Around September a wave of weakness began to settle in. Again, it was one of those things that was hard to define. I immediately stopped running. The last thing I needed was a screwed up leg in Vietnam. A couple weeks went by and I still didn't feel up to par. I stopped any type of exercising altogether and for the next few months took history correspondence courses for recreation.

I received an "early drop" to rotate home just before Christmas. Ginnie had done some pick and shovel work and had us booked to return to San Francisco on a ship. No, not just a ship, but a luxury liner. It had a number of allotted spaces for military families. She had called me while in Nam to get my date of rank. Whatever it was got us an outside double deluxe suite. The "Love Boat" could never have topped our trip back to the mainland.

                              ⊷⊶⊷

THE MS AUTOBIOGRAPHY BOOK

Command and Feeling Fit, Almost
1972 to mid–1974

After picking up our car in Oakland we made a quick, icy cold drive cross–country to Fort Bragg. I had been "command recommended," which meant if the Commanding General thought you were top–drawer material he would give you a command. It was like going out and winning your spurs all over again. My initial assignment was as the assistant G–3 for operations at the JFK Center for Military Assistance, the home of Special Forces. In a way the staff position was a smile from Lady Luck. Besides giving me a chance to size up how to do things right once I got a command, I also had the chance to start my parachuting again without being dropped at night onto postage stamp size drop zones. Over 4½ years had passed since I last parachuted. Would my body and my reflexes be up to it? I had also stopped running four or five months before arriving at Fort Bragg; were my legs up to it? This was an Airborne post, and that was synonymous with exercising and running — on asphalt, in sand, with boots as well as running shoes, rain or shine. If the legs or body were not up to it my military career would end, abruptly.

There was a running course through the woods nearby which was used by both individuals and groups, either running against the clock or at their own speed. It was called "The MATA Mile," named after one of the blocks of military assistance instruction taught at the Center. The course was laid out over trails that meandered through the woods and ravines, up and down the steep hills. Portions of the course were in deep North Carolina sand. On the first run, I found out that it was much more than a mile in distance. For the first couple of weeks I would go down every morning and run, but never the full distance. When I felt confident I could do the full course, I went for it. It was like the movie "Rocky" with the hero running up the steps in the park. All I needed was the background music to make it complete. Thereafter, I got hold of the G–3 sergeant major who had been trying to get a physical fitness program going. But, he always seemed short of people; they just had some other "very important thing" to do. I had him put "the word" out that PT was at 0600 hours in the morning. Anyone missing would be answerable to me.

The first parachute jump was fine. I went through a couple of hours of refresher training the day before. This was very important since we were now using the new MC-1 steerable parachute. Knowing how to handle the chute was the difference between very good jumps or hitting the ground like a steam engine going open throttle.

Around the beginning of July, 1971 I started to lose the sight in my right eye again. By the fourth of July I couldn't see out of it. I told myself not to do anything yet. Just wait. Hold off parachuting and ease up on hard running. Give it a month, then make a decision. Within the next two weeks, like a swinging gate, the eyesight came back.

"I need you to go over to the western part of the state and check a team out," the Deputy Commander of the Center, a colonel, said. "I would go myself, but I have another commitment." He said he had an aircraft laid on for the next day to fly over there, and ground transportation to meet the aircraft for a drive up to the team's location. So far, so good. "The team is doing spelunking in some underground caves," he said, with the straightest face I've ever seen. The next day I found myself at the base of a small mountain looking up to where the team guide was pointing. Well, if I ever wanted to check the body out this was as good a place as any. After climbing to the top of the rugged mountain I met the team leader. Stopping for a rest to catch my breath and be outfitted with a coal miner's-type hard hat equipped with a flashlight on top of it, I entered a small opening and swung down into a dark cave. I was impressed with the team's efforts, and more importantly with my body. It was holding up! Crawling, swinging and climbing around those dark caves was the best test I could have taken for things to come.

I spent about 14 months as the assistant G-3 and also as the G-3, a feather in my cap since the G-3 was a full colonel's slot. In March,

1972 I was given command of a Special Forces Battalion. The battalion is the first level of command where the unit is fundamentally self-sustaining. Whether it is good or bad depends principally on you. My next eighteen months of "pushing a battalion" would be the hardest, yet most rewarding of all my jobs in the Army. I ran with the best and made any parachute jump the battalion did, day or night, on small or large drop zones, with calm or marginal winds. I did it all and never looked back to see if the beast was following. A week before I was to give up my command, it tapped me on the shoulder.

We had the MATA mile runs, as I described, and we had unit runs. The whole Special Forces Group would assemble on the parade field early in the morning and go through a set of the "Army Daily Dozen" exercises. Then, by battalions in column, we would run a predetermined route along the various streets of our cantonment. On this particular day the body was telling me to take it easy, but I couldn't listen to it. A good commander not only runs along side his troops, but doubles back and around to ensure all are making the run together with no one falling out. It was a fast pace. We were leading the Group and my SCUBA teams, the very best runners, were leading the battalion. The end of the run was in sight when my leg gave out on me and I "crashed and burned" off the side of the road. Lying there bruised and scraped while the remainder of the battalions passed by was something I do not recall fondly. I hobbled to the hospital with a hairline fracture of the foot. From that point on my physical fitness would be on a slow downhill glide.

After my change of command I moved up to the Group Headquarters as the Deputy Commander. I had curtailed my running until the fracture had mended. When I started running again, because of a different work schedule, it was a slow jog around a nearby golf course in the early mornings, at first light. The Officers Career Branch in Washington started overtures of an assignment to the Pentagon, since that was viewed as a stepping stone for promotion. I wanted nothing to do with the Pentagon, thank you very much. I found a position at a joint headquarters at MacDill Air Force Base in Tampa,

Florida. There would be outside activities in the form of joint exercises, and my position would require dealing with Special Forces/Special Operations; it would also be a parachute position. I took it.

Before leaving Fort Bragg there was one last job I had to perform; I was to serve as commander of troops for a military parade/review which was tied into our Organizational Day. It was mid-June and already hot, as I, with a four-man staff behind me, marched onto the parade field leading the band and the Special Forces Group of 1,000 troops. The stands were filled with spectators. As the commander of troops I would be responsible for giving all the commands, which would then be repeated by the subordinate commanders. It entailed a number of *"about face"* movements. As I faced the reviewing stand I would do an *"about face,"* give a command, and then another *"about face."* This procedure would then be repeated for other commands. It wasn't long before my right leg began to get weak. The last few sets of turns for giving the commands was pure agony. Finally the last command, *"pass in review,"* was given to start the band and troops marching pass the reviewing stand. I, with the staff, led the band and troops. Trying to march with a weak leg, keep in step with the music and march straight was pure hell. Years earlier that engineer officer had told me I angled off to the right while walking. I had never noticed it until the parade. All the other times I had led my battalion in parades there was always another unit in front, close enough to guide myself in a straight line. But now there was just the open field and objects too distant to guide on. A member of the staff behind me softly called out "edge left" whenever I started to "wander"; then, to keep me in step, he called out the beat. Somehow I made it past the reviewing stand with the *"eyes right,"* and saluting. I then wheeled the staff off the parade field to review the troops as they passed. The thought struck me right then and there that "I ain't going to make it if I have to do many more parades as commander of troops!" We left for Florida the following week.

The Beast and I Come to Terms — Sort of
mid-1974 to mid-1978

Shortly after getting settled in the new headquarters, called Readiness Command (REDCOM), I was asked to return temporarily to Fort Bragg as an observer for a large exercise which included parachuting into Fort Polk, Louisiana with a couple of Special Forces teams. At Fort Bragg I boarded a C-130 aircraft for the 4 or 5-hour flight, part of which was night, low-level flying, always a sure bet for having some of the younger troopers taste their dinner for a second time as they up-chucked into a burp-bag. At the given time we chuted up in the aircraft. We would be jumping blind; that is, no markings would appear on the DZ. The aircraft would be guided by a beacon signal. A night jump, yes, but with a full moon it would make it seem more like daylight. Three times we received the hand signal from the jumpmaster to stand up, only to be signaled back down, since the aircraft couldn't pick up the beacon. The bright moon started to fade, and when we finally exited the aircraft it was pitch black outside without even a view of the horizon. Not being able to judge where the ground was and what obstacles were below could be costly. I made something less than a perfect landing but was not injured. Finding the assembly point, somewhere on the edge of the DZ, to drop off the parachute was another matter. It was hot and humid. A good deal of strength had been sapped from standing up and down in the aircraft as well as the parachute jump itself. Now it seemed I had hardly any strength left to carry the main parachute, reserve parachute, and other gear in a kit bag on my back. Having been the last man out of the aircraft, I had the greatest distance to walk. It was a stop-and-go process. Finally about 50 yards from the assembly point my body just stopped. I simply sat down in a pool of sweat in the darkness. When I judged myself strong enough to continue I finally made it to the turn-in-point. I had the dubious honor of being the last man in.

After a shower that evening I sat down with a drink and reassessed the jump and my capabilities. I had never experienced what I had just gone through on that drop zone. I was now faced with a new problem: being able to carry my gear off a drop zone. It is an old airborne ethos that each and every man, from private to general, carries his own chute and gear off the drop zone. If I couldn't do that each time I parachuted, maybe it was time to raise my hand. There were a number of factors which put me out in the middle of nowhere on that hot, coal–black night. I had expended a lot of my energy just parachuting, leaving nothing in reserve to move off the DZ. Okay, let's try to compensate. With the steerable parachute I had the ability to move laterally while descending. What about cutting the walking distance to the assembly point? Why not shoot for that point, or as close as I could get? Anything to reduce the distance which I had to carry that gear off the drop zone would help. From than on, as I exited an aircraft or helicopter, I wasn't looking for the softest or safest spot to land, but rather the nearest spot for turning in my chute. For the next four years at MacDill I would land among the cows in their pastures, apple orchards, and even send trash barrels rolling as I hit the ground, but for the most part I would land close enough to carry my gear off the drop zone airborne style, on my own back.

During that assignment I did more traveling than I had before. In most cases there were no real problems except when it was out of the country, say to Europe or Korea. Jet lag was the least of my problems; time zone changes threw my body functions off schedule. Up to then I had found I could control my bowels if I had a movement first thing in the morning. Diarrhea was another problem which would have to be dealt with separately; my only defense was not to get it. For the normal situation, I had to maintain the schedule my body was used to, which was on Florida time. If it meant getting up at two or three o'clock in the morning while visiting a particular distant country for my daily bowel movement, I complied with that schedule.

Since physical fitness was up to the individual, I set up my own program of exercises and an early run at 0600 each morning. I also bought a slant board for sit ups. Fifty without stopping was my norm. By 1976 I started to feel my balance was off. It wasn't a noticeable thing, but I sensed it. My sit ups now required a short rest/break before I could complete my set of fifty; furthermore, my running was becoming a major problem. My legs were getting tired about a mile out, with the return mile becoming harder to run. To compensate over the next year I reduced the length of the run. Next, I reduced the pace, but in the end the foot drop reappeared, and I tripped and fell. The leg just got tired and I would stumble into a fall. Frustration set in. This really wasn't exercising; a short run at a slow pace did nothing for me. What else could I do? I decided to try riding a ten–speed bike. I reworked my schedule. Since I lived on the base I would go home for lunch, put on some workout clothes, and with Ginnie, who also had a bike, do a fast five or six miles. After cooling down, a shower, and a sandwich, I returned to work. It was good exercise, but my legs were getting "spongy" after stopping. On weekends we would bike around Tampa bay, stop midway for a lunch we carried, then bike back, 26 miles altogether. I could do that kind of exercising as long as I didn't have to walk immediately after biking. My legs were simply too weak. After a 10 or 15 minute rest, the leg strength returned.

That summer I participated in a large–scale joint exercise at Yakima, Washington. At the end of the exercise I split from the exercise people who were returning to MacDill, and flew up to Alaska for a meeting. A couple of days later I took the "red eye" flight into Dallas. After landing in the morning, I found the flight to Tampa had been cancelled because of mechanical problems. I put a call in to Ginnie to tell her what my new arrival time would be. She said, "How does 95 sound to you?" She had just been called from the office. I was number 95 on the new colonels' list! I had made it! Even though I had declined a Washington assignment and was carrying the beast on my back to boot, I made it!

In the fall of 1977 I had been designated as the Chief of Staff for an unconventional warfare task force which would take part in a large–scale exercise in the panhandle of Florida. A task force is a temporary grouping of people and units for a particular mission. The staff is joint; that is, from all branches of the service. The challenge for any chief of staff is to rapidly mold that grouping of individuals into a smooth running team capable of 24-hour, round-the-clock operation. For some time now, I had felt I was running on 7 rather than 8 cylinders. Tired at the end of the day, my balance somewhat off, to walk any great distance I had to stop every so often to rest my legs for a few seconds. I knew I would be under a lot of pressure during this exercise. It would be a day-and-night treadmill, and I would rather have all 8 cylinders working. I decided to go and see a flight surgeon I knew, and discuss it with him. Since there wasn't a resident neurologist on the base he sent me to a civilian physician. There I explained my medical history and my improvement after taking a steroid treatment. I had been told by a friend never to recommend your own treatment to a doctor; let him come up with the solution. He was skeptical, but said he would put me on it for a short time. When I returned a week later and he checked me out, he was impressed at the improvement. My balance was back and my legs were strong, among other things. He gave me a steroid prescription for the exercise period. I went the distance, day and night, fast-paced while working with a joint force of Navy SEALS, Air Force Special Operations, and Army Special Forces. I had a saying that if one did not blow his own horn, someone else would use it as a spittoon. So let me just say the whole effort was a huge success. The general who was the commander of the task force was so delighted with my efforts he asked me when would I be ready to rotate, to transfer back to Fort Bragg and work for him. I declined.

Preparations for my next assignment had already been set in motion. In the early summer of 1978 I would take over a position on the Commander In Chief, Pacific (CINCPAC) staff in Hawaii, and be the senior U.S. officer responsible for unconventional warfare/special operations in the Pacific theater. It was also another parachute position.

Before leaving I made another visit to the Tampa neurologist to discuss my future. Unpredictable. As a backup he gave me a letter of introduction to another civilian neurologist in Hawaii.

Hawaiian Papaya, Aussie Beer, Korean Kimchi, and New Challenges mid–1978 to mid–1982

Our home was located at Fort Shafter, and the CINCPAC head-quarters was at Camp Smith, a U.S. Marine base about fifteen minutes driving time away. My new job was as Chief of the Special Operations Division, another joint assignment. Our duty day started about 7 A.M., when I would arrive at the office; there I would grab a cup of coffee and a handful of message traffic, review it, and along with other division chiefs meet with our boss, a Marine two-star general. At 7:15 A.M. I had to revamp my PT program. There would be no time for early outside exercising. The best I could do at "o–dark–thirty" in the morning was to include a series of sit ups on the slant board while watching the TV news, and on weekends, take a bike ride around the post. However, I found something in Hawaii that I didn't have to deal with in Florida — hills. It seems all of the island of Oahu is nothing but hills. Even with a ten–speed bike I was having trouble going up the hills. Coming down was a disaster. Trying to shift gears would sooner or later cause me to lose my balance, resulting in a "crash & burn." After one really bad accident, some individual stopped and loaded me and my bike into his truck for the ride home. At the time Ginnie was out shopping.

When she returned she found me sitting on the bed with an ice pack over a bloody forehead. She put her foot down. She had had enough of seeing me with bumps and bruises, and now a bloody head. She took my bike away from me and "ordered" me to find a new exercise! She was right. It was only a matter of time before I started breaking bones. "Why don't you try swimming?" she asked. "There's a large pool at Camp Smith." I loved snorkeling but had never done any lap swimming. It was an Olympic size pool. I would do it if only to say I had tried it. I didn't think it was real exercising until that first swim. After a few laps I found myself stopping to catch my breath. Okay! I'll work this into my schedule. As time passed I found swimming was just the thing I needed. I could take an early lunch break and beat the crowd. I finally set my goal for a half mile. It didn't happen overnight, but once I made it, knowing I had broken the mental barrier of getting there, I was satisfied with swimming that distance.

Whenever I finished swimming and climbed out of the pool my legs were "spongy." I worked it out to where I had to take only a few steps to a nearby pool chair; after a few minutes' rest my walking improved, and as the water cooled in the winter (yes, even in Hawaii, the pool water temperature would drop because Camp Smith was located at a higher elevation) my legs would regain their strength for the rest of the afternoon. Imagine, each time I walked to the pool, a distance of around 400 yards, I would have to stop once or twice to let my legs rest. But after a cold water swim it was an easy walk back, and then up three flights of stairs with no problem. Over the years I would become a believer in cold water swims.

Part of my job was to travel out along the Pacific rim to visit various countries and establish face-to-face contacts with others involved in the special operations business. Sometimes I could visit up to four countries on a trip, such as the Philippines, Indonesia, Hong Kong, and Western Australia. With this type of traveling, international airports became my nemesis. All the inherent travel problems came to rest on my shoulders — time zone changes, jet lag, customs checks at 3 in the morning, hitting the ground running for briefings, meetings, and social activities, all crammed into short time periods. No matter when I started a trip, and they were usually at night, my arrival back to Honolulu would be around 7:30 A.M. It would be close to 9 A.M. before clearing U.S. customs. Ginnie would always be there in her little yellow MGB. Following the short drive home and some private time together, I would sleep for the rest of the day. After a light dinner I would then sleep again. It would take me a few days to shed the exhaustion entirely, but I was already back to the normal 7 A.M. work schedule the following morning.

If I were to maintain that sort of pace, I decided it would be best to consult with a neurologist. I used the name that had been given to me in Tampa. After the physical checks I explained my traveling problems. The doctor decided to give me a ration of Prednisone. He said if I continued to react as well as I did, then I wasn't "burned out" with MS. I would use it as required, keeping within the prescribed dosage and time limits. Thereafter, I would visit him every six months for a checkup.

Balance and foot drop were usually more evident when I was tired. While visiting the New Zealanders as well as the Australians, I was introduced to their custom, which probably started with the Brits, of stopping work around 10 A.M. for a coffee/tea/snack break. It was a time for the commander to informally meet with his staff and subordinate commanders. As a guest I was invited to participate. The coffee or tea was poured and given in a cup and saucer, and that would be my silent dilemma for those visits. Standing, juggling cup and saucer while carrying on spirited conversation was always a challenge. It was a balancing act equal at times to the highwire show of a three-ring circus.

In another part of the Pacific I would visit Korea at least three times a year. As the senior Unconventional Warfare/Special Operations officer, I would become the deputy commander of a combined task force for exercises, with a Korean general as commander. One day while out in a helicopter inspecting troops in the field, I felt myself getting weak. I excused myself from the general's party and went back to the chopper. As I attempted to climb in I could not raise my leg high enough to sit on the floor of the chopper and hoist myself up and in. Each time I tried I became more tired. The Korean pilot looked back at me but said nothing. I finally backed up to the door, and with my arms lifted my body in. When the general and his party arrived he put on the headset as was normal when flying. Nothing was said to me as we flew back to the headquarters, but the inscrutable oriental mind was at work. The next day, for another chopper trip to inspect troops in the field, I found the helicopter we were to use had a running board or step on it. Again, not a word was said relating to the day before. From then on the choppers I flew in were all equipped with steps.

At the general's headquarters there was a wide, stately, circular staircase. In the last year or two of the tour I started tripping as I went up the stairs. If I did not concentrate on lifting my boots over each step, the foot drop would catch me off guard. I had to look down as I raised my boots. Over tea one day the general asked if I might have a neurological problem! It was obvious to the Koreans that I did have some kind of a problem, and as hosts they tried to ensure the problem would not hinder me.

On another trip by jeep, we stopped at a Korean subordinate headquarters for lunch. I loved Korean food and their meals could be counted on to be spicy hot and tasty. At the end of the lunch meal, apples were always served, as was customary. The Koreans were very proud of their apples, and they were always served with the skin still on, along with paring knives. They never ate apples with the skin still on. It was an art to pare the skin off in one continuous peel, which they did easily. I learned early on that I could not pare apples! The fingers just didn't do the job as they should. So, I simply didn't try peeling the apple, but left it on the plate. The host commander reached over for the apple, pared it, sliced it up, and passed the plate back to me with a gracious smile. Thereafter, it was never a surprise to see an already pared apple served to me, or the host doing it as I sat next to him.

On that trip, as we finished the meal and went outside, I saw a helicopter waiting for us. It was parked on a lower level which was surrounded with huge rock formations somewhat like an open air amphitheater. There was a short, steeply winding path down to the lower field. "Well here I am again!" I said to myself. Why can't I just have level places to walk instead of trying to be a billy goat? Just then a Korean colonel friend came up next to me. I used to introduce him to other Americans as a German officer who spoke Korean! He was fluent in German, besides English, and had attended one of the West German military courses in that country. He simply smiled and walked along my side stabilizing me as we went down the steep path. Once on level ground he smiled again but said nothing. I just gave a big thanks.

Traveling to those countries to observe or participate in the exercises would usually terminate with a party and a request to say "a few words," be it an officers club — Western Australia, a large gym — New Zealand, a large ballroom — Korea, or an open field, anywhere. As each party progressed I would have to take special note of exactly where I had to stand to say those "few words." Standing on the floor was okay as long as I moved the body to keep from stiffening up; stages could be my downfall, for the stairs up to the stage usually had no rails! Those impromptu speeches where I had to climb up onto a large crate or box could prove to be a catastrophe if I wasn't careful. My ability to maintain my balance was always stretched to the fullest, both in standing on any of the platforms as well as getting off them.

Ginnie had been a rock by my side, never quite sure what to expect as I traveled off island. Would I have a problem? She put no demands on me, except to get me back in one piece. However, as our 25th wedding anniversary was approaching, she asked that I be home to celebrate it with her. She had endured the vicissitudes of an Army wife to the fullest. Two weeks after our marriage I was carted from the field into the hospital at Fort Benning, Georgia with pneumonia. Six months after our first son was born, I departed for Korea for fourteen months. After I joined Special Forces, Ginnie became pregnant again; she only asked that I be there when she gave birth. It would be close. I was scheduled to depart for a six-month tour in Laos. She was late, and the departure date could not be changed. We finally went for a ride on a long unimproved bumpy road on the Fort Bragg military reservation. That night I took her to the hospital. The next afternoon she was released with our newborn son in her arms, and we drove to the airport for my departure! I returned in October of that year, and was put on a 72-hour alert status near Christmas. I pulled out right after the New Year for 4½ months in the jungles of Central America.

Despite all of this, I promised I would return in time to celebrate our 25th wedding anniversary together. The trip was for an annual large-scale exercise in Korea. Because of commitments at the office, I departed at the very last minute via commercial airlines, and was booked to return the same way. The exercise over, critiques and social functions just about out of the way, I was scheduled to depart the following afternoon. That morning a Korean Air Line 747 jumbo jet aircraft crashed on the only runway at Kimpo air terminal! The wreckage would remain on the runway until it had been inspected. Military aircraft leaving from the Osan Air Base were booked to the fullest. Would I make it home in time? "Yes, I shall be home in time." Brave words, but as each day dragged on, they seemed hollow.

Eventually, it was announced that the runway was cleared. My new booking was another day away. Now, if everything else went right, and I mean *everything*, I would arrive in Hawaii on the morning of our anniversary. I noted that my body was becoming weak. I just about lost it walking through Kimpo for the afternoon flight. In the aircraft I felt myself going down in ways I had never experienced previously. We would land at Narita Airport in Japan for a few hours, and catch another 747 aircraft to Hawaii. It was dark when we landed. Having flown that route many times before, I knew the procedures. The aircraft could roll up to the satellite terminal, or it could stop on the apron and have the high steps rolled out to it; then the disembarking passengers would board small buses to the terminal where there were more stairs up to the waiting area. If the aircraft stopped short of the terminal I would never make it down those stairs outside the aircraft. I prayed. My prayer was answered; the aircraft rolled up to the terminal with the moveable passageway extending to the door of the aircraft. We were told to take everything with us as we departed from the plane. I was so weak I knew I couldn't carry even my small handbag, let alone myself off the aircraft and up the ramp. As passengers started to move I signalled one of the officers who was from the States and had worked with me on the exercise. He carried my bag and supported me as I went up the passageway. Once in the terminal I flopped down into a chair and didn't move. Others came and asked if I needed any medical help or any kind of assistance. No. This was time for the steroids. I sat for about two hours frozen in one of those terminal chairs I called "Japan's revenge," the most uncomfortable chair of any I have ever sat in. It was certainly not made for the western-size body. When boarding time came for the final leg of the flight, the same officer returned ready to just about carry me on board. No thanks. Just take my bag and I'll be fine. The steroids had started to work. I walked down the passageway myself. The six-hour flight was uneventful. After landing in Hawaii I picked up my own bag and walked out. In the customs area I grabbed my luggage and tossed it into a cart for the march through the U.S. Customs inspection booth. Those officers who had helped me at Narita just looked in amazement as I thanked them for their assistance and wished them an "aloha" with a smile. Ginnie was outside in her yellow MGB waiting as usual.

That evening our 25th anniversary party was in a friend's house. Looking at a picture brings back a deluge of memories. The d'kanes were in colorful aloha shirts, and the wahines wore gorgeous muumuus; all were wearing leis. Our leis were made of Venda orchids. Kona breezes blew in the soft fragrance of Plumeria bushes outside the lanai. A large easy chair was my throne, while Ginnie sat on one of the overstuffed arms. We both had a glass of champagne, raising our glasses to the numerous toasts that evening. Tired, yes, but there was a sense of exhilaration, for it was our night and we were among good friends who also felt the moment. After all, a twenty-fifth anniversary only comes once! Ginnie had selected a poem for our chaplain friend to read as part of the evening's festivities. On a table close by, was a gift to us of a large ceramic Hawaiian-style plate to commemorate the date. Our friends had all signed the plate, which would later be taken to a store for baking and glazing. The last few lines of the poem were written in the center of the plate:

I Love You Not Only for What You Are
But for What I Am When I Am With You
You Have Done it by Being Yourself

The anniversary was actually a full week of celebrations, along with private, intimate dinners in town, and later at a club on the slope of Diamondhead overlooking Honolulu's city lights. In the meantime, word was carried back to Fort Bragg that I had suffered some kind of stroke while traveling on the aircraft. So it went.

Starting in the late 1970s I found that I could not walk barefooted, whether it was on a floor or rug, or even on sand. The bottoms of my feet reacted, causing me to look and feel like I was walking on sharp jagged rocks or broken glass. I hobbled. It was most noticeable at the swimming pool when I had to walk barefooted about 30 yards to the shower.

Of more concern, there is a Hawaiian custom of taking one's shoes off before entering a house. Being invited to various homes for cocktails or dinner presented a real problem. I simply could not take off the shoes and walk in a reasonable manner. So I wore my shoes into the houses and carried a story that I had a foot problem caused from being in the jungles. The excuse of "jungle rot" goes a long way.

Being on airborne status in Hawaii also presented a slight problem, since there were only two small organizations on the entire island that parachuted: a U.S. Marine reserve Force Recon unit and a Naval EOD unit. To maintain proficiency I would have to "straphang" with those units if the opportunity presented itself, or parachute with units of Free World countries while visiting them when possible. It was always dicey, since each organization had its own rules for parachuting. I always had to be careful not to put myself into a position I couldn't handle. On one occasion, while visiting a Navy SEAL exercise at Subic Bay in the Philippines, I decided to straphang for a parachute jump from a C-130 aircraft off the coast. There was to be a New Zealand Special Air Service (SAS) team with a rubber boat, rigged with a parachute, which would exit the aircraft first while I followed close behind. They would, as part of the exercise, link up with a submarine.

My normal uniform for those kinds of jumps was T–shirt, shorts, and canvas sneakers. A SEAL officer, who was a member of my division, asked if I wanted a set of scuba fins to wear. I said no. I couldn't imagine myself flopping along the full length of the aircraft keeping my balance and exiting in a reasonable time. "Well then," he offered, "why don't you strap them to your belly band (of the main parachute), go barefooted, and once out of the aircraft put the fins on?"

Again, no thank you. It only took a brief moment to review my tasks: going out the rear of the aircraft, opening the chute, checking the canopy, looking around to insure no other jumpers were close by, and then checking below to see where to land in order to be picked up by a SEAL boat. Then I would have to deal with a set of other procedures, including the unsnapping of one of the risers of the parachute. It would be held in the crook of my arm until just before hitting the water, when it would be released, thereby spilling the air from the chute to insure I would not be dragged across the water. Should I try doing all those things while being dropped from about 1,000 ft. above the ocean while trying to put fins on at the same time? No way! I had confidence in my ability to tread water with the parachute still on until pickup, provided I did everything else right. And I would do everything else right provided I didn't have to be distracted by those damned fins! Army types always gave the navy SEALS headaches.

In comparison, jumps on land usually presented no real problems. In Korea we always jumped on a DZ which was an island in the middle of the Han River outside of Seoul. There was always a jeep to pick me up. If it was a helicopter jump and we were making a couple of jumps, we would be driven back to the chopper and chuted up again and make another jump. When the jeep came out the second time for the long drive back to the headquarters there was usually a cold Korean beer handed to me as we started back. Other countries SAS units, including those from Australia and New Zealand, had a truck driving along the route of the drop to pick up the jumpers and their chutes.

By 1980 the weight of the main and reserve parachutes were starting to make themselves felt if I had to jump from an aircraft and was not first in line to exit. My right leg would usually drag as I moved toward the door. My exits became the object of a good-natured joke with the Australians. The commander of the SAS Regiment, who became a good friend of mine (and I swear looked exactly like the brother of "Crocodile Dundee") demonstrated after a few drinks, with a full dose of exaggeration, my exiting a C-130. We all had a laugh. I could take that kind of camaraderie; however, my balance and walking did not go unnoticed at CINCPAC Headquarters, and at the HQ there was no humor involved.

"Boss, I've known you since Florida, and your balance and walking seem to be getting worse." "JD," one of the Air Force Special Operations officers in the division, was always observant and up-front. My fall-back story was the "middle ear problem" for affecting my balance and "the old back injury from parachuting" for affecting my walk. If he had noticed, others could as well.

Some months later one of my Army officers who was of Chinese descent (and an outstanding linguist) stopped into the office to tell me some others had seen me getting out of the pool after a swim as I staggered to the chair. "They asked if you drank on duty. I know you don't, and told them so, but I just wanted to let you know what was asked." The crowning blow came when another colonel I sometimes drove with to work told me how the Deputy J3, an Air Force one star general who was in my chain of command, asked if I ever came to work drunk! "Never!" was his reply. I wanted simply to go to the general's office, shut the door, and tell him what my real problem was, and it wasn't booze. But to do that would have been a disaster. All I could do was to gut it out and be more conscious of my walking and balance, and to protect my back from "latrine rumors."

I came face to face with the "mother of all fears" in March 1982: diarrhea while flying. I had just finished my final large scale exercise in Korea. For almost four years I had drunk the local water and eaten the local food with no problem. But a bug was in the air during the last visit, and for a number of us, it meant fever and diarrhea. Traveling was out of the question. By luck, my replacement who was out to observe the exercise had a later return flight. Since we both were traveling by commercial air we switched bookings so he could leave a few days early, thereby giving me a chance to recover. On my travel day I met one of my division NCOs who had also been hit by the same bug. We would return together. The fever had subsided but the bowels were still loose. The whole trip consisted of gulping various diarrhea medicines. When we changed aircraft at Narita, a large group of Japanese on a guided tour boarded the aircraft. Having traveled with those large groups before, I knew what to expect; on "wake up" call the next morning when the aircraft was about two hours out from Hawaii there would be a line six deep waiting outside the restrooms, all of them carrying their toothbrushes and other toiletries. If nature nudged me within that time frame I would never make it to the restroom in time. I didn't sleep the whole flight. Lady Luck smiled on me that morning. I beat the crowd, but it was way too close for comfort.

Snorkeling was one of our big relaxations while in Hawaii. There was a state park called Hanauma Bay on the southern side of the island just before the Holona Blowhole. At least once a week, while I was on the island, we would drive over to it for a couple of hours of snorkeling. The park was surrounded by reefs which kept the big (dangerous) fish out. With a handful of bread crumbs we could enjoy all the underwater color that Hawaii is famous for just by watching the feeding fish. The parking area was at the top of some very high cliffs. To get down to the bay after parking we had to first go down a number of levels which contained mainly steps and sloped ramps; next was a walk down the steep road, and at the bottom of the road was a walk across the sand. The first time we snorkeled at the park in 1971 I ran all the way up after finishing. In 1978 I walked down and up without stopping. As we moved into 1982 it was a challenge to walk down. I could only make it with numerous stops. The return, because of being in the water for a time, could be negotiated without too much trouble. Would the day come when I could only enjoy the bay from the top of the cliffs? It was a thought I tried to lock away.

Being in the business I was in you just had to think you were omnipotent, capable of doing anything without harm, but the thought of not being able to negotiate those cliffs kept lingering. Would that day ever come? How soon? I didn't know the answer, but our last swim there told me it wasn't too far beyond the horizon.

The tour was now winding toward completion. Where would my next assignment be? Washington offered me places some would call exotic (depending on your taste) if I wanted to remain in the Pacific area: Katmandu, Manila, or Singapore, for openers. The Koreans wanted me to be assigned to Korea in a special operations position. All were tempting. But there were two considerations drawing me back to the mainland. We thought that within the next year or two, one son, if not both of them, would be married. We wanted to be stateside instead of half a world away when that time came. Taking stock of myself was the other consideration. By my own measurements I had lost ground — not enough to call it quits, but I wanted to be in the States if things took a real turn downward. It was time to leave. On the evening of departure many of our friends came to give us an Aloha send-off: a smile, a hug, some with tears, all accompanied by the placing of the traditional lei around our necks. As we boarded the 747 aircraft our necks were covered with leis, so many that we could not turn our heads. One word said it all: "Aloha."

Gen. Robert E. Lee and I Have Something in Common — We Both Surrendered in Virginia mid-1982 to mid-1984

First we drove to Yellowstone National Park. We had been among the palm trees and pineapple groves for too long. We wanted to drive through the tall pines and see the last snow still remaining at the higher elevations.

At the scheduled time we arrived at Fort Lee, Virginia. I would be the new commander of the Readiness Group located there. RG Lee, as it was known, was a tenant unit. The Group was located there as a geographic convenience. My higher headquarters was located at Fort Meade, Maryland. We worked with the Reserve and National Guard units in the Commonwealth of Virginia.

It was a choice assignment, with my boss about 150 miles away. I knew I had been selected over a couple of other colonels who had, on paper, better credentials. Why I had been selected, I didn't know. However, a possible reason came from a friend who said he knew the individual I was replacing, and "there probably was low morale in the unit." He was right, and with low morale comes low efficiency. Reinforcing this perception was the commanding general, with three stars, who stopped down for a visit shortly after I arrived and said the unit had a morale problem. The unspoken words were: "Fix it." Sometimes a reputation precedes the individual. I had a reputation of taking care of my people, and in return getting the very best from them. So that's why I was selected.

I was into my 27th year of military service. This would be my last tour before mandatory retirement in 1985 with a total of thirty years service. That was my goal — 30 years of military service. It wasn't long, though, before I was asking myself if I could make it to 1985 and retirement.

Little problems were becoming more noticeable. I couldn't walk more than fifty yards without stopping. The Group headquarters was spread out in separate buildings. I was having a hard time just walking from one building to another without stopping. I had set up a physical fitness program for the Group, and even though I knew my running days were over, it bothered me that "the old man" could not run along with the troops. I had fallen back on the old standbys of "bad back" and "old jump injury," but the fact was I wasn't running. When I drove a car my right foot was having trouble moving from the gas pedal to the brake pedal. I could drive short distances, but extended trips across the state, which could be 400 miles one way, or up to the higher headquarters, were beginning to wear on me; besides the weak leg, my whole body became stiff from sitting or standing for long periods. On first visits to the various reserve units I would go with one of my people for introductions; thereafter, I would drive myself. I could, of course, have used one of our sedans and drivers for the visits, but the norm was to drive oneself. It was decision time again.

Everything pointed to the increased degree of physical deterioration. The walking was the most obvious. My bike exercising on a stationary-exerciser which I started in 1980 had gone from a half-hour of biking in two segments of 15 minutes to just one period of 10 or 12 minutes. My set of 50 sit ups was now down to 15 in groups of 2 or 3 with lengthy rest periods between them. Fort Lee had an Olympic-size indoor pool of which I took full advantage. But my swimming capability had diminished. After a couple of laps in the pool my right leg would become more of a "rudder" than a leg propelling me forward in the water. My strength had dropped off to where I couldn't even carry grocery bags. The stiffness was now accompanied with a weak back. I couldn't bend over for any length of time without a need to stretch out and rest my back. If I was home for lunch after a swim, I had to rest before going back to work. There was no doubt I had gone downhill, but the car driving was my biggest concern. I could not do my job properly if I couldn't get to those distant locations. Maybe this was the time to "hang it up," yet something held me back. I owed one to the general who had picked me for the job. He could have gone with others, but he chose me. He wanted me to raise the morale and efficiency of this unit, and I felt obligated to do just that.

Ginnie and I talked about the future and my desires at least to reach the goals I had set for the Group. I figured it would take about a year to get the morale and efficiency up to a point where I was satisfied. That would be late fall, 1983. My own goal of 30 years service was put on the back burner. If I could just hold on until I was satisfied with the Group, then anything else as far as remaining in the service would be a bonus. To make it to that point, I would need Ginnie's help.

I could handle the driving to some distant locations to check how we were performing our duties, but for other locations Ginnie would have to drive me. We used private cars on many of the trips, and I had encouraged those married to take their wives along for weekends when they had to stay at motels; therefore, Ginnie accompanying me would not be out of the ordinary. On trips to the higher headquarters at Fort Meade, she would have to go with me. I could not handle the traffic around the Washington, D.C. beltway. On the other hand, most of those trips were tied in with an official evening function, and wives were encouraged to attend when possible. When I did go with other people from the Group for unit visits, they always took extra care, without my asking, to get me as close to the location as possible to reduce my walking. Okay. I would gut it out, this was my "last hurrah," and hopefully I would finish with my head up.

For the next year I was focused on making my set of goals into measured accomplishments. By late 1983 the morale, along with the efficiency were more than just up. Things clicked, and when they did, you knew you were there. The unit had passed its Inspector General's inspection with no deficiencies, and following right on its heels was a country-wide mobilization exercise. I had been tapped as the evaluator for Fort Lee and other distant posts while the Group executed its mobilization plans with selected reserve and National Guard units. The holidays followed shortly thereafter. We would celebrate them to the fullest with the Group, savoring every minute, for it would be our last Christmas while in active military service. As January 1984 rolled in, it was now my turn.

I called the executive officer of the local military hospital, whom I knew fairly well, and said I wanted to meet with him. With a knot in my stomach I was about to raise my hand and "come in from the cold." The short walk into the hospital was the final step to surrender. Although I was still on my feet, the beast had won, but I had at least given him a run for his money. Like General Lee my head was up as I took those final steps.

The Group had been told I was visiting the hospital because of my "bad back." During my meeting with the executive officer I asked him to hold any information concerning my condition until I talked to my Group. I disliked latrine rumors. Any information should come from me, and no one else. Within a couple of days I was on my way to Walter Reed Hospital outside of Washington, D.C. After the initial examinations by several neurologists, a couple of nurses carrying my records stopped by and asked "Where have you been for all these years?" I couldn't contain myself. "Having a good time!" was my reply.

Epilogue
mid-1984 to mid-1991

The Army had told me I was disabled and medically retired me with 29 years service. The Veterans Administration had gone even further and proclaimed I was not just disabled, but was totally and permanently disabled. However, in my own mind, I didn't see it quite that way. Granted, I had limitations, but I was still on my feet. I was an "able disabled."

Our home, which we designed and had built, was in the Panhandle of Florida. I threw myself into gardening since I had never had a chance to do it before. Flowers, shrubs, trees, and vegetables thrived in spite of my lack of a green thumb. My limitations were now a part of my life, but I could live with them. Early on I had acquired a "nickel philosophy." I have only so many nickels to spend in a day, and I would spend them wisely. Those nickels represented my strength and physical capabilities. Some days I would be a miser stretching my nickels over the whole day, while other times I would be the big spender and use all my nickels to the point where I would go bankrupt before the end of the day. When I reached that point Ginnie would step in to do the things I couldn't handle.

Ginnie announced from the beginning that the maintenance of the pool was her job and I was not to get involved with it. All I had to do was swim in it. As the pool temperatures dipped in the late fall I continued to swim. The revelation that I found years ago still held; I walked better after a cold water swim. Swimming in water of the 60 degree range was fine, but as it went into the 50 degree range something kicked in — common sense. Swimming in water that cold dropped my body temperature, and it took too long for me to warm up again. Thereafter, for the month or so that the water remained below 60 degrees I returned to my bike exerciser or pushed and pulled the wood cart loaded with logs for the fireplace. Basically I was seeking anything for some exercise while waiting for the day the water temperature reached 60 degrees again, so I could proclaim "Pool's open!"

Florida has been a natural jump–off point to the Caribbean for snorkeling trips. Getting over the sand to the water and putting the fins on are the greatest challenges, but once in the water I am my own captain. Our last trip was to Cancun, Mexico for our thirty–fifth wedding anniversary. It was a trip for the whole family; a full week of snorkeling and celebrating yet another milestone.

In 1985 I joined an MS support group and later was invited to become a member of the board of trustees for the MS Chapter located about 70 miles away from our home in Niceville. My experience with other MSers gave me insights on the need for humor and fellowship. A smile and a laugh goes a long way. I became the Bob Hope of our group. Making jokes about myself and my disabilities brought laughter and ultimately a desire to talk instead of just sitting and listening.

I also have had the chance either to talk to or correspond with other military people released from the service because of MS. The old chain of command still lives. Some just wanted contact with someone who had the rank and was in the same boat, someone who understood them and their problems because of having been there. I've also had contact with others who had been recently diagnosed with MS, about to start their own long trek through the maze of red tape in preparation for being medically retired from the service. My words are always the same: once the neurologist determines it is MS, all he can do is to check your progress, and give medication as needed — he can't cure you, and he certainly isn't going to tell you how to live the rest of your life. It is up to each person to take care of their own body and make the best of what he or she has, because nobody else will. I've had some positive feedback, and that makes all the phone calls and letter writing worthwhile.

In 1989 a therapist, my fourth one, told me I didn't have a hamstring in my right leg and was surprised I was still walking. She obviously had missed *"True Grit 101"* in her education about disabled people. I am still on my feet. I walk as gracefully as the son of Frankenstein, but I'm still on my feet. I will use a wheelchair when going through airports, Disney World, and other places where the distances are too far to walk.

When we reached the status of grandparents things were set in motion to sell our home in Niceville and move to west central Florida where the family ties are, and build a new home. I continue a routine of a 500–yard swim and leg exercises in the pool.

In retrospect, I was not mentally or emotionally ready in 1984 for retirement. Coupled with my physical limitations, this made things terribly rough on Ginnie. She would slowly take over those manly jobs which would decimate me if I attempted to do them. She did everything, from climbing the ladder, to brushing the pine needles off the house roof, to carrying the groceries, becoming a master carpenter with the saw and hammer, and taking over driving responsibilities. I have never been a good second–in–command in anything. At times I became a demanding tyrant. Ginnie would tell me she had been a good SFer's wife for 29 years and now she was trying to be a good MSer's wife. Unspoken was her need for my help in doing that job. It took a lot of self–searching on my part. Our lives have taken a new direction, and will continue to require a number of adjustments to handle the new situations arising as we travel down that dark road. Today, as always, Ginnie remains the wind beneath my wings.

Bodytrapper. Soulgrinder.

by: *Kayla Sand*

In hills and on the rising western sweep of the Great Plains, multiple sclerosis is common. In my circle of friends — vibrant, intelligent, active women all — MS sneaks in and savages a life here and there like a rapist on the prowl.

Now Chris can't walk, and her arms are halting, too. Now Wanda's voice has changed. She struggles to be understood. I strain to understand her. Kathy was fortunate at first. MS tiptoed into her life. For several years, she could ignore it. It grew bolder. Today she has a tough time about the ranch. Balance is essential for riding a cowhorse. She teeters and totters and can barely handle a trail ride on a poke. And a few months ago, the eyes of Muriel, owner of the nicest dress store in town, started to blur. Her hands and feet began to tingle, and she began to forget things. Two weeks ago, she too, heard the news.

And then there was me. Having divorced. Having survived a prolonged and vicious custody campaign by the father of my son. Having seen my son split down the middle. Having remarried and moved a thousand and a half miles away. I was about as high on the Holmes–Rahe scale of traumatic events as a person could get. According to Holmes–Rahe predictors, I was bound to get sick. But I would have preferred to be a little ill — or very sick, temporarily. I would have made a deal with God. I would have given up my appendix or my gall bladder. Even my womb. But MS hit me in the head, and out tumbled all of my dreams.

At first, I just wanted to know what was wrong. I had been in a state of malaise about my health for years, but symptoms always came and went until I learned to make self–deprecating hypochondriacal jokes to diminish power of my puzzlement. But this time, jokes didn't suffice. An array of harpies surrounded me: errant feelings of electricity when bending my neck; the blunting of touch in my fingers; difficult-to-describe sensory bombardment when I walked through a supermarket or the woods; a burning cape around my shoulders. I clawed helplessly as fog crept in and surrounded me. I feared something terrible lurked in the core of myself, in my fine brain. I haunted a library and sought books to catch and tag this mysterious and terrible adversary. A brain tumor? Mental illness? I found multiple sclerosis. I diagnosed myself.

Doctors were baffled, but I hesitated to tell them my conclusion. Psychosomatic is always a word in the background when female patients complain of vague symptoms. I wanted to avoid awkward referrals to psychiatrists. But more than that, I was hoping to be proven wrong. So I said nothing. I prayed for a simple, benign explanation. I didn't look sick. Wasn't throwing up. Wasn't losing weight. Finally, I mustered the courage to mention multiple sclerosis. I was referred to a neurologist. There, I touched my nose with my eyes closed. Stood steadily with my eyes shut. Had all the right reflexes — just a little brisk, with a little quiver in an eye. A little hesitance at the prick of a pin on a hand. That's all; but enough, with my description of wandering electricity to warrant an MRI to "rule out MS."

It didn't rule out MS. Instead it showed a brain, which to the eye of a lay-person (me) looked like a photo-negative of a wheel of Danish Havarti cheese. I saw a grim lineup of shots of my brain alongside those of a normal brain, which my neurologist, a medical school professor, put up to illustrate the difference.

The neurologist, perplexed by my weak attempt at humor, explained patiently, kindly, that unlike the Havarti, the spots on my brain slices weren't holes — just lesions. But of course, we weren't talking about cheese. We weren't looking at advertising proofs for a deli. We weren't even talking about a vestigial organ. We were talking *brain*. Mine.

We weren't talking imminent death, although my life had become uninsurable. I read about the woman left with only the blink of her eyes to command from her bodytrap. And another woman, with barely more. And another. Death held no terror like those specters.

Suicide is a seductive option when life becomes an uncontrollable free-fall. I contemplated taking my life as one last gesture of defiance to an unkind fate. The Baltimore Catholic catechism intervened. Over the years of parochial education, the nuns had managed to instill in me an unalterable sense of right and wrong, and the implications therein. In their books, suicide was a mortal sin, and an irrevocable one at that. Over the years, the Catholic church has become kinder and enlightened about sicknesses of the mind. Now it withholds its judgement of suicides. But the nuns' admonitions stuck with me, and I was imaginative enough to envision going from muddle on earth into everlasting Dismal Swamp in the hereafter. So I live on.

As I said, multiple sclerosis strikes often in the communities and countryside of the western Great Plains where I lived for many years. It is common in Wisconsin, where I grew up. I watched a bright cousin slowly fade from a distance. But I didn't know much about MS before I got it.

After I became an MS person, I read everything I could get my hands on about the illness. Unschooled in medicine, I learned about the anatomy of the human brain and central nervous system, plus the immune system. I studied everybody's' theories.

I see a prominent neurologist annually for a few reasons: he is involved in research, and therefore keeps abreast of conventional medical research, which my Western mind refuses to dismiss as a source of hope. He is also a kind man who takes time to thoughtfully answer the rambling lists of questions engendered by my reading on the subject. He reassures me.

However, I have long since broadened my search for help beyond scientifically supported definitions. I will try anything that shouldn't hurt and might help. I contemplate my t-cells, believed to be misguided. I have conversations with them when I think I am at highest risk, such as when I have a cold, after an upset, while travelling, or when it's hot. Does mental imaging work? I try it. Does diet help? I eat carefully. Relaxation therapy? I pampered myself with regular visits to a clinic for months, learning progressive relaxation and biofeedback.

The efficacy of hyperbaric oxygen is doubtful, but I heard it wouldn't hurt, so I tried it. My health insurance didn't pay; that hurt. Sensibly, from insurance companies' point of view, health insurance policies exclude experimental treatments. But the mean effect, from my vantage point, is that almost all treatments for incurable, uncontrollable diseases like MS are technically experimental. So MS is a relatively cheap disease for most health insurance companies. Common mercies are strained from our family budget: massage to ease the interminable ache of muscles laboring to obey garbled messages; chiropractic adjustments to relieve the painful confusion of my back.

I have heard many heartening words since learning to pick my brain out from a line-up. The wisest thought came from a physician who has survived MS for many years. A battery of psychological tests indicated that she had the psychological defense of denial down to a fine art. Psychological dogma indicates that direct address of problems is the healthiest response. However, the good doctor reflected on the matter, and shrugged, "What more sensible way to cope with life when a chronic, incurable illness has crept into your brain?" Denial. I do not have denial down to a fine art yet, but I work hard on it.

My husband — The first few months of our marriage were inauspicious. My husband had a demanding new job, and while mastering that, he pulled from his great soul the strength to accompany me into the vortex of my private hell. The neurologist who diagnosed my illness expressed his condolences when he met my husband. Hardly anybody else had thought to do that.

I seldom read anything encouraging about marriages where MS makes three. It's tough to be healthy and vigorous and live with a young person who lives with MS, only remembering vitality. We do it with humor. Black humor usually, but our Irish-Jewish combined heritage lends itself well to the genre. We ferment our spit and pass it off as champagne.

We travel. I push myself to keep up with my husband. And with myself. After three years, I still hike up and down steep hillsides, hoping my twisting legs will continue to carry me. Damn the pain. I trudge through tropical foliage, dumping ice water on my hair, becoming stringy and drippy like the weeping figs around me. All the while, I look up — and up further — my eye follows unwavering trunks to see the glorious heads of tall cabbage palms.

I find no crisp ending for an MS story. I know multiple sclerosis grinds upon spirits over years as ineluctably as does desperate poverty. I keep in touch with a friend who is brainscarred like me. Our Christmas cards are painstakingly bright. We speak of children or other friends or pets. We avoid our year's losses. We reunite carefully, like new mothers of deformed children: afraid of pity, afraid to pity. We exchange pain-coping tips lightly; cookie recipes, by our offhand tone. Then we exalt small brightnesses, aware of the vastness of our own sad possibilities, and preferring to smile for our reunion.

MS-related literature is full of the word "hope." As a magic word of commerce, "hope" replaces "sex" when selling anything related to MS. And hope for MS is as elusive and ethereal as the perfect union of bodies and souls.

Part–time Mother

by: *Mary Martinez*

"I knew this would happen," my mind affirmed in righteous disbelief while my heart whispered a desperate prayer, "Dear God, please don't let my baby die." I tried to drag my lame body down the porch steps as his stubby two–year–old legs propelled him with animation along the sidewalk, closer to the traffic on the busy street. I screamed his name through scrambled sounds of birds singing, wind rattling leaves on trees, honking horns and roaring engines while my son moved, as if in slow motion, deeper into my nightmare.

For two years I'd dreaded this "what if" moment, and now it was happening. What if he got away from me, what if he ran into the street, what if he got stuck in a tree, what if he fell down the stairs, what if he rolled down the bank into the water? My white fingers clutched the railing helplessly as he skipped farther down the road.

God didn't let him die. His gentle hand reached down and stopped Joe at the sidewalk's edge. He stood there for an eternity, swinging his arms, watching, thinking, examining, oblivious to my frantic calls. When he turned and saw Mom sitting on the steps, a smile spread across his face. His legs whirled along the pavement, up the stairs, and he jumped into my numb, trembling arms. I cradled and rocked him, as remorse froze the tears forming in my eyes. What right did I have to be a mother, with a body too frail to stand, legs that could not run, arms too weak to snatch him out of danger? My child had a disabled mother. He deserved better than that.

Never in my life had I wanted anything as much as I wanted a baby, my own baby. The oldest girl in a family of eight, I was an "assistant" mother most of my life. I took my brothers to Little League, decorated Christmas cookies with my sisters, drove carloads of pets and kids to the pool or root beer stand on sweaty summer afternoons. But they were my mother's children.

So when the doctor said, "You are seven weeks pregnant," I avoided thinking about words spoken eight months earlier by another doctor, "You have multiple sclerosis." The strange things I was feeling — numbness, dizziness, stumbling, "electric shocks," double vision — all had a name. Doctor after doctor (I'd lost track of the number) poked and pricked me, frowned, grasped their chins and echoed, "I can find nothing wrong with you." After four years, I had more psychiatric referrals than I had parking tickets. But I wasn't crazy after all. Now I knew. I had a degenerative disease of the nervous system, with an unknown cause, a yet undiscovered cure, and an unpredictable prognosis. The pamphlet said that MS "...strikes young adults, just as they are starting to live." It could attack at any time, affecting any part of my body. At that moment my symptoms were bothersome, but they only marginally interfered with "normal" activities. And at that moment multiple sclerosis wasn't real; I was going to have a baby.

I called the MS Society for information and slammed down the receiver when the voice said, "We advise you not to get pregnant."

But I *was* pregnant! The doctor assured me there was no evidence that I could pass the disease on to "the fetus," and that many women go into remission during pregnancy. His statements supported my longing, and after a turbulent pregnancy I delivered a premature — but perfect — baby boy. I was a mother. I could not think of the unknown possibilities of an ephemeral disease.

Joe was so tiny and helpless. When I nestled his fragile body his big dark eyes caught and held mine in complete trust until they closed again to restless newborn sleep. He was the most wonderful thing I'd ever seen in my life, and fun, and a little intimidating. My arms quivered as I lifted his four and one half pound body into a mixing bowl, the perfect size bathtub for those potato knees and twig arms. I was afraid I might break that flimsy collection of bones packaged in too much skin. He almost disappeared when I dressed him. I sat for hours and held him, touched his fuzzy hair, checked his perfect toes, straightened his long thin fingers — a pianist for sure — and watched them retract to a tight fist. I shot roll after roll of film.

I was rapturous the first time he smiled. I did silly things to prompt that toothless grin. I talked to him all the time, even when he was asleep. I told him how wonderful he was, how much I loved him. I told him of all the things we would do together when spring came; how we would walk along the beach, feed the ducks, plant a garden, pick wild blackberries. I wished he could talk to me, tell me what he thought as discovery and impression burst into his mind, making his whole body erupt with mirth. I wanted to hold him all the time, and I did. I didn't think about the food crusting onto the dishes in the sink, or the ironing board unattended in the corner.

Then one day I couldn't hold him. My three-month dream turned into a nightmare on Halloween afternoon when MS — like a bad joke — unmasked its malignant face. I was painting the trim in the dining room of our neglected rental house that sat twenty feet off the waterfront as the fog rolled in across the bay. Joe observed me from his infant seat tucked in the corner of the sparsely furnished room. I was sure he laughed when I climbed the ladder and "accidentally" dropped the freshly dipped paint brush.

As I pivoted to watch it splat, the room swayed and lurched. Simultaneously, nausea swept through my stomach and my entire body turned to jelly. I eased down the ladder and collapsed to the security of the floor, motionless, though the walls, windows, and ceiling rushed around me. I must have blacked out, because I was aware of nothing until I heard Joe crying. The room was dark. I bent my legs to sit up, but they did not move. Panic exploded through me as I realized I could not go to my baby. My mind knew the requisite motions but my limbs were frozen. I felt like I was sitting in a car with a dead battery, twisting the ignition key. Through a blur of time and space as thick and shapeless as the fog outside, I dragged myself over to Joe. I picked the pacifier from his lap and, with slapping lunges, finally lodged it between his lips. My arm was too exhausted to reach up with a reassuring touch, so I lay on the floor and listened as my baby's urgent cries turned to whimpering sobs, then to silent sleep. Foghorns moaned somewhere in another world.

My mother flew in two days later. "Don't worry about it, dear. Anyway, I owe you," she assured me as she propped up my inert body with pillows and tucked my baby close so I could feed him. I reached to touch his sweet face, but my disconnected arm was concrete on the bed. Tears splashed on his balding head. His black eyes hooked mine, still trusting. And he was smiling. "No God, don't let this happen," my mind wailed. My body trembled, but it wasn't moving as horror tornadoed through my being. "I need to hold him, feed him, pick him up when he falls. Let it happen later, when he is older. Not now, not yet." This wasn't supposed to happen. Then Grandma lifted my baby away and walked him to sleep, her steps out of sync with the rhythm of my sobs. This torture never dulled as it was repeated three or four times every day.

Days, weeks later — it seemed like years — my fingers could again touch him, my arms hold him, though they were not strong enough to lift him. But hope returned. Maybe I would yet be able to take care of my baby. In the meantime, Grandma's sure arms carried him. Grandma had rice cereal splattered on her glasses. Grandma's bodice was drenched with suds after his kicking baths. Grandma kissed his toes when she changed him. I sat, slumped on the sofa, an observer, an outsider. I tried to believe he was getting the best care. And he was. Whose loving attendance could top that of a mother of eight, a first-time grandmother? Mine! I closed my eyes to trap the tears, lulled into defiant resignation with the gentle hum of Brahms' *Lullaby*.

Then I could sit up for short periods of time. I got down on the cold floor with my baby as he sat, rocking unsteadily, arms flailing to grasp a toy. I was the perfect playmate for him. I had his six-month balance, strength, and coordination. His blocks squirted from my fingers as they did his, crashing to the floor from atop the shallow stack. He would chortle and clap, sure I was doing it to entertain him. But I was thirty years older than he was. His infant neurons were coalescing into confident directors, allowing tiny fingers to grasp and hold a raisin, a dust ball. My adult neurons were fragmenting, struggling to cool the inflammation and shrug away the scar tissue, to recall the fine motor control that once so effortlessly and unthinkingly allowed me to pick up popcorn and put it in my mouth.

I can still see him bobbing through the living room, to the dining room, into the family room, his bare feet slapping the hardwood floor, his dad's gray jacket draped over his shoulders dragging behind. He was a bird with a big tail to steady an unsure, ill-proportioned body. Each step fascinated me, and I studied the power, the muscles, the motion. He didn't know — and didn't care — how tenuous those early steps were. Delight drove the cadence of his feet. A squeal accelerated his pace and he fell into the hug of my waiting arms. Watching him explore the potential of his new-found skill distracted the self pity and anger of my own damaged proficiency.

Three weeks before Joe's first birthday I lost the sight in my good eye. By then I had memorized the texts of his little books, so I could fake it. "All that deep, deep, deep snow. All that snow had to go." As I turned my face sideways to kiss his pudgy cheek, my heart moaned, "What next? He deserves better than this."

So this was what MS is all about. I was the same person, one who loved life, loved people, loved being active and involved, living in a different, unreliable body, one that could — and did — change drastically within moments, without warning.

We made four moves in the next four years, while I tried to adapt to the capricious extremes of multiple sclerosis. Joe was my singular constant through this upheaval. He steadied my hesitant acceptance of my disability and taught my shattered self-confidence how to take that first rough step into new cities, new neighborhoods, new friendships, new lives, while anchoring my heart in his gleeful delight with the discovery of life. He countered my dread of tomorrow. I awoke each morning intimidated by what new MS symptom might intrude on this day, but also with anticipation of what new discovery my son might make.

The concentration of our time together receded as he noticed an outside world waiting to be explored. I was no longer the matrix of his experience. He could play in the yard with friends, go to the park with "helpers," do errands with his dad, take long walks with Grandpa. But always, he burst through the door, jumped into my lap, or snuggled close to show me his treasure — a butterfly, a rusty railroad spike, a rock." I think it's gold, Mom. Pure gold." I got his quiet time. We smelled the flowers, watched the "moonrise," talked about snakes. Dull stuff compared to his high-powered adventures with others. I watched him run and jump with pain in my heart, a wretched ache that he was missing something, cheated by a mother who was unable to race him to the car, to run beside his first wobbly bike ride, to throw a fast ball. I convinced my heart that he didn't know mothers were supposed to do those things. But every time he paused in his play and looked back at me, something in his eyes burned agony into my soul. Then, seconds later he zoomed down the driveway on his tricycle, forgetting, or unaware of Mom's inability to be by his side. He had a part-time mother, but it was a condition he could live with, a condition I had to live with.

His dad carried him, kicking and screeching, to the car. "You'll have fun at school." I chirped and waved, thankful for the short distance that concealed my own tears. He did have fun, and with an additional three hours to rest I gained extra scraps of energy. Maybe I was through the worst, the most excruciating demands of this misadventure.

But school days brought new challenges to trip up the tightrope balance of disabled motherhood. One day Joe suddenly stopped going to kindergarten, refused to step outside the house. He pressed close and clutched my arm when I rested, and followed like a hungry puppy when I fixed dinner or loaded the dryer. After three days of subtle queries I learned that his best friend's mother had told her son I had "a disease" and I "would probably die soon."

"Why can't you go?" He stamped his feet and twisted his face. "All the other mothers will be there." Each word of my reply increased in volume as my muscles pulled tighter with guilt and frustration. "I'm not *like* all the other mothers." I didn't explain to him about the stairs to the auditorium, about the deep snow. He was the victim and the scapegoat of my frustration and pain. He could never know how much I wanted to go to his first Christmas play.

Junior high brought a complete turnaround. Now the gym was ground-level accessible, but he announced the date of the school band concert with a condition: "If you need your cane or wheelchair..." — the pause was long and loud — "...maybe you should stay home and rest."

The effects of those MS ghosts that came that Halloween day still haunt me. Physically, some of my symptoms relapse and remit. Some, like fatigue and weakness, are my lifelong partners and severely restrict "normal" activity. I am ambulatory much of the time with the aid of a cane on bad days; but, it's to the wheelchair on very bad days, and my bed on worse days.

However, there are no aids to ease the emotional effects of those MS monsters. Physical deficits, such as my inability to drive a car, have left deep emotional scars that don't remit. When Joe gashed his mouth on the coffee table, I dabbed his bloody face with cold soaks for two hours while we waited for a ride to the emergency room. So many times my heart shattered when he came through the door shivering like a river rat after walking home from school in the rain. How many times he rode the bus home burning with fever when his father couldn't leave work and no neighbors were available. He does deserve better than that.

Somehow, those things resolved. What troubles me more is the long-term effects my disability will have on him. Once, I ripped to pieces a magazine picture of decorated Halloween cookies. White frosting woven into spider webs against the ginger cookies, gum drops cut and pressed to make a black cat, smiling peanut eyes of the pumpkin cookies mocked my inability to make those silly Halloween specialities. But those cookies represent the extras that make every holiday hurt, the extras I can't do for my son. My meager strength, coordination and energies are spent on minimum household chores. Nothing is left for the unnecessary luxury of cookies, let alone decorated cookies. Holidays happen just fine without cookies, but those little extras are the big things that make traditions into happy memories. What traditions will he give to his children? Extras say, "I love you. You are special." I can't say it like that. Will he know in the years to come how much I loved him, how much I wanted to do for him? Or will he be anesthetized or oblivious to the details that make life special?

Today my little "preemie" stands at least a head taller than his mom. Now we sit and read college brochures instead of Verne and Wells. The mother who held that tiny baby in strong arms now takes his arm to go downstairs or walk on slippery pavement. The physical demands of being a mother with a chronic debilitating disease have lessened. The emotional demands are cumulative and ongoing. I've yet to cry my eyes dry. Every time I can't lift my arm, my legs buckle and drop me to the floor, my vision gets fuzzy, I still beg, "Dear Lord, not now, not yet." I still feel an insidious terror that Joe carries an increased susceptibility to multiple sclerosis. I die a little every time his foot "goes to sleep." I still feel sad that he has never known me any other way, always his mother who has MS, but I no longer try to convince myself that he doesn't know the difference. I still feel unsettled by how frivolously the phrase "my dysfunctional family" slips into his sentences. I still feel the sting of the missed walks in the park, the gingerbread houses we never built, that I never pushed his swing, or pulled his sled, or took him to the root beer stand. And it still hurts, every single day.

But I was delirious with pride when I saw him "dressed up" for his first dance, when the band director urged him to take a bow after his percussion solo (my cane and I were there), when he received his Academic Achievement Award. My heart glows when I hear him laugh, when he says, "Love ya, Mom," or "Let me do that for you."

Maybe, given the risks of my disease, the decision to go ahead with that pregnancy was selfish. And definitely, he does deserve better than this. But maybe when the doctor said "You have multiple sclerosis," God said, "She is going to need more courage and strength than she thinks she has, a stellar good reason to fight this wretched disease. I will give her a wonderful baby boy."

A Sense of Place

by: Karen G. Stone

Varied as plants lie the reasons for a garden. It could be a full-fledged truck garden or a patch of lawn just big enough for a chair. Dilettantes or fanatics in our growing endeavors, pride in the results can be equally overgrown or sparing. Our gardens can have an impressionistic French–country look or a pristine Japanese layout. The tiniest of seeds grow in ways so different that gardens are never the same, even if in the same place. But a place it is.

I have recently discovered a new meaning to what kind of place my garden is. A prelude to this discovery was watching my neighbor, Dalt, water his small front yard lawn every morning. It was not a big yard, and the four trees colored liquid amber cast their shadows over the entire area. Dalt hand–watered with a hose. He could have easily set up a sprinkler. Dalt didn't really need to do a daily watering, which he did along with a cup of hot black coffee in one hand and the hose in the other. Snoopy, a very small but protective mutt, would join Dalt in the morning ritual. Daily, I passed by about this time on my way to the post office. And stopped. Dalt and I never spent less than twenty minutes talking about fishing, the weather, the passing season. Our discussions were, of course, part of the routine.

While talking to Dalt, I would watch him water. He was methodical. Like someone sweeping the porch from one end to the other, he never missed a spot. And the tree trunks would be sprayed down as well. I realized this was Dalt's way of being religious, meditative, whatever. And it was his way of greeting the day... a vignette that has never left my memory.

Years later, I found myself spending much time planting, at random, the courtyard space in front of the south side of our house. It is encircled by a five-foot-high adobe wall. Because of this particular design, the space is like a big eardrum, catching and echoing the sounds of birds, thunder, children playing, and of course, barking dogs. It is not a large space, but big enough for five dwarf fruit trees, three chairs and two side tables, and a stone bench. Just at the base of the soft, curving adobe wall lies a flower bed that is, perhaps, three feet wide. It contains a mixture of flowers, herbs, and typical garden variety plants. Some year, I will plant a small lawn in the center of this semi–circular space, but for now, I put up with cropped weeds. At least it looks green.

Until a couple of years ago, my attitude about my courtyard space was one of fun and entertainment. Having a place of my own was new, and I realized that I could plant something here and watch it grow for a very long time.

Then, with my body playing uncooperative and unbelievable tricks, newly disabled, I wept and raged and grieved. Where I could do this most freely turned out to be the garden. Instead of listening to the barking dogs and playing children, this big eardrum turned to me. It listened and calmed. It accepted my rage and tears and continued to grow and to give. With cane alongside, I could still hobble out to the garden.

Lying on the cool earth, I would watch the clouds. Hummingbirds checked out my bright red t-shirt. Sparrows ate the growing Amaranth grain. Daily, around 11 o'clock, Sylvester, the plucky and punctual roadrunner, would run the wall's rim, scouring grasshoppers. He cocked both his head and tail while eyeballing his intruder, namely me. I laughed.

Roadrunners are common birds in this area. They are, in fact, the state bird of my residence, New Mexico. These birds have legendary bits and pieces of lore both spoken and written about them, but what I like the best is their Spanish name, "Paisano." Paisano is often translated as "peasant," and I cannot think of a better name for a bird so tuned to the earth.

Peasant reminds me of my Grandma Jenny, who came from Lithuania, and who fought in the Bolshevik revolution. She ended up living with her daughter in Sonoma, the heart of California's wine country. My childhood visits there gave me an introductory understanding of garden spaces.

Grandma's trailer had an arbor before her door, running the length of her abode. She had planted, at the base of the supporting posts, climbing roses. We spent many hours under this shaded space, hours watching the bees, the hummingbirds, hours just talking as she did some sewing.

Now, I consecrate my garden place. It provides a place also to visit and talk. It gives me herbs, tomatoes, pears, and joy. It remains steady in presence throughout the changing seasons and with my changing body. From this, I learn, likewise, to be steadfastly strong. Which surprises me. I never thought planting a seed could do so much. But, in so doing, I am giving a place to that very seed, and in turn, it grows to be part of my garden space.

Even kids sense the specialness. We sit in this garden and watch the sun's setting stillness on the background mountains, often talking until total darkness. Because one of the trees is named after Grandpa Howard, his presence feels near. The kids especially like this and talk about him a lot. In fact, all the trees here have names. It adds to the personalness of the place. Most are named after people, so the garden has become quite a center, and yet, there are wonderful moments of solitude. It is during these quiet periods that I really get a sense of the place, with expanding seeds, visiting birds, an eardrum listening...

Autumn

by: Ruth Greer

From the windows of my house I am watching the trees turn shades of gold and red. A particular maple at the end of the driveway is a brilliant scarlet. The sun is lower in the sky this time of year, and it seems to light the leaves from underneath, making them glow. The beauty of autumn helps me to appreciate being alive.

I miss going into the woods more than can be expressed, but I have in my memory the smells and sights and deep delights of my favorite places. I've visited the mysterious swamp with its many orchids and lovely pitcher plants and mounds of delicate mosses. I have sat for hours on a stump watching nuthatches and squirrels, having deer go by so closely I could have touched them. I know when and where the bright yellow and red mushrooms pop up. I know where there is an incredibly beautiful black and green fern. I have watched the sandhill cranes dance.

Thoughts that I may never do these things again is painful and brings tears, but the experience remains with me. This summer I thoroughly enjoyed watching bluebirds build their nests on the garden fence. Wild canaries swooped down to eat dandelion seeds outside the kitchen window. An indigo bunting joined them, the first I had ever seen. He was such a bright blue he reminded me of a Christmas tree light. A mama bear and her cubs rolled and cavorted in the hayfield south of the house. A few days ago I watched geese and swans fly overhead. The air has turned brisk, and mornings are misty. It's good to be here.

Making Cookies

On the morning of Bryant's tenth birthday, Jenny asked, "Well, Bryant, what are you going to do?"

"I don't know," he replied, with tears in his eyes. He was not looking at me.

I asked, "What's the matter?"

Jenny slammed down her spoon. "Mom! It's his birthday! He's supposed to bring a treat!"

Bryant looked up at me. "Do you think you could make some cookies?" he asked doubtfully. My heart sank.

"Bring me the flour. Bring me a bowl. Get a wooden spoon. I need a stick of butter. Do we have any chocolate chips?" I took charge. Cookies were going to be made.

The kids brought me everything I needed, and I began. My hands were too shaky to measure, but I told Jenny how to do it. I didn't dare use the mixer. My hands were too weak to hold onto the bowl, but Bryant held it firmly. I took the wooden spoon and began to stir, but the spoon wouldn't move in the thick batter. I couldn't grip the spoon handle strongly enough. Stephen stirred. I started plopping spoonfuls of dough onto the cookie sheet, but it was going too slowly. The bus was due in twenty minutes. Everyone dug in with spoons, and we soon had a batch of chocolate-chip cookies in the oven. Jenny took them out ten minutes later, and I showed Bryant how to layer them in a tin box with sheets of wax paper between the still-warm cookies. The three of them grabbed books and jackets and lunch buckets and ran out the door. Bryant stopped halfway down the driveway and waved, a big grin on his face.

I remember that as a very low day, the day I couldn't stir the cookies. It was gloomy all morning, thinking over and over, what kind of a mom can't make cookies? Not much of a mom.

My children's perspective is a little different. They remember feeling cheered up to see me with flour on my nose! Jenny says, "That was the day I knew everything was going to be all right."

Perspective. It makes such a difference.

⸰⸰⸰⸰

Enter Diagnosis 13

On a January day in 1984, I dropped a cup of coffee. I was raising the cup to my mouth, and it just fell out of my hand. I leaned against the kitchen counter and took a few deep breaths to still the panic. No doubt about it, there was something wrong with my hand. They lied to me again! I was screaming inside. Meningitis, they said. Over and done with. Uphill all the way from now on. Steady recuperation. Ha.

I called the doctor. Nothing can be wrong with your hand, he said. It has to be stress. What's bothering you?

What's bothering me is that something is wrong with my hand! Shaking all over, I hung up.

In a few days, I could not open or close my hand, and my arm was heavy. My husband and I didn't talk about it. I made an appointment with another doctor, another neurologist. He ordered tests, and we drove the hundred miles to the hospital. Again. No jokes along the way. I imagined myself throwing money out the window like confetti as we sped down the highway.

Most of the tests were familiar, pinching and poking, electric shocks, needles. I watched squiggly lines on a TV screen. They put me in a whirlpool with very warm water swirling up to my neck. After the whirlpool, I was terribly embarrassed to find I couldn't dress myself, or even sit up without help.

"We suspect you have multiple sclerosis," the new doctor said, looking at the curtain rod above my bed.

"What does that mean?" I asked, to keep the conversation going.

"You will end up in a wheelchair," he said, and left.

My mind went blank.

My roommate was an elderly woman with terminal cancer. She had been weeping softly most of the day. She said, "Oh, my dear, I'm so sorry." I didn't want to add to her distress. I assured her I was fine.

Ordinarily, people were in and out of our room all evening, but that night no one even peeked in the door. After midnight, I went into the bathroom and turned on the water and cried until there were no more tears.

Protest

At first it couldn't be serious
I had to be okay
Lying in bed, day after day
I said, I'm all right
I'm fine
This isn't happening.
Of course it was real
I couldn't get up
I was a prisoner
But still, I thought
All is well
It has to be
Then
I saw
I was broken
My parts didn't work
But still, I pretended
    How are you?
    I'm fine, thanks.
I got better
Little by little
A portion of wellness
Sticks for props
Awkwardness
And pain, of course
Patched over with a smile
Of course
Inside
I grieve
I rant
I dispute
I covet
I want

Myself
Back
But hush, it could be worse
Look how bad it is for other people
You're lucky
Lucky
Lucky
I turn away
No more sad stories
Please
It doesn't help
I hurt
And still
I want
Myself
Back.

Little Joys

Still alive
Months after thinking to end it all
I savor being.
Warm breezes stroke my face
And little joys creep in:
Wildflowers in the uncut lawn,
Butterflies drinking from a puddle,
Eagles playing in the sky.

Carried to a sunny spot,
I feel the warmth on my skin
And marvel.
Dark thoughts hang around
Waiting for me to open the door...
Not today.
Today I drink sunshine.

Facing It

I lost myself, somehow, a few years ago.
It might have been in the woods
when I fell.
Or it might have been the accident...
deer on the road, brakes, ice, a hard bump.
Or perhaps it was one of the blows from that baseball bat
that said "Ted Williams."
Or maybe none of the above.
A disease. A creeping menace in my bones.
No, the bones are fine, the problem is the nerves.
What nerve!
How dare they take my life away!
I was fine, fine, strong and happy.
Happy? Was I ever happy?
Anyway, I was strong.
I danced.
Then I lost myself.
I was gone for awhile, in some netherworld,
and when I came back,
I was stiff
clumsy
paralyzed, they called it.
I didn't.
I called it an unfair trade,
Not my idea!
Tilt tables, parallel bars, braces, braces,
wretched accoutrements of *disease*
Not me, not me
Not me.
Hard times, folks, everybody has hard times.
Grin and bear it
Life goes on...
It doesn't have to.
This unwieldy body

Can die.
I know a way.
What's the use? *Why am I still here?????*
I don't really want to die.
But why, why, why am I still here
like this?
Progress
So very slow.
Pull and drag when once I danced?
Come on, don't expect me to rejoice.
I am not what I want to be.
I grieve.
Say goodbye, goodbye.
Ready or not, here we live.
As is.
God it hurts, God.
Help.

The Persistence of Memory

by: Ben Ellis & Russ Kendall

Soldotna, Alaska — Notebook and pen in hand, Corinne Willard battles fear and a body that has turned on itself.

It is a struggle the 41 year-old multiple sclerosis victim knows quite well. Too well. Nearly a dozen attacks in five years have taken a heavy toll on her petite frame. The last, in 1988, assaulted her brain, robbing her of her short-term memory. The woman who was 30 credits away from achieving a doctorate in special education now has difficulty remembering her children's ages.

The notebook in her lap contains her life: memories this wife and mother of three teenagers can't recall.

"Time is very precious to me," she said, sitting close to her husband Larry. "It must be, for me to record my every minute of my waking time in a notebook."

So detailed is her accounting, a penlight and miniature clock is attached in key chain fashion to the notebook; if she gets up during the night, she can record she was awake.

To date she has logged her last year and a half's thoughts and actions on nearly 8,000 pages.

Proof and verification that her memory may be returning is paramount to her at this point in her recovery.

Patting her husband's leg, she quickly says, "I'm going to answer this first and I'll let him verify it. I honestly think my short-term memory is back.

"But I do not trust myself. I'm too afraid that I'm going to make a mistake. I'm constantly asking him (if I'm right) before he will tell me. And he lets me do that, without getting angry at me."

Her husband agrees that "some of her short-term memory is back, but a lot of it we go through enough so that some gets into her long-term memory. If we don't, she usually won't remember it after 10 minutes."

At night, in the quiet of her bedroom, Willard uses her notebook to test herself.

"When I'm alone, I try to remember what has happened during the day, each and every event. I want to know where I've gone, who I've been with and what we have done as a family."

After jotting down what she remembers, she compares it to her daily journal.

Most nights she passes the exam.

"It proves to me that I'm starting to remember," Willard says.

The fear that she will not remember or that she will recall things incorrectly constantly haunts the former elementary schoolteacher.

"There is a tremendous fear that I am not going to be correct with my first evaluation of the situation," she said. "The name of a person I meet on the street. I'm so afraid that I might make a mistake. Still, there is a question in my mind that says you need to be positive."

Struggling to get her memory back is just the latest battle Willard has waged against MS.

First stricken in 1986, she can recall the day the tingling began in her left leg. It then progressed to both legs and soon she had no feeling in either leg.

Finally forced to use a cane to get around her classroom, Willard resigned from the Kenai Peninsula Borough school system in 1987.

She was forced to trade her cane for a wheelchair, then a hospital bed, and eventually, round-the-clock assistance after she lost control of all of her bodily functions from the waist down, as the disease ravaged her body.

"It's so hard to accept that you have to have an RN with you every minute of the day. I was definitely an independent person before the attacks, downright stubborn," she said. "It's been a tremendous turnaround."

"It's got to be a huge adjustment. Our whole lives have changed because of me," Willard added. "The environment we live in has changed because of me."

"It's not as difficult now," her husband said. "The most difficult time was when she was confined to the bed and needed 24-hour care."

Each attack has brought its own definition of fear, according to Willard.

First, there was having to deal with her paralysis and the thought she might never walk again. Slowly, feeling began to return to her legs. After years of rehabilitation, she can tentatively move about under her own power.

Then there was a period when her eyesight became blurry and the fear of blindness became paramount. After seven months, her visual impairment retreated as quickly as it came.

"Each attack was like a slap in the face," she said. "I didn't know it was coming. It just happened."

Willard has tried several drugs, including steroids, to battle the disease," but the side effects were worse than what they were supposed to cure," Larry Willard said.

The support she has received from her husband and their children (16 year-old son Jos, and daughters Jessica, 14, and Jeni, 12) is the source of her strength.

"We really do have a good system," Willard said.

The children do a little more around the house, her husband added, but they have handled it well.

Using many of the same techniques she used as a special education teacher, Willard has always figured out a way to cope.

The notebook in her lap is her latest testimony.

A sticker on Book 24's cover reads: "Nothing more is needed to know. All is correct and checked."

Above the affirmation are lists of her children's names and ages, her husband's and parents' telephone numbers, and a calendar.

"He checks it and I either put it in quotes or have him sign it. And then I know that if something happens or I'm stuck somewhere all I need is this crazy book," she said.

"It means more to me than anything," she added. "I'm scared to go anywhere without it."

While she averages about eight notebook pages a day, a busy schedule can result in logging 12 to 14 pages.

"I time everything. See," she said, "everything is: 1:15 — I tell you... 1:25 — you've asked me..."

"So when I come home," Larry Willard begins, "and ask her about her day then she goes back — "

" — and he sits down and I read him my pages," she finishes.

It is a tight dance of love by this husband and wife of 21 years. Often they intertwine their conversations. She wants to validate her memory; he supports her areas of vulnerability without degrading her dignity.

"We've always been each other's best friend," he said.

"We keep working on it every day. And bless his heart," she said, patting his thigh again, "he answers me without getting angry, and he's heard it a hundred thousand times. There is always that wink of the eye or the smile that says 'It's OK, go ahead.' I trust it 100 percent. It always comes through."

She said she thinks she can look forward to the day she can leave her notebook home.

"I think I do and, yet, I'm not sure. I will go somewhere and leave it in the car. Of course, the door is locked," she added. "But, I always have a smaller notebook in my pocket if I need it, just in case."

Willard would rather not think about what debilitating blow the disease could deliver next.

"My coping is tears, by myself, somewhere," she said. "When I'm in a real bad state I have to go to my bedroom, because in there I have everything I need to read to verify who I am and where I'm at and that things are OK."

"Sometimes," she added, "it's just fear and tears."

—————

The Notebook

I had been photographing Corinne Willard about four hours. I was sitting with Corinne and her sister, a registered nurse. I had come to see Corinne as a bright, loving, strong woman, determined not only to hold on to the memories she still has, but to fight for and win back the ones taken from her by multiple sclerosis.

I asked if she could remember events that took place in the years before she was stricken.

"Sometimes I can," she said, adding that she still recalls the classroom where she taught special education. What about her family, I asked, changing to the present. Could she remember her children's names and their ages? She was silent for a few moments as she struggled, not only to answer the question, but also to remember what she had just been asked. She tentatively said that her oldest child, Jos, was 16. Then she opened her ever-present notebook to the front page where such information is written. The page verified that her son is in fact 16 years old.

She sat there a moment before tears began slowly running down her cheeks. More tears came, her face moist, her eyes full.

"I didn't know my own son's age for sure," she said, her head bowed. "I had to check the book..."

Her sister handed her a tissue and she dabbed at her salty cheeks. A moment later she raised her head and with a slightly perplexed expression put two fingers to her cheekbone.

"Was I crying?" she asked.

"Yes," her sister said.

"Why?"

"You just let some feelings out," her sister reassured her. "It was OK."

— *Russ Kendall*
The Anchorage Times
Anchorage, Alaska

June 15, 1989: The Telling Test

by: Beverly Zajicek

Today I am beside myself with fear. Why call it anxiety? It is ugly, uncontrollable fear. I am praying constantly for courage and, of course, extrication from what seems the inevitable diagnosis. My arms and legs are weak today. It is from this cursed fear that I'm so exhausted.

Lynn (my sister) calls at 8 A.M. She wants to know more details of my symptoms. I don't want to talk about them, but I know she wants to hear.

Vick and I go to the Museum of Science and Industry before my MRI appointment. I see all of the technology. It is mind-boggling. With all of this knowledge, why can't man figure out MS?

I try to take my friend Vi's advice and not focus on negative thoughts, but their content could be reality. Yet, I know that while my mind is dealing with facts and rational thoughts of the worst, my emotions still hope for the best, the silver lining. I feel that if bad news comes, I will shout, "No, it cannot be. It will not be. It isn't!"

Vick tells me that my face looks sweet today. I laugh and say sometimes that happens. He says, "I know." A few minutes later, I wonder if he'd said that because he knows how nervous I am. No, I don't think so. I think he was absolutely sincere. That's the kind of person he is. I need to depend on that sincerity.

We are traveling to the MRI facility. The swell of fear has subsided for an unknown reason; it comes and goes... This is it. I'm in God's hands. But I know I always have been!

I pray with Vick in the waiting room. As they prepare me, they tell me they're on time, but that the woman ahead of me is slow. That may mean she has trouble moving. The people who take this test are sick. I am taking this test. When the technician is ready for me, she asks if I can walk. That shocks me! I answer her with surprise and possibly a little indignation. I repent of that.

As this machine probes my brain, I think nothing but health. I pray, asking for health and wholeness, but giving myself to God's will. It's amazing how close one can be to the Lord when there is a need. Shouldn't I have been this way daily? I spend the rest of my time singing songs of praise in my mind. This is a mystical, transcendent experience.

It is over. Now, more waiting.

Lynn calls again. She has started the prayer chain at Church of Our Saviour. She's anxious to know about the test. She hurts for me. She speaks of the unfairness of this for me and Vick. She's concerned for herself. From the beginning, I could feel that tension. I hated to tell her about this for that reason. She wants to hear my symptoms again. She's making mental notes and comparing her health with mine. It hurts me to go through these, but for her, I will. She says now she's going to have diarrhea until I find out the results. I share that affliction!

When we go to bed, Vick wants to have intercourse, but both of us are too tired. I'm glad he wants me. I have thought at times what it would be like not to be able to hug him and return his embraces. I think I couldn't tolerate it. Could he?

For the Love of You

If I could gather you in my arms and take you to the farthest corner of the world where there was a secret cavern and you could be made whole, I would do it. We would fly on the North Wind and you would be safe with me. I would protect you.

And when the secret cavern had worked its wonder, you would glow and be radiant, as you once were. Your eyes would spark with life and silver beams of energy would flash around you as you moved. And my broken heart would be mended, and I could laugh, deep, heart–healing laughter, once again.

HOPELESS

Hopeless is a lonely word.
It echoes in an empty heart
And leaves the spirit desolate.
But hope, no matter how slight,
Gives life meaning.
And what dilemma can be without hope?
For each new day brings to the horizon

POSSIBILITY

Symbiosis

The I that is me
Lives in this body.
We both were once one,
Myself and this flesh.
Now, I am still me,
But this trapping is foreign,
Only a husk,
That no life can express.

So look in me deeply
And see me quite clearly,
And know that my spirit
Is still free in flight.
And love me completely
To give yourself fully,
So through our shared sorrow
Your soul might have sight.

Thirty-five

by: O. Kathleen McCauley

Thirty-five was supposed to be magic. Old enough to be credible but young enough to be crazy. I looked forward to it.

Then my left hand began an unfamiliar tingling. And the tests began. Tubes and tunnels, blood in vials, X-rays, shocks, invaded spinal cords. Doctors and nurses thick as flies.

On September 25, 1987, in my thirty-fifth year, with husband Bob at my side, we listened to a nervous doctor read my test results that confirmed a horrible suspicion: multiple sclerosis.

It wasn't out of the blue. It had been a real possibility, consuming thoughts and cluttering dreams for a month. But there was no preparation. We were devastated. And that terribly outdated medical book I'd just read gave a life expectancy of five to twenty years. We focused on the fact that I could be dead by forty. No magic there.

Our emotions were predictable. We cried, held each other and tried like hell to make it okay. The doctor left on an emergency as if he were unable to handle relating such bad news. Not much comfort from that guy. We left the office through an employee exit, avoiding curious eyes, dragging fear behind us.

When we reached our van Billy Joel was on the radio singing *Only The Good Die Young*. Bob clicked it off. I'll never forget that.

At home we sat on our patio, talking about monumental things that surface during a crisis. And washed it all down with beer. Life, at that very moment was cruelly jerked into perspective. The weather was near perfection — sunny, balmy. As if nothing was wrong. I could have shot down the sun with my grief.

Later that evening we celebrated a friend's birthday at a local bar we usually frequented on Friday nights. People were laughing and carrying on like they do when the weekend comes. I couldn't smell the smoke or taste the wine, and felt like I was wearing lead clothing. My brain felt lobotomized, my body defective, my screams silent. I was sitting in that bar alone, waiting to die. The truth is, I already had. And nobody knew it.

—The years have softened. My disease is careful with me. I don't need a chair with spokes or diapers or doctors on call. I've read everything I could get my hands on. But days remain filled to the brim with all kinds of emotions. I try to keep the bad ones at bay, especially fear. You learn to be good at it, playing the game. And you're reminded of nauseating maxims about becoming a better person after going through hell. But you know, there's truth there. One goddam hard way to learn a lesson, though.

Death is not the issue anymore. There are far worse things anyway. The issue is trying to accept what life dumps in your lap and remaining sane in the process. Never underestimate the power of those you love, a good screamer of a cry, a fine glass of wine. You have to kiss the disease good night.

DAY

Sunrise.
A morning filled with rooms.
The cat praying to the sun with
folded paws and stillness
while cars pass by with dedication.
Her dressing gown dusts the
floor as she checks the day
through window glass
noticing it's fall.
Leaves kiss the ground
to please her
then quietly sleep until wind
comes.
She washes till her darkness
fills the drain
leaving her white and new,
smelling of soap.
Clothes cover her quickly.
The cat stretches and turns
as she sits watching.
Her hand touching its fur
sharing heat.
Doors gently close as she steps
outside,
the air biting and clear
as her thoughts,
tiny roses at her feet,
mums at her side.
She drives away alone
holding the day like a baby.

Living, Learning, and Coping

by: Lisa Anne McCoy

"Lisa, why don't we have your mother step into my office while I talk with the both of you?"

Those words were the first spoken to me by a doctor, and should have warned me that something was seriously wrong. Ironically, I didn't panic about it — I just smiled inwardly as the doctor poked his head into the waiting room where my mother was sitting, and asked her to join us inside.

"Lisa, after consulting with Dr. "X," and after getting the preliminary results from the tests that have already been run, it is our mutual opinion that you have multiple sclerosis."

What was that supposed to mean to me? I was only nineteen years old, had just gotten my start at a major university in Boston, and had only sought out a doctor to find why I was having trouble with my knees locking on me and my sense of touch becoming numb. I never thought of something so serious and permanent being the culprit. I didn't even really know what the words "multiple sclerosis" meant. The doctor must have rambled on about the disease and its implications, but I don't remember much of what he said. I was too busy thinking, "This will be all right. He's told me I have some horrible sounding thing, but if it's only a little backward bending of the knees and a little numbness, then I can handle it."

The problem was that was not all there was to it. I was anxious to get back to Boston and the routine of school, so I did so. Looking back, I'm not sure why this news didn't stop me, or didn't at least make me take a break and re-evaluate what I wanted to do, but it didn't. I went back to school, proceeded with my classes, and tried to act as normally as possible. The problem was that MS only allowed me to do this for so long before it interceded again. Soon my walking became more and more difficult, and it was hard for my friends to understand why I wanted to stop and rest, when our dorm was only a hundred yards away. I found that the MS was not something that could be ignored, and I had to travel back and forth to Worcester, where I became a new patient at the MS Clinic at the University of Massachusetts Medical Center. So many tests were run on me—CAT scans, neurological tests, and so on. And so many pins were stuck up and down my legs to determine if I could still distinguish from "dull" and "sharp" that it became routine and almost like a game.

Unfortunately, it wasn't a game.

Family and friends had to be told, explanations had to be made, excuses had to be given to professors whenever a class or exam was missed. At times, it was even harder to talk to people and tell them what had happened to me than it was to live with the disease. Of course, this was all at the beginning stages, and not all the surprises had been revealed to me yet. Like having to go to use the bathroom umpteen times a day. Like getting so weak from the sun and heat that being outdoors only led to catastrophe. Like having to use a cane, then crutches, and then, at times, even a wheelchair. Like having to spend some of the prime years of one's life thinking about the next hospital stay and what kind of treatment would be tried on you, instead of thinking about one's first apartment, or one's next vacation, or one's next romantic relationship.

The first time I was admitted to a hospital, I was a total wreck. Everything was alien to me, and I had no idea what was going to happen. My doctor, whom I trusted, saw me in his office during a regular checkup, and said I should go into the hospital right away. I could barely walk at that point even with the aid of a cane and another person, so I was placed in a wheelchair and sent down to the emergency ward, which is where I had to be admitted, as it was after hours for the admitting office. After that experience, I was finally brought up to a private room and told I would be receiving the drug ACTH for five days. The problem at that point was that ACTH was something they gave you intravenously, and they first had to place a needle in a vein. But I didn't want a needle put into me. I was nineteen years old, but when it came to things like that, I might as well have been nine. Nothing like this had ever happened to me before, and I wasn't prepared to deal with it. A nurse came into my room to insert the needle into me, but I cried and rebelled so much that I made her job impossible. She tried to reason with me, but I was beyond reason at that point. So she called in another nurse. I still wouldn't let them stick a needle in me, so they finally relented and decided it could wait until morning since, by this time, it was very late in the day.

The next morning came much too quickly, and so did the nurses. A new shift was working, but they no doubt had read the notes of the nurses from the night before. This time, a male nurse came into the room and told me in a stern voice that I had to have the needle inserted, no ifs, ands, or buts. Of course, I finally let them do it. I made them wrap over the needle with a bunch of gauze so I wouldn't be able to see it. Even now, five years after that first time, I still make them wrap gauze around the needle. It is just something I don't want to see. And, if a little piece of gauze helps me cope with the experience, then I'll always ask for it, and never be embarrassed by doing so.

But even after I had received the ACTH, I was no better off five days later than when I was admitted to the hospital. It just didn't work.

So my doctor went back to the drawing board, and less than a month later, I was back in the hospital. This time, I was going to receive methylprednisolone.

This treatment was a wonder drug for me. When I went into the hospital, I could barely sit up in my bed, or make it through a day without becoming completely exhausted. But at the end of ten days with this treatment, I could walk up and down the halls, walk up and down the stairs, just walk, *walk,* **WALK!** I had to use Canadian crutches when I walked, but this didn't bother me in the least. The only important thing to me was that I could walk! During this hospital stay,

I also had a physical therapist assigned to me. It was the first time I had had one, and she really put me through the rigors! Beth gave me a whole exercise routine for me to do myself, watched me walk on the stairs (to make sure I did it as safely as possible), and scheduled me to come back and see her several times a week, so that we could work on building up my strength and endurance.

When I was released from the hospital, I realized my entire outlook had changed for the better. Not only had I gotten a lot of my strength back, but a lot of my confidence came back, too. I also noticed that an invisible veil had been lifted from me. It's funny, because I never knew it was there before, but after the treatment, I felt so much lighter in spirit, after feeling that I had spent the last year or so in darkness. Not anymore, though. This treatment gave me so much! I spent the first couple of months getting back into the swing of life; afterwards, I actually felt confident enough to look for a job. Not wanting to get in over my head, I started working for a temporary agency so that I could be free to say no to a job offer if need be. But a funny thing happened. I never found the need to say "No," and I actually got my first permanent job through this agency, working for a local law firm. This job eventually wasn't enough for me, and there was a time when I began toying with the idea of going back to school to get a degree in counseling. However, this never materialized, so I stayed in my field, which is business.

While all these "normal" decisions of life were coming and going, MS stayed with me. Sadly, my wonder drug wasn't a permanent thing. After about six or seven months, my strength started declining again, so my doctor put me back into the hospital for a "booster" treatment. This treatment did its job as well as it could, and I found myself back into the routine of life a week later.

I was still determined to get on with my life, so I did a couple of things to help myself. First, I took driving lessons to learn how to drive using hand controls. I even bought a new car, complete with the necessary equipment, so I would have some independence. I also went back to work at the temporary agency. They assigned me to the accounting office of a company, while giving me the impression that the job would last perhaps three days. After the first day, though, this company asked me if I was interested in a permanent position. I ended up taking the job, and found myself commuting to work in my new car, acting as normal as could be expected. Eventually, I even had the strength and determination to move out on my own for the very first time. I found a little 3-room apartment, moved in, and for the first time felt like a real working member of society.

But no matter how hard I wanted it to be so, I could only be "normal" up to a point. I still had to visit doctors, and I still went into the hospital every few months for treatments. But the treatments weren't cooperating, and weren't doing their job, until finally, it became useless to even spend the time doing that.

This meant that it was back to the drawing board for my doctor and me. Because my disease continued in its progressive course, something obviously had to be done. The only real option left open to me was chemotherapy — a word, in itself, that scared the hell out of me.

My doctor wanted me to get a second opinion, so I went to Boston for further evaluation. After asking me a million and one questions (just how many people remember the exact chronological details of the last five years of their life?), it was the opinion of the doctors there, too, that I was ready for chemo. But was I? This decision took a lot of thought. Not only would it mean a hospital stay of a couple of weeks, but I had to commit myself to going into the hospital one day every two months for the next two years. Maybe it was the thought of all those needles, but I wasn't quick to give my OK on this one. Besides, there were a lot of side effects that had to be taken into account, the biggest one being the possibility of becoming sterile. How many people in their mid-twenties are faced with a decision like that? How many even give it a thought? Well, I had to, and I ended up making the decision to go ahead with the chemotherapy.

That hospital stay was the worst experience of my life, and even now, two years later, I can get uncomfortable just thinking about it.

The problem is that chemo, no matter what form, is comprised of such powerful drugs. Also, I had to receive fluids around the clock, which meant that some form of IV was going into me twenty–four hours a day. This meant that I had to go to the bathroom about twenty–three hours a day. This is more difficult than one might at first imagine, because chemotherapy really knocks you out; just sitting on the side of the bed was a major endeavor. Also, I had to deal with the expected effects of the chemo, namely nausea, vomiting, total weakness, and so on. All in all, it was not a pretty picture, and I wouldn't wish it on my worst enemy.

Right after this treatment was completed, I had to stay home and have as little contact with anybody as possible for the next week, because my immune system was so compromised at this point. Besides the actual horrors of the experience, I had to wait a few months before a decision could be made about the success or failure of my treatment. It wasn't like other treatments, after which my doctor and I knew the results right away; I had to go through all this stuff only to wait around to see if it did any good. In the meantime I had my two month's visit for booster shots to look forward to. Yippee.

Being faced with this disease is the most difficult thing to deal with. I remember being in the hospital one time and having a couple of doctors interview me. One of the questions was, "What's the most difficult thing about MS that you've had to deal with?" Without hesitation, my answer was that "It's always changing. You never know what's around the next corner; whether you'll be able to get out of bed the next morning, or whether you're going to lose some other function of your body soon."

It's also the most challenging thing I can think of. So many people take their lives for granted. They might be touched by a close one's problems, but unless something happens to them personally, they really have no idea what it's like to be unwell. They don't have to think about how they're going to get down a set of stairs, or how they're going to get their clothes on, or how they're going to hold a fork in a weakened hand. Those things just come naturally, and might be seen as a God-given right, but having had MS for the past nine years, I've come to take nothing for granted. Sure, I've had to make all kinds of adjustments in my life, had to slow down a great deal, and forego a lot of experiences. Not a day goes by without my wishing I didn't have this disease. But it's not going to be the end of me. I won't let it. I still want to have a job, have friendships, have "normal" worries like everyone else. And, yes, doing these things are all the more difficult for me, but I'm stubborn enough to plow ahead and live my life as fully as possible, MS or no.

Survival

by: *Mary Ellen Putnam, C.S.J.*

Step by step
With leaden feet
Burdened and heavy.
Step by step.
From one now to another.

Step by step
Walking, from or to?

Faltering, tired, weary
From here, to there, to where?

Step by step.
One step at a time.
Slowly, cautiously, singly.
Step
    by step
        by step
            by step.

Dream Space

Within the chasms of each one's inner depth
There lies unfurrowed,
A sacred space, DREAM SPACE,
Where walking is not allowed.

Each one's DREAM SPACE is determined
By one's willingness to have visions.
To look to the future.
To hope, To plan.
Where tomorrows become today.

DREAM SPACE,
A foot, a mile.
For some, an endless highway.
Reaching. Stretching. Turning. Winding.
Where one becomes while continuing to be.
DREAM SPACE.

Minute Meditations

If we are patient, our stumbling stones will become stepping stones.

I saw, far off on a hill, a cross that now stands bare.
And as I looked, I suddenly knew,
That I must now hang there.

Often it is when you are most helpless that you are most helpful, for it gives those who need to be needed the opportunity to be.

We must allow others to wander aimlessly, through the chasms of their very being, for it is in that emptiness that life has meaning.

You are welcome to hop on my elevator, but I'm not sure in which direction it's going!

Journey invites us not only to go on but to grow on.

It is the rocks and stones in the brook that absorb the powerful force of the waterfall.

Winter, a time when the brook is no longer free to babble. It is only after the piercing cold and haunting silence of winter that Spring can have its turn.

Bridges,
      Connections and crossing.
      Leaving behind and leading forward.
      How easy to stop in the middle
      And be distracted by the reflections.

Sometimes solving a problem is like blowing up a balloon, the harder you try, the bigger it gets.

Balance

I lie here hostage to a disease.
Afraid of the unknown.
My spirit is being bent and stripped.
Subtly my body is changing.
Balance, the key is balance.
How does one balance a failing body
And an active creative mind?

I lie here hostage to a disease.
Outside my window a forest with trees now stripped bare.
Changed, awaiting the onslaught of winter.
How do the trees endure the cold and winds?
How do they balance to survive?

Reality,
Many of these trees are already broken,
Their tree hearts fractured.
Some of those trees need to bow humbly
    And lean on a nearby stronger tree for support.
Some trees will bear up under the
    weight of the snow and ice.
Some will topple, unable to bear the weight of
    one more snowflake.
Oh trees of the forest,
Are you too afraid of the unknowns?

The Colors of Sunset —
Living With Multiple Sclerosis

by: Lindy A. Newell

Chapter One
My Initial Diagnosis

When I woke up I was disoriented. Slowly I opened my eyes and searched the room for clues as to where I was. Wood paneling, plastic horses and a nautical window became familiar, but there was something wrong. It was a strange sensation; I thought I must have something in my eye.

I wandered to the bathroom to investigate. Looking out of my right eye, there was a spider web shadow across my field of vision. I was certain that it must just be the sticky fluid that coagulates in the corner of your eyes at night. I tried to rub it out. I tried washing it away. I was unsuccessful.

By the following day I couldn't see anything through this eye. Frantic, I called one of the city's two ophthalmologists to make an appointment. His receptionist told me that the earliest I could be seen would be in three days. "Damn," I thought, "I'm not talking about a sty or a speck of dirt! One of my eyes is blind." My desperation must have been recognized at the second office.

The following morning, at that doctor's office, I began what would be a thorough lesson about the realities of the medical profession. I was amazed. The physician checked my eyes, gave me a pat on the back, a prescription for Prednisone, and a diagnosis of retrobulbar neuritis. "That's all?" I wondered. "My eye is blind and he's not going to do anything more?" But there wasn't anything more for him to do. There were no pills or eye drops that would ensure a recovery.

I didn't know that there were areas in which medicine is not sovereign. I had never imagined being up against a medical problem that could not be remedied. It was difficult to believe that what was happening to me was really happening. I was twenty years old.

In the shower one morning a few months later, I noticed that a section of my neck and shoulder on one side, felt sunburned. I hadn't been sunbathing, and passed it off as having happened while I was sitting in the sun studying the day before. Soon the mysterious burning sensation felt more like tingling. The next day my left arm and the left side of my neck and shoulder felt as though they had "gone to sleep." The tingling sensation didn't go away as I expected, and within two days my arm, as well as a totally symmetrical portion of my upper torso, were numb. In another day my arm had begun to weaken.

Suspecting a connection between my blind eye and my frozen arm, and still believing in the miracles of modern science, I made an appointment at the school clinic. Thus began the frightening, frustrating, and lengthy series of appointments in and out of the school infirmary.

For a month I was without the use of my left arm, and I was afraid. I was shuffled between lab technicians and physicians. Forced to waive my life–long fear of needles, I relinquished fresh vials of blood every other day. My head was X–rayed from every conceivable angle and I repeated answers to questions about my medical history, about my family, and about my sleeping habits. I understood little of the complexity of medical diagnosis, and as far as I could see, these questions, projections, and tests had very little to do with me or with the fact that I wasn't well. I suddenly felt assaulted by a foreign culture. I didn't understand the customs and I couldn't speak the language. It had all been frustrating and I was tired.

I asked questions that seemed to be ignored. I received unintelligible accounts of illnesses I might have. After the results of the latest tests were studied, each diagnosis was dependably refuted. I had always thought that if you had medical problems (psychiatry excepted), you walked into a doctor's office, showed or told the physician what was wrong, he prescribed something, and you went away with the assurance that there was relief in sight. I never imagined that it could be like this; so many tests, so much ambiguity, so many dead ends. The diagnostic options were narrowed down, and I was referred to a neurologist.

The nervous system specialist introduced me to the neurological exam, and it included a spinal tap. I was awed by the long needle, and by the fact that it was going into my back. I fainted. Laying on my side on the small exam table and facing the wall, I revived to find that I had relaxed enough so that the doctor was able to insert the needle between my vertebrae.

But fainting proved to be contagious. Moments after I had regained consciousness, I heard what sounded like a body dropping to the floor. The physician's nurse had fainted, too. Though I couldn't see what was going on, I imagined that the doctor was unnerved. I hoped that maintaining the correct angle of the needle in my spine was high on his list of concerns while he filled the vials with my spinal fluid. I knew he also wanted to assess the condition of his nurse. Just one of these tasks seemed to me to be formidable. I hoped that he was up to it.

Within seconds of her fall I heard the nurse ask, "What happened?" and we all breathed a sigh of relief. Our ensuing laughter, over what could have been an all-around embarrassing situation, helped to ease us all through a generally unpleasant procedure.

The neurologist told me that he would have the results of my spinal tap within ten days to two weeks, and that he would call then to discuss my medical condition. A week and a half passed and I still hadn't heard from him. Never had time elapsed so slowly. I began to call his office every day. By the time he finally returned my calls, it was only to arrange for another appointment the following week. He wouldn't give me any information over the phone.

Sitting across the desk from him, almost a month since the spinal tap, I'd had plenty of time to expect the worst. I awaited his words telling me that I had some condition such as an inoperable brain tumor, and only weeks to live. Instead the man was not definitive. He was not the perfect television doctor. I needed support, and I was not prepared for any more ambiguity. I was annoyed; I wanted answers. All he would say was that I had a 90% probability of having an illness known as multiple sclerosis.

I almost didn't notice his sullenness. I was impatient with the care he took to explain my diagnosis. I couldn't see the road that lay ahead or the potential paths his words mapped out. Then, my only reactions were anger and relief. "Well, it took you all long enough," I thought sarcastically. "At least I finally know." I was naive.

No single test is used to diagnose MS. A history of MS symptoms helps point a neurologist toward a diagnosis of the disease. A spinal tap is only one indicator, and is not always positive when administered to a person with multiple sclerosis. Other tests, including an electroencephalogram or a myelogram, can take a neurologist still closer to a diagnosis of MS. However, until the advent of the magnetic resonance imager (MRI), a diagnosis of multiple sclerosis could not be made with certainty.

My diagnosis was made more rapidly than most. I had two sets of symptoms that were readily attributable to multiple sclerosis and they came within three months of each other. But in the time since I received my diagnosis, I have met many other MS patients with histories that spanned years before their illness could be named.

There is no one to blame for this. It is true that medicine is not perfect. Technological advances like the MRI make it more perfect. It is also true that most physicians are not eager to confer a diagnosis of MS on anyone. Multiple sclerosis is incurable, and not easy for either the physician or patient from its onset. Stripped of the traditional roles of healer and healed, each can be left overwhelmed by a feeling of helplessness. Each can choose, however, to learn from one another as they stumble together toward an unpredictable future.

——◼◆◼——

Chapter Two
The Doctor — Patient Relationship

At times it's hard for me to understand
Why, out of all the people in the world,
We have come together with such intensity;
Why we continue this hoax, this paradox.
Lacking any familiar means of reciprocity,
We are bound instead in a culturally provided structure.
Our relationship rests on the history of malady and cure,
diseased and healer.
I call you doctor.
Squares of fine white paper hang in plain black frames upon
    your wall;
Stamps of approval, evidence to verify your godliness.
I sometimes treat you like a god,
Believing as I should that when I need it your power will
    materialize before me
And through a process too complex for me to even try to understand,
My ills will be miraculously healed and you will turn
    with disinterested assurance
And perform another miracle, while I stand in awe.
But what happens when you say that there is nothing you can do?
In place of expectations for a hero, I realize we stand together,

Gazing at our equality, at our humanity, into a void.
I wonder how it feels, what it's like to be you.
The rules that govern our exchanges won't allow you time for
      lengthy self-disclosure,
But when we persist, stripped and helpless in the rubble of
      the ritual we perpetuate,
My wonder ceases and I look you in the eye, disappointed,
      angry, and in love.
Then we touch.

Sometimes I say, "I'm sinking and I can't keep up."
You hold me.
For all your wisdom, all the knowledge that medical science
      makes available to you,
It is not with science that you treat me, but with your heart.
You call me patient, but you travel with me beyond the
      demands of this absurd association.
More than the hangings on your wall or your relentless dedication,
It is these glimpses at your depth, brimming with the courage to
      care that nurture my affection and respect for you.
They remind me that we stand together in this fantastic bond
      and that I need not understand.

                        ◄─·─✖◆✖─·─►

      I didn't understand how unrealistic my expectations for medicine
were until I received the confirmation of my diagnosis of multiple
sclerosis. Up until this time, with the exception of colds, which
everybody knew no one could cure, medicine and physicians had
been able to successfully treat whatever maladies I got. I had further
assumed that they would always be able to mend any abuse I might
endure or any bugs I might fall victim to. It was with this vague and

infeasible notion that I approached Dr. B. Robert Aigner and his sensitive receptionist.

When Bob confirmed the diagnosis made in Berkeley it was only the beginning of my awakening to the reality of chronic illness. My relationship with Bob has been indispensable to me for 18 years. Bob is clear, direct, and straightforward in his communication. His candor frightened me in the beginning because he seemed to hold all the cards, and the deck appeared to be stacked against me.

Upon closer examination, my relationship with Bob has been one of the most curative associations of my life. Other neurologists have told me that they have nothing to offer me or any MS patient. Other MS patients have told me they see their neurologist once a year and that he is an inconsequential, almost irrelevant figure in their lives. Many patients do not receive support or assistance from their doctors and do not expect any. This is sad, for both parties.

For about a year I worked with a man who had MS and his wife who had no relationship with his physician. This young man got a bladder infection which went untreated, and he died needlessly because he was never comfortable calling his physician, and consequently never sought treatment. His death could have been prevented had he taken time to establish this vital connection with his physician.

At first, I didn't want to get a confirming diagnosis. I could see no reason for it, given the nature of the illness and the diagnostic process. After my experience in Berkeley with the spinal tap and my subsequent excruciating headache from the procedure, I didn't want to have any more to do with doctors, and particularly wanted nothing further to do with neurologists. Nevertheless, I made the appointment, and arrived for it in fear and trembling at Bob's office in September, 1973.

He could see how frightened I was. He said that he wanted me to have another test, but reassured me that he could get the results from the spinal tap I'd had just weeks earlier, and that there would be no reason at the present time to repeat it. I appreciated his honesty and sensitivity at that first meeting, as I have since.

Bob knew that in order to treat me effectively our relationship would have to include two-way communication. Reciprocity developed easily between us. I've been fortunate in that I respond favorably to steroid drugs, so he has successfully treated me with these, too.

I placed all my unresolved transference issues from parents and previous physicians onto Bob's shoulders. For several years, I was alternately in love with him and cursing him. He accepted my need to work through issues surrounding dependency and acceptance. He knew that this would be important as my MS progressed. He made it clear that as his patient he cared about how I felt and what was going on in my life.

After several years, I was on a first-name basis with him. He has been able to give me what I need, often before I know what it is. He has always been accessible to me. He has always been supportive. I have sometimes needed him quickly, and he's been there, ready to accept my anger or my tears.

The doctor-patient relationship is crucial as it surrounds MS. It isn't easy for the patient or physician, because neither can fall back on conventional roles. Trust between the two must be implicit. I can think of no one with whom I feel more trusting. Bob quarterbacks the rest of my medical team. It is a winner. In the course of living with MS, I have needed the advice of other specialists. Bob has offered choices and given me his appraisal, which I appreciate and respect.

I needed a great deal from Bob in the beginning. We met at a time when his career and reputation were blossoming. There was room for me and many of my needs in his life. There is still. I know and love his family. Clearly, this is not a typical relationship, but certain elements within it can be applied to more traditional roles.

The patient needs to feel that the physician is genuinely interested in his or her well being. It is imperative to select a physician whom you can trust and upon whom you can rely. The physician–patient relationship will be an ongoing one. With Bob and me, it's been important that we be close geographically, as well as in our ability to communicate. He takes time to explain tests and procedures; he always answers my questions, and he recommends treatments, other doctors, and medications. He stays current on new developments in research, and keeps me apprised of them. He listens to what my experience is, and takes it into account when planning treatments or medications. All these qualities go into the makeup of an ideal physician, and need to be considered in any decision about whom to choose as a health care provider.

Bob and I are able to resolve differences between us and those surrounding MS. Fifteen years ago I was working on my master's thesis. I wanted to use his other MS patients in a support group designed specifically for MS patients. In the beginning we disagreed about some elements of the group, but we worked through these to the satisfaction of us both. My expectations for him have grown more realistic. It's important that we can talk, and important that we trust. Early on, Bob became an essential mainstay for me on my journey through life with MS. This he remains today.

Chapter Three
Adjusting

My diagnosis of MS acted like a death sentence in what had previously been an active and healthy life. Although I had not yet read Dr. Elisabeth Kubler–Ross' book, *On Death and Dying*, I followed her five stages of dying (denial, anger, bargaining, depression, and acceptance) as if my diagnosis had been terminal.

After hearing the neurologist utter the words that pronounced me unwell, for better or worse for the rest of my life, I felt numb. Multiple sclerosis didn't mean much to me. I had only two examples of what it could do to my body, and no way to comprehend being no longer well forever. I was blessed with my naiveté.

Fear was not among my predominate emotions at the outset. Confusion and anxiety reigned supreme. As hard as I tried, I couldn't put the nightmare of the diagnostic process behind me. I worked at denial without success. I felt alienated from myself and from my friends. In grasping at denial, I created for myself an intense isolation.

Rather than naming an illness that I may have had for years, it was as if I had been physically changed as a consequence of the diagnosis. I began to hate to be alone. My fear became pronounced. I was afraid the intensity of my feelings would break me apart. I got angry. Denial, anger, bargaining, and depression then vied for the dominant position in my mind.

My disease was active from its onset. I responded emotionally to each assault upon my body. One day I was depressed because I had been actively not well for so many months. The next day I was angry, and I bargained with my neurologist and with God for just a small break from the fatigue and sacrifice. When no bargain could be reached, I argued some more.

The process of adjusting to MS, its losses as well as its gains, is an ongoing one. I have found that with each loss to MS, I go through the same five stages as a part of my adjustment. Sometimes I go through one stage two or three times, and I may pass through another stage only briefly.

When I am sad because of abilities I've lost, or when I am afraid of losing more, I cry. Crying is my most ardent ally, for with my tears, resentment, anger, pain and fear can be washed from me. Crying is a talent that I've relearned. It serves me well.

My sight, my speech, or my ability to raise an arm are all gifts that I never know when I may lose. I have already lost much of my independence. My sight is poor and I can no longer drive a car. My endurance has been dwarfed and I cannot participate in the activities that I used to. Again, crying helps to take the resentment and the bitterness about my losses from me.

Another set of adjustments have to do with examining expecta- tions that I have for myself or others. This is not always a well defined process. My own emotions often disguise my true expectations, for myself or someone else. But communicating my needs to those around me, or checking to make sure my expectations for others are reasonable is my responsibility. Expectations can be dangerous and can potentially result in resentment, disappointment, or frustration. I try to use them sparingly.

Too many holidays have been ruined because I didn't accept my inability to do what "I had always been able to do before." One year, determined to continue to help decorate the Christmas tree, I stood on the toes of one foot to hang an angel from one of the highest branches. In the process, I fell into the tree. I clung to a heavy chair, which followed me and the partially decorated tree to the floor. I wasn't hurt. The tree had cushioned my fall. Miraculously, no ornaments were broken, though they lay strewn across the living room. Of the injuries I received in the fall, my ego was the most badly bruised. My tears were the tears of fright, of loss, and of embarrassment.

It's too easy to push myself beyond my limits and get tired and frustrated. The tears that came that Christmas many years ago were understandable in light of my need to surrender another ability. But if I push and frustrate myself to tears, it's because I've been unable to accept my limitations or to communicate them adequately.

It's often difficult to remain clear about the conflicting emotions within me. Once I have examined what I'd like to do and compared it with what I will be able to do, I need to let those around me know how I will need their help. Asking for help is not easy, especially when you're used to doing things yourself. Asking for help becomes a double edged sword. First, because you have been independent for so long. And then because it begins to feel as though you're always asking someone for something.

To complicate matters still further, I become impatient when someone doesn't do something the way I would like to have it done. I too often expect that whomever I have asked will be able to step in and accomplish a task exactly the way I would have done it. The sad fact of the matter is that more times than not this will not be true. It is a fact I must simply recognize and accept. Saying that I can't do this or that hurts, especially if it has been an activity that I've enjoyed. But others are frequently more than willing to do things for me if I can gracefully accept their help. If I can accomplish this, I don't always have to accept the loss.

It takes less, now, to get me to lie down and rest. I wouldn't think of pushing a vacuum cleaner or scrubbing the refrigerator. There are some tasks that I'm grateful to be no longer responsible for. Anymore, I try to come first. In theory, protecting my health has priority over just about anything. If there's an easy way to avoid extreme fatigue, I try to remember to put on the brakes.

I watch my body now for clues about which direction it may be moving. Keeping track of this is almost automatic and unconscious. The unpredictability seems tamer than it did eighteen years ago. But I am still alarmed at the onset of an exacerbation, not knowing how far it may go or how many losses it may leave me with.

Nancy Mairs made these observations in her book, *Plaintext*: accepting loss is a part of what living is all about. It's also a part of what living with MS is about. Sometimes, with MS, the loss is reversible. Sometimes I have regained abilities. I have even enjoyed a taste of the independence for which I once grieved. Unlike most losses in life, a loss to MS isn't always permanent. But I cry the same tears, and grow angry and sometimes depressed on the same road toward adjusting.

So strange to hear the words fall from my mouth, as dripping candle wax, building indiscriminate walls and pathways, exertive and hesitant, at last, barely audible. It's still my voice I hear, my thoughts, my words, mostly articulate, though sometimes scattered and seldom clever or profound. My words, flowing, but no longer from beyond the boundaries of my mind.

Strange to be unable to rely on such a thing as balance, as a step, assumed endurance and control — no longer valid. Experiences taken so much for granted, so little appreciated, our having too long depended on their consistency.

As each new restriction infringes on my independence, as it frustrates and offends me, the same encounter intensifies my gratitude for the miracles held within a life. Not content to settle for the prison walls, I begin exploring for the alternatives neglected in my formal education. I struggle to discover veiled possibilities, to recognize and then accept my temporal realities.

I'm sometimes faced by a lonely terror and by the burden of utter isolation. But beneath my deep and wrenching sobs, out of bleak and darkest hopelessness, emerges a profound joy — a cause for celebration, a glimpse at wonder, at my capacity to feel, to grow, to experience my intrinsic role within the beauty, the absurdity that is simply, life and death.

I wonder. Would I be as committed to or as frightened by my chartless voyage were I the person trying to look in? I cannot say. But I've been touched by the lives extended to me. I've drawn strength from their compassion and support, grown through their confrontations, and have been sustained by their courage to travel with me.

Sometimes still, I am disconnected, alienated, detached and only looking in. The observer studying the observed. Concerned that I may stumble. Made uneasy by unquestioned pride or unexamined values, unaware. Until again my legs shake and falter beneath my weight, or another day's weary and monotonous fatigue consumes me, and again, I am confronted by my limitations, by my self. Through each opposition, past each battleground, peace comes more readily. I am left more certain of my unity with the magic that surrounds me, of which I am a part.

Strange is this experience, this journey, this person I continue to become. Through the disability and the pain, I'm joyous for my opportunity to marvel, for a moment, at the depths of life.

⊷⊶ ⊠◆⊠ ⊶⊷

Chapter Four
Bridging the Gap

My diagnosis of multiple sclerosis left me feeling stigmatized and alone. While I was in the hospital, Bob invited other of his hospitalized MS patients to stop by my room and introduce themselves. I know his intentions were good, but after I'd met three or four people 25 or 30 years my senior who had fleeting trouble with their eyesight or weakness in one leg, I felt even more an outcast.

I was reminded of my traveler status. I was deep within a country I knew nothing about. People tried to reach out to me, but as in a dream I couldn't seem to grasp the hands extended to me. These people had lived longer with MS than I and had found some degree of acceptance — something still far out of my reach. I was still too frightened and too angry to respond to their gestures of friendship. I needed a map to guide me on this journey and I didn't see how they could help. I was afraid and discouraged.

I seemed to be the youngest MS patient in the world, though I knew better. The first woman with MS that I had counseled was seven years younger and far more impacted by MS than I. The way I learned of Jill seemed to be such a long shot that I was convinced that fate was stepping in, encouraging me to meet with her — to work with other MS patients.

After swimming one day at the main pool of the apartment complex where I lived, I started talking with a woman who turned out to be a nurse employed at a nursing home nearby. I had recently received my master's degree in mental health counseling with an emphasis in chronic illness. She asked me if I would consider visiting a patient in the place where she worked. The patient had MS and was only sixteen, she told me. I went to the home to meet and visit with Jill. I saw her only three times.

Jill's illness horrified me. I left her that first day and went home and cried. I cried for Jill. I cried for myself. Suddenly, possibilities for my future became clear and tangible. Jill not only couldn't walk, she could not talk, and pointed with a spastic arm toward letters on a board to converse. A bag hung from her hospital bed filled with urine. Through Jill, my imagination could see my possible future, and it terrified me.

Aside from Jill, who was a lot more affected by MS than I was, it was clear that even so, I was more unwell than most of the other MS patients who had come to visit me while I was in the hospital. I was unable to relate to their acceptance of MS, and was feeling too poorly to identify with people who were far less affected by the disease than I was. As far as I could tell, we didn't have the same illness at all.

I was preparing to leave the hospital after a successful treatment with ACTH. With the encouragement of Bob, I stopped by the room of one of his partner's patients.

Cheryl McEachern had just been admitted a few days earlier. I knocked tentatively on her door as I entered the room. She was attached to an IV pole by clear tubing that actually connected the bottle to her arm. This was a procedure I'd just completed. I suspected Cheryl's bottle was full of ACTH, too. Upon questioning, my suspicion proved correct. This, and the closeness of our ages, immediately established a camaraderie between us, and the chasm between myself and the rest of the world around me began to disappear.

Cheryl and I talked non-stop. Discovering that we had so many abnormal physical experiences in common, and that we spoke the same language, was a liberating and validating experience. We both felt as though these were things that we would never be able to explain to another soul, and yet, with each other, no explanation was necessary. After no less than forty minutes, I emerged from Cheryl's room feeling as though a bridge had been built across an abyss that had separated me from humankind since my diagnosis.

MS has been a powerful life experience, and as in other experiences, I have lost a little more of my prior naiveté. I have been crippled, but not pulverized by this test. I never anticipated anything like this, but I try to remember that very little of life is successfully anticipated. Life lets me in on only as much as I can handle. I gain the strength I'll need along the way.

The map I longed for so desperately was supplied gradually as my journey proceeded. The path that I have stumbled along in darkness has been illuminated as I live with MS. An important segment was offered during another early hospitalization. I was depressed because I didn't seem to be getting any better despite bed rest and a week's worth of ACTH.

When Bob came into my room I almost screamed at him, "Why don't I feel any better?" I was impatient, and I felt very sorry for myself. I was extremely tired, frightened, and disappointed that the drug had not been working more effectively. He responded directly and emphatically. He said, "Lindy, you have multiple sclerosis. It won't kill you, but it'll kill you emotionally if you let it." I heard the words more clearly than I ever had before.

They frightened me, but I've never forgotten them. They have helped me to not let emotional death consume me when self-pity and depression have threatened to.

One night, a week or so after I'd been released from the hospital, I panicked. I feared that I could no longer bear the weight of MS. Anxiety filled me. On Bob's advice, I had cut back on my daily dosage of medication. I called my psychiatrist, Glenn Strand. I told him that I was overcome with anxiety and depression, and begged him to do something.

Glenn suggested calmly and quietly that perhaps the experience I was having was directly related to the great reduction of ACTH I'd had during the last week. He said that it may very well be that the physical experience was responsible for the psychological one I was having.

Redefining the experience by relating my anxiety and depression to the medication I was taking significantly altered my perception of it. I knew that what he said was technically accurate. It was true that I was taking the most powerful drug available to fight MS. I felt less responsible for feeling anxious and depressed, and thus less intimidated by the feelings. Being reminded of this perspective was liberating, not only during this withdrawal from the drug, but in subsequent ACTH withdrawals. Another section of my map was in place.

⊷⊶⊷

Chapter Five
The Hospital

I was terrified the first time I was admitted to the hospital for treatment of the symptoms of MS. I got undressed and into bed. My legs shook so fiercely that my nurse was prompted to ask if the shaking was due to MS or to fear. She had unwittingly given me additional information which added to my trepidation. I didn't know before she asked that MS could cause your legs to shake. "Fear," I responded certainly. Especially in the beginning, as my visits to the hospital increased, so did my anxiety.

Here was more unknown territory to explore, and I didn't know where to begin. Each time, my body was assaulted by fatigue as I had never felt it before. Not even after I had snow skied all day and danced into the night had my very being protested so vehemently against each move. Each exacerbation began by making its presence evident with this oppressive fatigue.

I was often frightened because I didn't know what would happen to me or how much pain I might have to endure. One procedure that I came to depend on was the intravenous administration of ACTH. Once I found that ACTH worked faster and more effectively when it was introduced directly into my bloodstream, this became the automatic treatment of choice. But my veins are small, and it took more than a couple of jabs to get a needle safely ensconced within one of them. As someone who had passed out the first time blood was taken from my arm, I dreaded this IV procedure. The more frightened I was, the more trouble the nurses had. Finally, after more than a decade and a half, I understand that this procedure is necessary and inevitable. I've been through it enough times that my fear has subsided. I know the IV nurses hurt with me when their job takes longer than usual. The task is now easier for me, as well as for the nurses.

I look to the bruises on my arms as indications that something in my body still works correctly. My bruises still go through their array of colors and still heal predictably. I watch this healing process, and in it find solace. Something in my body still works right, though another part of it does not.

Beyond this I had no idea of what I could expect from my body or from the hospital environment. There were always other atypical sensations or lost abilities which accompanied the extreme fatigue. During one early hospitalization, I was having trouble with my vision. I had already lost the sight in one eye, and I was afraid that I might go blind. Many sleepless nights went by while I contemplated life without my sight. I was hospitalized another time in an effort to try to control minor seizures — seizures that I'd attributed to an unknown psychological problem. At the mental health center where I was training to lead a Gestalt group, I beat pillows and screamed at the seizures to stop. After weeks without success, I called Bob. When

I realized that MS was responsible, it occurred to me that there was much about the illness I didn't know. I was afraid, then, that I might die.

There is no nighttime in the hospital. Life slows down, but nothing ever stops. Nurses continue to check on patients as part of their routine. It is quieter than during the day, and lights are turned down or off, but in contrast the moans and screams of semiconscious neighbors penetrate the stillness.

At first, these cries cut deeply into me. I identified with the screamer as I projected him — alone, afraid, apprehensive, and intimidated by the hospital walls. After listening to the same explanation from many nurses and physicians, that the screams emanated from disoriented patients, my projections eased. I learned to turn down the volume of the unfailing shrieks and to focus on feelings of my own.

On many levels, I was confronted by loss. A very basic loss of health is denoted just by admission to the hospital. I had, at best, a temporary respite from the current exacerbation to hope for and to look forward to. Hospitalization also signifies a loss of independence, a loss of the ability to freely move around, a loss of privacy, a loss of everything familiar.

I associated hospitals with places people died, not where they went to get well. My most significant memories about hospitals surrounded death, and I was haunted by the feelings that accompanied the recollections.

During my first visits to the hospital my traveler status was epitomized. As in a foreign country, I couldn't speak the language. I didn't understand the standards, the customs, the rules and regulations, or the appropriate etiquette. And I was there, ostensibly, without a passport.

The nurses were understanding, but before I got to know them, I was unsure of how much I could depend upon them. They were busy, especially during the day, with beds to change, baths to give, preparing patients for surgery, and distributing breakfast, lunch, and at least two rounds of medications. My modesty was offended as busy nurses came and went with no time to check to see if I was dressed after a shower.

I found that ACTH had some disconcerting side effects. My skin broke out, my stomach burned, my entire system raced. My digestive tract and my menstrual cycle were thrown off, and I bloated from retaining water. It's easier to tolerate these side effects when I can keep in mind that MS is still an incurable illness. I appreciate the fact that ACTH works so well in treating my symptoms that it gives me an opportunity to almost forget this for awhile.

I learned a great deal as my time in the hospital grew. I learned early that the medical profession is made up of human beings with human frailties. At first I was angry "for having been deceived" for so many years. But doctors and nurses hadn't told me they were infallible, I had just assumed it. Having lived so many years with the illusion that medicine was able to perform near–miracles, the realization that medicine had limitations, and that doctors and nurses were people was disheartening.

However, realizing that this human dimension was a part of the medical professionals around me gave me another glimpse beyond myself and MS. I began to make friends among the staff. When I could see them in a more realistic light, I realized there were many that I wanted to be my friends. I recognized the hospital as a safe haven. At the hospital, I was learning how to best care for myself during an exacerbation. I finally understood that medical professionals are people. They make allowances for a patient's lack of courtesy in the face of pain or fear. But like other people, they appreciate being treated with civility.

To survive in the hospital and feel less a prisoner, I've found that learning to be an indulgent patient is essential. The duality of the homonym is not accidental. Learning patience will make your life in general, and your hospital stay in particular, a more gratifying experience. Being polite and friendly are qualities that are not difficult to enact, and will usually be responded to in kind. When grief or fear overtake me and I cry, I can almost always find a nurse who will hold me and let my tears flow. I've found the hospital to be a microcosm of the world, with some sensitive and perceptive additions. Now that I have been a patient on so many occasions and have worked with some of the staff, both as a patient and a professional, I've found that hospital personnel are friends at a time when friends are badly needed, and are too often at a premium.

Chapter Six
Pitfalls Along the Path

As Bob left my hospital room one morning, I picked up a shoe and threw it with all my strength into the door behind him. I hated him for having to leave. Like a spoiled child, I cried and cried until a nurse came into my room and asked me what was wrong. I couldn't very well say that I was afraid to be in the hospital without my physician. So I muttered his name between sobs and hoped my tears would express my frustration and fear. During my early visits to the hospital, Bob was the only person I recognized as my ally.

Grasping out in desperation, I held onto Bob tightly. I feared the day he would no longer be available to me. Until I got to know the staff, I depended on him to provide me with support. He always did, but he encouraged me to realize that I had other allies, both in and out of the hospital, who would share the burden of my illness.

One way in which my communication with Bob was tested surrounded issues of dependency. During my initial hospitalizations, he came to see me in the morning and again at night. Those first few years he responded frequently to my hunger for his reassurance that he cared and was concerned. He did until I began to expect it. It was at this point that he figured I should know that he could be depended on without so many reassurances.

We have been through many hospitalizations and an active case of MS together. Even when I knew Bob was on my team, when I was first admitted to the hospital I felt powerless. I was reacting to my loss of independence that as a patient I felt so keenly, and to my illness, which in the hospital I was forced to acknowledge. My fear was of its progression, of my growing dependence, and of all the variables still unknown to me.

Dependence can be as insidious as the illness with which we live. It is especially frustrating to those of us who have always worked to be independent, to get along on our own. The gradual process of needing more and more help to live is disconcerting. As we grow older this process is supposed to be moving in the opposite direction.

We are required to say good–bye to much of our lives as MS progresses. Many of the losses in the beginning were reversible, but the anger and grief I felt over them was real. We never know where the loss will stop. This experience is frightening, often leaving anger or sadness in its wake. Expressing these feelings is imperative. Feeling them as they become apparent to us presents a formidable challenge.

Before I had my diagnosis of MS, I had already lost the sight in my right eye. In the process, I lost my ability to accurately perceive depth. Suddenly, I couldn't catch a frisbee or parallel park. I was extremely tired. I didn't have the energy to dance or ski, two activities that I'd enjoyed previously a great deal. Following my departure from the ski slopes came my loss of friends that had been primarily skiing buddies.

As an MS patient, I have become very familiar with loss. Though it wasn't my style, I found that working my way through the grieving process was important if I didn't want to become overwhelmed with depression. It seems ironic that one secret to staying ahead of depression is to cry, to get angry, to scream or to yell. But I have found that it is healthy to express sadness, fear, and anger. Not to do this means giving these feelings an opportunity to enlarge, to be pushed back inside, and to become twisted.

I also take an antidepressant each night. I get a dry mouth from this, but no earth-shattering side effects. In fact, a positive side effect is that the Imipramine controls the pain in my legs. I also work on grieving. It makes sense to me to do the most I can not to let depression interfere more than necessary with my life. I've gotten to the point where I experience the emotions associated with these losses as simply part of my life.

There is a fine line between healthy mourning and getting caught in feeling sorry for yourself. Unfortunately, there is no easy way to distinguish between the two. A faculty member in my graduate program said that if you feel anything for longer than five minutes, it's a con; that if you feel mad, sad, afraid, or glad longer than that, you are deceiving yourself or someone else. I would extend the time for feelings associated with losses to MS, but not a lot, at least not in one sitting. Ideally, the emotions that go with living will wash over me. I should be able to feel sorrow and joy as they appear, without having to think about them.

A great deal of thought and discussion with people in positions to help is sometimes required once you have begun the grieving process. A good question, once you have cried about your inability to do something you have enjoyed is: "How can I continue to do it?"

If you have lost your sight or ability to hold a book, the Library for the Blind and Physically Handicapped offers a good alternative to enable you to continue to be able to read. There are many agencies to aid the visually impaired. Physical, occupational, or speech therapists can be helpful, too. And nurses are excellent people to talk with about anything. These people are first available in the hospital. The point that I want to make is that available resources for help are much larger than I believed them to be 18 years ago, and they're growing all the time.

The last issue that I want to discuss here is isolation. Before I received my diagnosis of MS, this was not a problem for me. My life was always full of friends, family, and activities. Once I began to live with MS, with my energy cut in half, I found myself more and more isolated. I became aware that many of the other MS patients I saw were also isolated, and consequently suffering from this lack of contact with people.

It is important that we not let MS, any more than it has to, cut us off from friends and family. For example, when I no longer had the energy to ski, I lost my comrades in the sport. But, while my being in the hospital for a week or two at a time forced changes in the kind of work I did, it didn't affect my ability to work. Friends and associates gained through work are valuable. While communication with them may not be at the same level it is with family and friends outside the work place, it is nonetheless important and should be continued as long as possible.

Eventually, it will be clear to you that adjustments in your work must be made. Finally, the time will come when you will know that the best thing you can do for yourself is to retire. It will take beating your head into the same brick wall before you will give up your position at work. Sometimes a lack of energy will be the proverbial straw that breaks the camel's back. You'll know when it's time to quit.

After 18 years, I know that I have support beyond Bob, in nurses and other hospital personnel, and from friends and family members. A solid base of support can never be too big. Though it is true that I have grown more and more dependent, I have also investigated and found greater resources among people who help me by dividing the chores I cannot do. These folks enable me to live alone in a clean apartment, and with food in the refrigerator. Living by myself is a luxury I never thought I'd have again. I had no medical insurance when I was diagnosed. But the state took over and covered my medical expenses. My helper friends are also covered by the state.

I allow myself to grieve over the children I will never have, the man I will not marry. My lack of endurance keeps me from situations where I have any opportunity to meet an available man. I could not raise a kitten again (eight years ago I just barely had the energy to get my cat through kittenhood). I could not raise a child. For these losses I grieve, and for others as well. Watching sad television shows, hearing tragic news, or having a misunderstanding with a friend can trigger tears that have more to do with my own sorrow than with the television, the news, or the misunderstanding.

I cry the tears that sometimes seem to come from out of nowhere with the same energy that I give to the ones I clearly understand. I believe that they both are equally important, and I know that the same cleansing of my spirit will result. I still grow depressed about physical losses, but more and more I have found ways to compensate for these "little deaths."

I am more isolated than I was eighteen years ago. By recognizing and taking care of my additional dependency needs my isolation is less than when I began to feel my initial movement from independence to dependence. It still seems like a step backward, this journey, courtesy of MS. After so many years it's not so frightening.

Finally, don't try to take more than one day at a time. If you find yourself imagining five or ten years down the line, stop! A good reason not to get involved in projecting too far into the future can be understood by examining my life and current living situation. When I thought, ten years ago, about what my life would be like today, I held images of myself bed-ridden and living in a nursing home. Instead, today my cat and I live alone with people to help cook and clean, drive me to appointments, and shop for me. I'm living almost as independently as I did eighteen years ago, and I never would have believed it possible just ten years past. Judging from my poor health at the time, no one would have. So try not to get stuck imagining what might happen, when you could be living your life instead, whatever it brings.

Chapter Seven
MS is a Family Affair

Chris immediately threw his arms around my neck and stated, "I'll go to the office and explain to them that we need to be closer to the ocean for my sister. I'll pay the extra — whatever it is." He went flying out of the apartment. I cried even harder. My half-brother was just seventeen when he, Mom, and I arrived on the salubrious island of Kauai. Chris' father had died a year earlier and had left him a significant portion of his estate. Chris had enough money to follow through on such a sensitive indulgence.

It was warm and humid. I was totally enervated by the time the electric cart that carried us to our accommodations finally arrived. There had been a five-hour plane ride, then another short hop, commuter style. Finally, a long taxi ride ensued from the airport to our outlying hotel. After checking in, we took an electric cart up a hill to reach our quarters. Wearily, we followed the bellhop up three flights of stairs. After traversing a long outside corridor, we entered our apartment. I pulled the drapes that blanketed sliding glass doors and revealed the expansive ocean. I began to cry.

Our apartment was six blocks up from the water. All I could think about was that long climb up the hill from the beach. I was afraid I might not be able to manage it even once a day. We came to Hawaii primarily to enjoy the warm ocean surf. Standing before the vast view, I let self-pity set in, and I thought, "I may as well be back in Seattle." It was at this point that Chris came to my rescue.

In this chapter, as in the next chapter about the importance of friends, it has been tempting to use the writing as an opportunity to thank my family for all that they do for me. When I have caught myself at this, I have not given in to the temptation, but I have not always caught myself. I realize that not every MS patient is lucky enough to have the kind of support from family members that I do. For some, this support is made up for by non-family, and yet others must get along the best they can.

Early on in my experience with MS, Bob told me repeatedly that MS was not just a personal illness, but that it affected each family member as well. I didn't like the idea that my family had the illness as I did. They weren't unwell. They didn't approach each night wondering what the morrow would bring. On the other hand, no one in the family has someone with whom they can be angry. MS is the target of all our anger, and consequently, stress develops between family members out of our frustration about having no control over the disease.

I was extremely angry those first years after I'd received my diagnosis. I didn't understand how my family could fathom my life, let alone live it. The way I saw it, I was the one with MS, not them! But as time has passed, I have better understood the ways in which MS is a family affair.

All have had ample opportunities to see me not well, to watch me struggle. They love me. They have been forced to observe as I have stumbled or fallen. This helplessness and the ensuing stress created by the illness have become ways in which MS is their illness as well as mine.

One day Mom came to my house. We were going to a movie. I was having trouble with weakness in one leg. When she arrived I should have been ready to leave. Instead, overcome with fatigue, I was still lying on the bed and in a nightgown. I hadn't told her I was having trouble. She asked why I was so far behind. I still hated to say that I was having an exacerbation of my MS. It seemed, in the beginning, that it was happening all the time.

I told her that I needed her help to get dressed. I stood up to take clothes from my chest of drawers and promptly fell back onto the bed. The next time I tried to stand, Mom helped me, but I was too heavy for her, and started to fall in spite of her strong arms. By the time I landed on the floor, we were both laughing and in tears.

I was determined then to go to the show. It was only later that I realized the importance of resting, especially during an exacerbation. Those first few years I was not accustomed to living with MS. I hadn't learned yet how best to take care of myself. With Mom's help that day, I finally got dressed with only one more fall.

For several years I experienced burning and throbbing pain in my legs, a rare symptom in MS. After I lived with Mom for awhile, she had watched as tears filled my eyes from the leg pain. She knew that it often kept me awake at night. She saw me consumed by fatigue. Unable to stay awake, some days I slept fourteen to twenty hours. Mom watched as I grew too tired to work, and stood by as I searched for something I could do to feel productive. Mom shared the illness with me.

The year I had to surrender my driver's license, Dad went with me. Before we arrived at the Department of Motor Vehicles, I knew that this would be it. Entering the building in my wheelchair effectively ended my driving days. I knew I couldn't stand long in a line, but going inside seated meant losing the license I held so dear. The official act of giving up the right to drive was not easy. Since Dad was close to having to do the same thing, he understood what I was feeling.

Dad drove me to appointments after I had to give up my license. I think that having to relinquish his own license was made that much more difficult knowing how I depended on him. When I was alone at Mom's house, Dad brought tasty lunches from a fast food restaurant. We had picnics on the kitchen table. He brought groceries. He called a couple of times each day to make sure I didn't need anything. I panicked when I overflowed the washing machine. Tears followed and Dad held me tightly before he went to get his wet vacuum. Dad has felt MS, too.

Chris is my half-brother. We share a mother and have different fathers. We lived together from his birth until I left home to go to college — ten years. I have other half-siblings, Dick and Ellen, from a former marriage of my stepfather. We didn't grow up together, but we've developed warm and close relationships.

When Dick told me that he, too, had received a diagnosis of MS it seemed that my entire extended family was now in on the experience. Both Ellen and Dick live in Portland. Dick and his girl friend, Kris, have come to see me when I've been hospitalized. He sends cards and flowers and generally makes it impossible for me not to count him as a real member of the family and someone I can depend upon. Ellen, too, has made this clear.

When Chris invited me to live with him in Olympia while he went to school, I accepted enthusiastically. The eight years age difference between us when we were growing up had seemed like decades, but Chris always knew how much I loved him. Years ago, my relationship with Chris had bordered on being a parent–child one rather than that of siblings. Recently in our history together, we have become good friends. In fact, in many ways our roles have been reversed, and he has held me while tears streamed down my cheeks. He has watched as my frustration has caused me to lash out indiscriminately at people I love. I couldn't ask for a more sensitive and understanding brother. Chris was willing to take on MS as a daily diet.

Moving back to Olympia after a ten–year separation put me back in the circle of a number of good friends. Having not worked for several years, I had rediscovered the satisfaction that comes from writing. Chris bought a computer. I could sit in a comfortable position, put the keyboard on my lap, and peck away. In Olympia, I was not isolated. Friends dropped by unannounced after work or at lunch time. Nearly every weekend, we played bridge. Frequently, when Dick and Kris came through town on their way home, they would stop for a hug, some conversation and a cup of coffee.

Dad purchased a bird feeder for me. Chris hung it in the magnolia tree outside the kitchen's bay windows. I began seriously to bird watch. Olympia is far enough from the big cities so that there is a splendid array of bird life. I could watch them at the feeder through the windows while I drank my morning coffee. Chris kept the feeder filled and "bird-word" spread about this bonanza.

Barn swallows built a nest under the eaves of our house, and in the springtime they returned to mate and raise several families. Since they are insect–eating birds, I could not watch them at the feeder, but under the eaves they were within close proximity and easily observed. Soon I combined my interests, and was writing stories about the birds.

In the fall, I felt well enough to enroll in a weekly writing class. Chris volunteered to drive me to the college and push my wheelchair in and out where the class was held. Frequently, we made an evening of it and dined together at the school cafeteria. I made more friends in the class, and my writing was taken seriously and encouraged. I thrived.

Eventually, Chris needed to be closer to Seattle. He bought a small apartment in the city and asked me to come and live in it. At first, leaving Olympia and the closeness of my friends disturbed me, but when I finished pursuing all the possible alternatives, Seattle began to look functional and exciting. I thought I would never again live by myself, for reasons of economics and needs. Chris took care of the finances by renting me a well-lit and cheery apartment.

Chris just recently married, and his wife is as wonderful as he is. When flowers are in bloom in the yard, she'll bring me large beautiful bouquets. When she makes apple muffins or soup she always remembers me. I couldn't ask for a finer in-law; Michelle's the younger sister that I never had.

Regardless of the type of family you live in, MS becomes a significant ingredient in each member's life. Mom, Chris and Michelle, Dad, and Dick and Ellen all know that any plans they make with me are provisional. I may really want to attend a workshop or make birthday plans, but I cannot do it too far in advance. If I set up the plans, it is with the knowledge that they might need to be changed at the last minute. Family and friends alike understand why any plans we make must be conditional, and subject to change or cancellation by how I am feeling. It can still be difficult and frustrating for us all, but more and more this tentativeness becomes just a part of living with multiple sclerosis.

Chapter Eight
Friends

Friends are vital to my life — like oxygen. So is the time I spend with my cat, Samson, and the time I spend alone. There is no question that getting through life with MS means that you must become your own best friend. Better than anyone you know your needs and what you must avoid. A delicate distribution must be maintained to appreciate each facet of life, and so to better appreciate its whole. When I lose this balance, I become inevitably depressed.

Sharing love with a friend is an amazing experience: fulfilling, gratifying, and validating. I understand this better now that I've lived 18 years with MS as a constant companion. Since much of my time is spent alone or in the company of my cat, I have ample opportunities for solitude. Untold hours are devoted to sleeping and resting, quiet healing time. Alone, listening to music, I reflect on my most recent MS–related hospital experience. I write and read. These important hours of silence are balanced by friends who share my laughter, tears, hugs, offer challenges and new perspectives, inspiration and comfort.

Samson, my cat, is a very rewarding part of my life. Time with him is a happy combination of alone time and time with friends. When I'm too drained to do anything else, I can always muster energy enough to feed him and to clean his litter box. When he's letting me know that one or the other of these things needs to be done, his meow is never intrusive. Because I know he needs me, his presence comes as an affirmation of my worth. He loves to cuddle and always seeks me out when I'm crying to comfort me.

I call Samson my little boy. I know that he will be the closest creature to a child of my own I'll ever know. And so I use a mother's privilege to love and spoil him. He fills a lot of gaps in my life. His love is unconditional — even when I haven't showered for too long or am too involved in a task that leaves no room for him. He almost always lets me have my way. Consequently, I can be selfish and still be loved.

Friends teach flexibility, thereby helping me to better adjust. Some of my friends may say that it was I who showed them the way. But truly I have been the student and they the tolerant teachers. My friends give me more room than I give myself.

Friends are a deep and dependable well of love. They provide me with insights I might easily have overlooked. Friends live with the difficulties and frequent frustrations that come with MS. Those unwilling to do this I have lost along the path, or they have lost me.

Some friends take a little longer than others to realize what MS does to my body, and thus to my life. I surmise that this is true because of the difficulty they have with the limits that MS has put on my energy and time. It is difficult for them to listen to what I say about my limitations. Sometimes it takes a long time for them to really hear.

I cherish my friends far beyond their knowing. I write them. I make certain they know how important they are to and for me. In the spring and summer I give them flowers that surround my small apartment. Frequently, they bring me flowers or fresh fruit when it's in season. I look forward to their notes in the mail. They cook meals for me, change my bed, vacuum, clean. And so the time I spend with them is genuine quality time. Everyday activities become special when a friend is there to share.

My life is enriched by the love of my friends. They share their love with me in ways that make them ever-present in my life. Some have held me while I cry. Others escort me to a concert or a festival, and visit me in the hospital or at home. These magnanimous deeds make their presences live! Through kindnesses, cards, letters, and help, they allow me to bask, whenever I want, in their warmth. I treasure the love of my friends.

There are moments I've felt that all of this — even my writing — was being applauded only because I have MS. I even had trouble accepting that I got my master's degree the old-fashioned way. I worried that I hadn't earned the respect of my teachers and had only won their sympathy because of my illness.

I've secretly questioned my friends' motivation for remaining friends, especially when it seemed that I had so little to give back. While I can no longer fix meals or clean up afterward, I can offer tea or a soft drink, or tell someone I love them, or I can just listen. Ten years ago, I did not understand that my spirit is energizing. Even when fatigue has overcome me, I am still able to communicate this energy.

I don't make time for anything unless the provisional nature of MS is understood. Most folks seem to understand and accept this. At times, I still feel as though I am unduly disrupting plans when they have to be suddenly changed. This is a frame where my friends give me more room to have MS than I give myself. I know that they do this now without having to think of it.

I treasure my moments alone as I do moments with my friends. I can be intolerant about unannounced interruptions of this time. When I'm reading or writing and I'm still in my pajamas or nightgown, having not prepared myself for visitors, even a close friend can throw me for a loop just by dropping by. I know that a part of this is due to the amount of time MS forces me to spend in the bathroom on a regular basis. Without having to worry about receiving anyone from the world outside, I can take care of my personal hygiene, or concentrate on writing and being productive. This, too, is essential to my sanity.

My life must retain these delicate balances if I'm to continue my journey sanely and humanely along this path marked off by multiple sclerosis. With the company of Samson, caring friends, and my ability to enjoy time alone, the journey is made far easier.

Chapter Nine
I am Still a Sexual Being

— *The Last Wedding* —

Love permeated all.

In the moment the bride and groom were radiant, their happiness complete.

Up this high, streets and buildings were dwarfed and softened by the expanse of greens and blue.

Friends became family.

Your family became mine.

Cindy hooked her arms around my neck.

"You're wonderful."

"What you wrote for his birthday... Maybe I'm not supposed to know... I cried... He cried..."

A gift.

Always busy, you passed me slowly.

"What do you need?"

"You," I thought and answered, "Nothing."

I almost kissed you.

Easily, I reached for you with my mouth, then spontaneity was
   checked by reality.

Later, you rested with me for a moment and teased me with your foot.

I breathed you deeply.

Tonight I wept.

Tears ran across my cheeks and fell into tiny pools quickly
   absorbed by my shirt and jeans.

As satiated with sorrow as I had earlier been with joy.

Still, I'm grateful for all the love I'm given.

All I can return.

You are warm inside me.

━ ∙ ━ ✦ ━ ∙ ━

I spent many months trying to disown my sexuality when I
realized that I had lost much of the feeling below my neck. It had been
a gradual but insidious process, like so much of this disease. But I am
human; a part of me is sexual.

As far as it is possible, I find myself personalizing relationships.
Most people respond favorably to this and their responses are warm
and strong. I have many friends and they are important to me as I live

and sometimes struggle with MS. My family and friends are loving and my bonds to them are strong, but for the most part this does not address my sexual nature. It is easy for me to communicate with people and even my acquaintances with the mail carrier and the sensitive and creative soul who cuts my hair are satisfying. My self esteem is good.

So why has it been so difficult for me to acknowledge my sexuality? At first I was unaware of what this disease could potentially do to me. While initially the diagnosis of multiple sclerosis was a relief after so many tests, the diagnosis also frightened me terribly. Finally, the physical dimensions of the illness wore me out. I had no energy to be conscious of my sexuality.

Then the day came when my last sexual relationship ended. When my partner vanished, I feared that with him went any vestiges of sexuality in my being. Because sex had been frustrating since before my diagnosis of MS, I couldn't see any reason to stay involved in it.

Were it that easy.

My spontaneous interactions with people, for the most part, are satisfying. Through these, my unconscious mind is provided with needed material to construct dreams. I ski down deeply powdered slopes and hold and touch and kiss real men with scratchy whiskers. Consciously, I can use these encounters to fantasize. My sexuality is addressed in my unconscious and these dreams often reach my waking conscious mind. No wonder it's been said that ninety nine percent of sex takes place in your head. Dreaming and fantasizing are, clearly, mental activities.

MS has forced me to see my sexuality in a new light. My expectations about the reaction of others to me as a sexual being have undergone a complete transformation. For the most part, people react first to my wheelchair and not to me, the clothing that I wear, my hair style, or the overall impression that I make. The wheelchair seems to preclude any kind of sexual response. I have tried to deny this. I've been angry about it, depressed, afraid and lonely. For the most part, it is a reality.

My sexuality isn't dependent on someone's response to me. My sexual nature is a part of who I am. Some days I exude sexuality without thinking about it. Other days I neglect it badly. Some days I love the way my body feels. Other days my body is wracked with pain and I could not feel sexual if my life depended on it.

Journal Entry from January 10th, 1990

Another attempt tonight at masturbation. I climaxed — wonderfully. First time in about a year. Cytoxan? Hmmmm — I wonder... I guess it's worth it to try every now and then. (I had gone through an experimental regimen with high dose cyclophosphamide about a year earlier, but didn't know if I could attribute my success at masturbation to the Cytoxan or to one of many other variables.)

It's worth it, especially when you have reason to hope that some drug that you think may have interfered with your ability to climax is cut down or discontinued, or you experiment with a drug like Cytoxan — because there is always the possibility of your sexuality still existing even when you don't feel much like a sexual being. I guess I already knew that.

Frustration that I don't have a sexual partner is appeased, in part, by extrapolating from the knowledge that a relationship of any kind demands energy. A romantic relationship requires more than most. It's all energy I don't have.

In the past, I have dealt best with my frustration about sex by not anticipating orgasm as the be all and end all of my sexual expression. It's important to work with what you have or haven't got, by putting more emphasis on kissing and responding, touching and being touched, and always on communicating. It is important that you talk with your partner. Because I express myself best when I am writing, writing for me is another sexual outlet.

Fatigue is my most significant foe as far as my sexuality is concerned, as well as MS disability in general. Sleeping twelve to sixteen hour nights is not uncommon for me, and then I awake feeling as if I haven't slept at all. Often, I haven't the energy to brush my teeth, let alone to contemplate anything sexual.

Friends hold me. Hugs sustain me. Out of all, I miss kissing most. I no longer see a romantic relationship as out of the question, but I'm also not looking for one to develop. I know now that I encompass all that is essential for living. I don't feel incomplete as a person without a sexual partner. I do miss cuddling and sharing certain kinds of physical intimacy. But my friends have assured me that I am replete with love, and though I could complain about my lack of sexual intimacy, I see no reason for it. Many friends live deep inside me and keep me warm.

—•—❈❖❈—•—

Chapter Ten
After Eighteen Years — The Colors of Sunset

Eighteen years have elapsed since I lost the sight in my right eye and subsequently received my diagnosis of MS. This frightening malady has been a catalyst for change in my life. It has created and clarified as many options as it has ruled out. It has taught me a few things that I've failed to mention so far and would like to pass along, lest they be lost forever.

One of the basic notions I have learned during my MS years came to me as I observed the changing colors of a northwest sunset. You don't look at a sunset and say, "Well, it would be perfect if only there were more pink, if the orange were only brighter." You watch a sunset as it lives and passes through an array of colors and are mesmerized by the sheer beauty of it. Each hue, each color, is unique and perfect. Each has its own way of contributing to the sunset's life, to its short-lived beauty that enthralls the beholder. I've come to the awareness that if I can look at my life in the way I look at and appreciate a sunset it will hold out to me this self-same beauty and order.

Even during the worst of situations, my life was touched with expressions of love — which I compare to a sunset's changing colors. There could be nothing more beautiful than the love I receive from family and friends. The night following my first chemo treatment I vomited all night. When the day shift arrived, Bob was immediately contacted for a medication to stop the nausea and vomiting. This the night shift failed to do.

I said to a nurse whom I love and respect that I didn't know if I could make it through another night. Between my lack of sleep and constant nausea, I was ready to throw in the towel. Marge knew that as pitiful as I looked, I didn't need pity. She had been through what I was going through and she admonished me to continue the treatment. She said that if I could focus on being at the other side, being finished with the chemo, it would make my current situation tolerable. She said that if I tried to keep a clear image up front of a successful regimen, it would help me to get through the therapy. She held me while I cried.

Her presence in my life at that crucial time was another expression of the love she's offered me over the years. As the changing colors of a sunset express their own beauty and continuity, the same is true of the love I have received from Marge.

My mom called that morning, too. I didn't need to say too much before she knew that the darkness had been a nightmare. She came over as fast as she could. She also held me and allowed me to cry. Later, while I was still too nauseated to eat, she drove to a fast food restaurant to buy me a root beer float, which was all that appealed to me. My mother's and Marge's expressions of love, and the calls and visits I received from the rest of my family and my friends were what sustained me through an otherwise arduous time. From it, I received sustenance, just as the changing colors of a sunset promise a new day.

Obviously, MS and its many problems are difficult to see as beautiful or ordered. In fact, they can be ugly and frighteningly unpredictable. However, if you don't get caught too long in self-pity, anger, bitterness, or depression, your chances of living a more normal life increase.

I had no medical insurance when I was diagnosed with MS. My learnings began when I quickly discovered that no one was going to offer me medical insurance with my diagnosis. Before Social Security would cover me, I had to be disabled enough to need state welfare. For a person who had been a spoiled child of the upper-middle class, this social security and welfare procedure was humiliating. Just recognizing myself as a disabled person was debasing. Because I had been attending school when I was diagnosed instead of working, I was not eligible for Social Security Disability Insurance, but only Supplemental Security Income — the difference of a few hundred dollars a month. For awhile, I didn't think I deserved this help. Later, it became clear to me that I did. One often needs help when dealing with a foe as unremitting as MS.

It's a trap to look into every treatment that is publicized in *The National Enquirer* or in rigorous scientific journals. If you opt to do so, you can spend all your time checking into each one of these claims, and have no time left to live your life. MS will be controlling it.

Over eighteen years, I have gone through my share of "cure" treatments, but the number would have been even larger had I not followed Bob's counsel. The year following my diagnosis, without checking with him, I ate nothing but sunflower seeds for a week. Once, I underwent hyperbaric oxygen therapy for ten days. My most clear memory from this experience was the pain I felt in my ears each time the air pressure in the chamber increased. I've had trouble with my eustachian tubes all my life while descending in airplanes and scuba diving. They do not regulate in the way they should. I had not connected this with my experience in a hyperbaric chamber until it was too late, and my eardrums felt as if they'd burst. Between this and attempts to arrange predictable transportation to get to the office on time, any positive results were eradicated.

More recently, I went through a course of high dose chemo-therapy. This experiment was with Bob's knowledge, and it looked like it might hold real possibilities for calming my central nervous system. Bob and I would always have wondered whether or not Cytoxan would have quieted my illness if I hadn't tried it.

I enjoyed my bald head. I paraded it like a trophy until winter brought cooler temperatures and I had to cover it. By spring, new hair began to grow. Friends and family made bets that it was darker or curlier. As for color I couldn't be sure, but I'd noticed red highlights I hadn't before, and I'm even growing attached to the additional specks of gray. It curls now, and is reminiscent of thirty-five years ago, which I love. I never have to pay for a permanent, and it's easy to care for.

The first years after my diagnosis, I was angry, and there was no good outlet for this anger. So it seethed inside me and made me literally sick. I suffered one cold after another. But as I began to realize that I had an incurable illness and my life was going to have to change, the colds ceased. Mind over matter? It was a gradual process, to be sure, but reflecting on it, I am convinced that ones' body takes on what you don't work out in your head.

MS has created important opportunities for me since I have grown past the worst of my anger. I am depressed from time to time, but mostly I am filled with love and appreciation for my life, my family, and my friends. Living with MS and having worked with other MS patients, I have seen how much worse off I could be. Though I didn't know all it could entail prior to my most disabling symptoms appearing, I knew that I had MS, and that it could affect me further in any way at any time. Occasionally I get a glimpse of MS patients not as affected by the disease as I am, but I know that they, too, must deal with their own personal sword of Demosthenes on a daily basis.

For the most part, I am living the way I want. MS has produced bodily malfunctions that I could easily live without, but I more quickly lean toward loving life and the people around me. I think I get to the heart of living faster than I did before MS. I know now that I may not always be physically able to reach the quintessence of life. So while I am, I'm going to touch lives and be touched by them.

I no longer feel like an inexperienced traveler with multiple sclerosis, and so travel with an air of confidence. I've learned the customs and language of the hospital and medicine as they relate to MS. I've learned what to expect from potent medications. I've watched, unknowing, as a good friend got strung out on prescription medications, and then with great difficulty and determination un-hooked herself. Her experience has had a poignant effect on me and has increased my awareness of how I deal with these medications. I've learned the scope of symptoms that can be attributed to MS. Fatigue is the hardest for me to deal with, because I am never unaffected by it. My bladder is failing, and there are many unknowns ahead for me. I've learned that rest is the best way I can care for myself during an exacerbation.

The colors of a sunset. My! To get in on the experience while the sun is still yellow and just beginning its journey beyond the horizon is a treat. I've watched the yellow glow as it becomes gold, then orange and sometimes red, especially as it crosses a field of snow. Shafts of the brilliance often pierce the clouds. At the other side of the sky are pink wisps, clouds colored by the sunset. My life would be diminished without this exquisite phenomenon, just as it would be without the love I'm generously given.

I am now less afraid of physical pain than I was eighteen years ago. Having been through countless painful procedures, leg aches and head pain, hurting no longer frightens me. But physical experiences outside the norm, and ones I've not gone through remain terrifying. I am still concerned, particularly at the onset of an exacerbation. I know not where it will lead or when it will stop. I am far less alarmed now, however, than I was 18 years ago. I know my body and MS better, and life is easier because I do.

This illness of ours expresses itself in different ways in different people. I have found some whose MS looked a lot like mine for a few years and then changed direction. I had symptoms for a while ten years ago that went away and never came back. So much is unpredictable.

Family dynamics that are dysfunctional will be exaggerated when a person with MS or with any chronic illness is added to the picture. Rather than MS improving a strained situation, it often stretches it to the limit, or beyond.

For some reason, it may happen that a family is tempted to hide the diagnosis of MS from the sufferer, "for their own good." If the need for adjusting is kept from the patient, it also keeps the rest of the family from making their own individual, and necessary adjustments.

"But you look so good," is a comment I've heard time and time again. My mom calls me an optical illusion. The truth is that we can look good most of the time, and that how we appear has little to do with how we feel or how our illness is progressing. It's also true that the comment frequently comes from friends, and is merely a statement of fact. We need to let them know about the feelings that it sometimes triggers in us: "If I look so good, then how could I be so unwell?" If the thought has crossed our mind, then certainly it has occurred to others. And that leaves us uneasy.

We are all helpless to control MS, but we do have control over how we respond to it. There is a gamut of emotions that are predictable, but beyond and including these (addressed in chapter 3) it is possible to choose how you will react to your life with MS. Attitude is all-important.

Accepting what is, and what isn't, is of great consequence to our health and happiness. For instance, my wheelchair has shifted from a dreaded adversary to a welcome friend. It allows me to do things I couldn't do without it. I let go of more and more expectations and found myself struggling less, while being far happier. Summer sometimes gets too hot, and sometimes winter gets too cold. By moving as little as possible, ice water on a wash cloth placed on strategic parts of my body, fans and an air conditioner all help me stay cooler in the summer. Cuddling beneath my electric blanket with my cat keeps me warm in winter. Attempting to see the colors of a sunset in an overcast day is a generous effort. The colors will sneak into the day, invited by the attempt.

Bob Aigner tried to teach me about expectations. At the time he first brought it up, I didn't understand. All I wanted him to do was fix my body. He couldn't, but he tried to do the next best thing—a lesson in life — that life is the way it is, and not always the way you'd like it to be. Bob instructed me, "You're not well, and as your physician my hands are tied. You can change your perspectives, your expectations; see your disabilities, accept them, make the adjustments you need to make, and then move on."

At the time he was trying to teach me about expectations I heard the words, but I had no idea of how to apply them to myself. I hadn't lived long enough with MS to understand that I would have to abandon prior expectations I had for my body to function correctly. Fortunately, the words sunk in, and finally I understood.

I know the fleeting beauty of a sunset. The deepening and mellowing of colors and hues — predictable and orderly — and they remind me of the nuances of love that color my life. If only I keep myself open to the light of love by accepting what is, love will then help me to transcend the diagnosis that has disrupted my life and the lives of those who love me. What could be more imperative to living with courage and hope than love?

A Change of Attitude

by: Lee J. Draper

"Just hang in there, Little One, I know what you are going through. I, too, am frightened and feeling as insecure as you must be. My world, like yours, will never be the same again."

I was talking to an animal, a tiny little creature that had come into my life two days before. I heard the little thing before I found it, and when I did, I do not know what gave me the courage to pull this screaming "embryo" from the tree it was clinging to. I had seen things that looked like this before when watching nature shows on the TV, so I knew this strange-looking, hairless being had come from a pouch. Its mother must have died, or was hurt, or maybe the poor little thing had fallen out of the pouch. These thoughts raced through my mind as I searched through my yard for "something" to give this little thing back to. My empty yard told me we were both on our own.

I was to find out the next day that my tiny little creature was a Brushtail Possum. A little girl, they told me, as they pointed out the pouch on her almost transparent body. I also got the impression from the way they looked at her that they did not hold out much hope for her survival. I had seen that look before, that look of pity, from people who find out I have MS.

"Hang in there, Little One," I said." We have so much in common, you and I. I, too, have recently had to give up my safe little pouch — my job. My hand movements are like the movements of your little head and body — very shaky and uncoordinated, and even though my eyes, unlike yours, are open, I, too, have trouble focusing on things." She did not seem to notice my words. She just clung to me as I fed her from a bottle no bigger than the ones that little girls have for their favorite doll.

Feelings came over me then. Feelings I had not had in what seemed to be a long time, ones of usefulness and achievement. Me, I thought, why would anyone feel sorry for me? I had achieved the impossible. I had kept this little creature alive for two whole days. I knew the road ahead for both of us was not going to be an easy one. She, like me, was accustomed to a life of waking from sleep when she felt like it. She was also accustomed to having a "warm bottle" ready and in place any time she felt like a feed. With me, she had to be abruptly awakened every four hours, and sometimes, by the time we had both got our "shaky" parts (her head and my hands) working together, her bottle was cold. There were often times when we would both fall asleep from exhaustion.

The road may have been an exhausting one, but those feelings of usefulness and achievement were to stay with me over the weeks and months ahead. Her eyes eventually opened and a beautiful gray fur started to grow on her "see through" skin. As she grew and filled out, she also filled many little empty holes in my heart, holes left from the things I could no longer do. Having to leave my much-loved job of twenty years did not seem that important anymore. What I was now doing was more meaningful (if not as financially rewarding) than my job ever had been. My resentment at having to rely on other people for help was lessened; my little creature had to rely on me, and I did not mind that at all. Maybe other people liked to help me!

Over the months I watched her grow into what I believe was the most beautiful possum in Australia. We had a lot of fun together, as I took her everywhere with me. She was with me when I was hanging out the clothes, taking trips in the car, playing games in the yard, and even when I went to parties. At parties she was always the star attraction, and gave new meaning to the term "party animal." All the time I was learning from her, and the most important lesson she taught me was to have courage: courage to keep going when it appears life has dealt you a bad hand.

My Little Possum is now no longer in my life. The time came when she needed me no longer as her safe pouch. She was now, after living in my home for seven months, ready to live in her own home, the wild bush where she came from.

Yes, she taught me how to fill my empty holes, but she left me with one I did not have before, as I miss her very much. But the hole left by her is full of love and gratitude for the lessons she taught me. Maybe they were not lessons on how to handle MS, but how to look at this MS thing from a different point of view.

People say to me "It must make you feel good, to have saved a little wild animal." I just smile to myself. The reality of it is... *the little wild animal saved me.*

MS SYMPTOMS

by: Jeanette Stones

There is no pain with MS.
That's what the doctor said.
No pain.
So much pain
Diagnosed 29 years old
No pain
So much pain
Two years of pain,
Change
Learning to let go
Letting go
Change
So much pain.
Not physical pain
A pain very deep
Loss,
Lost
I don't know where to find it.
Tears
No tears
Sometimes the tears come so easily
Then they stop.
I am empty inside
Not always,
But sometimes so empty and alone.

There is no pain with MS
I reach down deep inside
To figure out what's there.
I am afraid.
I am afraid I won't be able
To walk,

To write,
That I will lose sight,
Coordination
Lose the ability
To take care of myself,
Lose everything!

There is no pain with MS
That's what the doctor said
There is no pain
Yes
There is.

Foxhole Dances

by: Ted-Luke Greene

"I'll go it alone." I wonder if many of us with MS have said that to ourselves at one time or another. I know I have. I think I didn't really understand its meaning for me until I went to a weekend workshop called "psychodrama."

The hope there was to get closer to one's feelings by creating a drama about them. There were fifteen of us with different backgrounds and issues. I was the only one with MS.

We sat around a raised platform as each of us was given time "on stage" to design and play out a drama about an issue in our life. We were supported by the "director-therapist" in our work.

At my turn I said, "I'd like to dance with death. My MS struggle feels like a piece of me dies each time a new episode begins. It may be my walking. It may be my vision. It may be my sense of touch. I lose a part of me for a while or forever."

For my drama I directed a young woman to slowly dance around me, moving her arms through my personal space. As she did so I dodged the "death energy" radiating from her movement. She raised her arms above me. I bent down and sidestepped her. She tried to wrap her arms around me. I dodged her. I could feel the struggle. It was familiar, particularly the energy I was expending. I was tiring physically, mentally, emotionally, and spiritually.

The director-therapist stopped us after ten minutes and had "death" return to her seat. She asked a Vietnam veteran to join me. "From what you each have said," she explained, "I see a certain sense of isolation you have in common. Talk to each other about it."

The vet explained that after all these years since the war, in addition to the visible reminders of one arm shot shorter and a scar across his cheek, he is so aware of a deeper inability to feel "close" to people. He has a sense of a deep chasm separating him from others. "That is," he noted," except for the very few who shared the Vietnam foxhole." People just cannot quite grasp the sense of his experiences then and how they are still with him. The sleeping and awake nightmares that recur. The deaths of buddies. The sense of futility, of being trapped in a world of chaos. He feels that people just cannot really understand what his life is like," where he is coming from."

I explained that I too feel as though I cannot quite "connect" except to those who have been in the "MS foxhole." Holding my hand to my throat, I try to explain to the few people who really want to know, by saying, "I start my day already having had it up to here, for I have gotten up and stumbled to the bathroom three to five times during the night. Later I get my seven-year-old to close the shirt buttons that are too small for my numb fingers to handle. And so the day gets into first gear. Second gear eventually comes as I push myself to deal with the world. Third remains a question, or I even end up in 'reverse' fatigue."

A few people in the group responded, "Well, I have a small bladder, so I, too, have to go to the rest room frequently."

"I, too, spill my coffee more than I used to, and I also get frustrated."

It wasn't until my friend and I were driving home that I realized what had been bothering me about the responses; why the chasm between me and the others seemed to widen instead of narrow. They had honestly tried to be supportive. I appreciated that. But my friend was familiar with the feel of my plight from her struggle with her husband being deaf the past ten years. She shared her reaction to the group responses and helped me to understand my own.

"I was mad," she explained. "They spoke as though they were in your situation. But it's the degree of the struggle that they missed. They didn't catch the extent of the desperation you were trying to convey. I see how you feel, like you reach out through a dense fog."

I learned that there are people dancing in their own foxholes, like the Vietnam vet. A foxhole is a lonely place. There is something special to reaching out across the chasms to others. Maybe a person's foxhole is a different shape, but can we move together nonetheless? I would like to pull myself out of the hole, grasp another's hand, and help him or her out of their foxhole. At least long enough for us to dance. Now that I have the sense that I am not the only dancer, I might put off death as a partner and dance with life instead.

A Personal Journey

by: Cecelia J. McGregor

I believe that I fall within the category of a person "newly diagnosed" with MS. The formal diagnosis came less than two years ago; my body, of course, was aware of the disease's existence long before that.

I trace the beginnings of noticeable symptoms to more than six years ago. However, as other specific conditions presented themselves, such as low blood pressure and low blood sugar, medical efforts and my awareness of my body were concentrated on those aspects of my health. I began experiencing migraine headaches around this period of time, and a major concern for me each day was the struggle against dizziness, loss of balance, and fatigue.

When the migraine headaches became so frequent that emergency room physicians refused to treat me unless I consulted a neurologist, that became the next step in the process. While I now consider my relationship with this neurologist to be an excellent one, I made many mistakes in the first couple of years that we were building this relationship. I found him difficult to talk to, and therefore gave him minimal information about my concerns. When the dizziness or the fatigue or the feeling of electrical shocks moving throughout my body became particularly worrisome I would schedule an appointment. Once I was in the neurologist's office I would feel embarrassed to be there and I would minimize not only my symptoms but also how I felt about them. I knew that something was seriously wrong because many things had changed, but my complaints sounded psychosomatic to me, and I could not talk honestly about them.

I had become unable to tolerate crowds of people; one example of this is that I had not been grocery shopping for years. I could not concentrate on a conversation or a task if any noise was present. I began to experience difficulty with memory, and was unable to read and then retain what I had read for any period of time. I began to be tired all of the time. Worst of all, I had begun to doubt myself and my abilities. I am a lawyer by profession and a judge by occupation. As a result, these cognitive deficits frightened me even more than the physical disabilities. I had become unable to maintain my balance, and I never knew where my legs would be, or whether they would respond to my directions. Almost none of this did I share with the neurologist, because I wanted to appear strong and in control; I did not want to be thought of as a crybaby or, worse yet, a hysterical female.

When the neurologist was unable to find anything physical to explain my complaints, even after a number of diagnostic tests, he suggested that perhaps I was experiencing stress which was contributing to the symptoms. I believe that I did at least tell him that I disagreed with that assessment, but I did not argue with him about it, because I had become unable to trust myself in my perception of what was happening. I feared that he might be correct, even though I had already given up a substantial portion of my legal work over and above my job as judge. I had been aware on a deeper level than my conscious self would admit that I could not continue to meet the demands of my life as it had been structured, and I had given up all legal work that no longer gave me pleasure. Since I was working only in areas which I truly enjoyed, I could not agree that my physical symptoms were caused by stress.

However, in spite of my awareness that stress was not the sole source of my symptoms, I continued to question my mental and emotional perceptions. One of my fears was that I knew I had to run for re-election as judge the following year, and I was afraid that perhaps I would not be capable of handling the demands of the job. In spite of my desire to be completely unemotional in the presence of the neurologist, I got tears in my eyes when discussing this concern. After some time, the neurologist suggested that I enter the hospital for diagnostic tests, which I did.

The MRI showed the presence of MS, although I was not to learn that until some time later in the privacy of the neurologist's office. During my hospital stay he informed me that the tests showed an abnormality in my brain, and that when all of the tests were completed we would talk about specifics. Although I did not know exactly what was wrong, I felt in one sense relieved. I was relieved to know that I was not a hypochondriac, that I had a right to be concerned, and that I was actually in touch with reality, rather than having lost it. This knowledge gave me permission to once again trust in myself; I felt that no physical difficulty could be as bad as experiencing that loss of the sense of myself which I had allowed to happen.

When the doctor initially told my husband and me the results of the test, he referred to it as "demyelination syndrome." Those words which sounded foreign to me at the time, are now so much a part of my consciousness that I cannot remember ever *not* knowing what they meant. The neurologist told me that essentially it is a diagnosis of "multiple sclerosis," and he explained a bit about the factual aspects of the disease. He encouraged me to read whatever I could find about it, and encouraged me then to return with any questions I might have. I have spoken with people who have MS who were devastated when they heard the words "multiple sclerosis." I had the luxury of having no idea what those words meant. I went home eager to learn about this disease, about which I knew nothing. Learn about it I did, and while what I read was not particularly encouraging, I found the whole subject to be fascinating from an objective standpoint. I was interested in the *possible* course of the illness, but it seemed rather removed from my current experience. Denial? Perhaps, but it afforded me the comfortable illusion that I could control the illness simply by knowing about it, and it allowed me time to regroup my faculties before significant problems surfaced.

My only child, who was nine years old at the time of the diagnosis, had come to the hospital to visit me during the period of diagnostic testing. We as parents had believed this to be a wise course of action:

to allow him to see that I was not actually sick, and that I was simply there for tests. Unfortunately, we were wrong. We discovered about a month after the diagnosis that he had been experiencing intense fears about my well-being and that his trip to the hospital had only reinforced his insecurity. He had seen me fall at home, and had thought about what would happen if I fell while crossing a major intersection as a vehicle was approaching. I am writing this with the benefit of hindsight. At the time, rather than talking to us and expressing his fears, he chose to act in a way which would put as much distance between us as possible. He refused to allow me to kiss or hug him, he picked fights with me, he made remarks that were uncharacteristically rude and cutting, and his grades dropped. He began to act out in school and became a discipline problem. I sought the advice of a neuropsychologist whose training would, I believed, enable him to explain the disruption which had occurred in our home. I felt okay about having MS, but I could not understand my son's volatile reaction to it.

During the course of my discussion with this doctor I was able to see that the three members of the household were traveling three different paths relative to MS. My son was frightened and angry. My husband seemed, in my opinion, to be unable to acknowledge the magnitude of the illness. I was personally working on ways to cope mechanically, refusing to acknowledge my own feelings of sadness, frustration, and fear. Perhaps the decisive moment in my personal acknowledgment of the effects of the illness came at an unexpected moment. I was watching television and a picture appeared of a person running with a kite. In that second I realized that I could no longer run without immense effort, and the sadness was overwhelming. I began to be angry with my husband for his denial of the severity of the illness. On the one hand, he wanted me to rest more so that I could be available to do all of those things which I had traditionally done. On the other hand he was frustrated that I was accepting less legal work, and thus, my financial contribution to the home had decreased markedly. I remember telling him that perhaps we should separate for awhile, that I could handle my own situation with MS, but not his and my son's, too. I felt as though I was on a tightrope and that no matter which way I moved it would be a disaster. I began to seek privacy in my public and private life, not engaging in social activities and not conversing with friends unless circumstances required it. I remember that I cried sometimes.

At some point I began to use a cane for enhanced mobility. It felt awkward and I was greatly embarrassed by it, but I knew I needed it for balance, and realized that it helped to reduce the fatigue. I was always self-conscious with its use, and it seemed that no matter where I put it, it was always in the way. But I also knew that it was a real aid to me in maintaining my professional life, and it allowed me to engage in other activities which otherwise would have been beyond me.

I had been diagnosed with MS in January; in the summer of that same year the physical symptoms worsened. The neurologist and I worked with medications to control the dizziness and fatigue and I was finally able to express to him one of my very real fears that my mental acuity was decreasing. I did not know anything about cognitive deficits caused by MS, but I learned a great deal that summer. I went through the standard battery of tests, some of which I could not complete, and I learned that in fact I was experiencing substantial impairment in my ability to process information quickly and to filter out irrelevant stimuli. I began to be conscious of a growing depression.

In the fall of that year I traveled alone to the state capital for the annual meeting of the MS Society, hoping to talk with others about their experiences and eager to hear the speakers' presentations. I had not been to a support group, and knew only two other people with MS. I was not prepared for the experience of the annual meeting. People were moving in all directions in motorized wheelchairs and three-wheelers. Others not in wheelchairs were obviously disabled. I was confronted for the first time, and at close range with the effects MS could produce. I felt the need to escape to the shelter of my hotel room. I just sat on the bed, trying to center myself and to fight what

I was able to recognize as panic. When I felt capable of it, I went back to the meeting, grateful that I required only a cane for mobility, and believing that my situation would likely remain the same for many years. I remember also being in awe of these people who would make the effort to attend the meeting, and I admired the inner strength I felt they possessed.

At the annual meeting, I made the acquaintance of a couple who lead the support group in my area. I had not felt the need to be a part of a support group, but I was pleased to meet them and to know that they could be a valuable resource to me in the future, should I ever require their expertise.

The Christmas season was rather more difficult than the year before. Christmas tends to be, for many people and for myself, a kind of "watershed time," a time when we can remember from one year to the next our situation at that point in the year. I could not help but reflect on the fact that I could do little shopping, something I had greatly enjoyed in the past. I reflected on the fact that I was physically weaker than the Christmas before, less stable in my movements, and more preoccupied with the everyday effects MS was having on my life. The one point upon which I felt some relief is that I had been able to resolve my fears about the cognitive deficits with the help of two able and compassionate doctors. A doctor to whom I was referred in Chicago, and to whom I remain very grateful, walked me through descriptions of cognitive deficits, and showed me how my body had been compensating for these deficits all along, well before I knew that I had MS. I had, without even being aware of it, changed my ways of doing things at work. I had begun to take extensive notes during hearings (to counteract possible memory loss); to use word associations (to aid in recall); to demand an unusual amount of quiet in the courtroom (to avoid sensory overload); and to be selective about the things that demanded my attention at any one time. This doctor encouraged me to realize that my body had been taking care of me all along with no conscious help from me at all. If it could do this *without* my help, how much more could it do with my conscious attention to developing compensatory functions?

This doctor also talked with me very seriously about the fact that my life had changed, and that I had not yet come to terms with that fact. I was, in his opinion, continuing to demand too much of my body. Although I had reduced the legal work I did off the bench, I had simply filled up that time doing different legal work and writing, and that combination gave me no true reprieve from the time demands I had experienced as a practicing lawyer. Once again, I was told gently and kindly that I was expecting more of my body than it could produce for any sustained period of time.

I could not at first bear the thought of giving up work that is important to me, not merely because that work gives me pleasure and a feeling of purpose, but also because of simple pride. I felt that my peers would think of me as only "half a lawyer," as someone who is not totally devoted to the law. Many of us as lawyers are taught either implicitly or explicitly that we are to live, breathe, and sleep the law. I could not imagine doing that, because walking itself required so much concentration that it seemed to me impossible to continue working with the resultant fatigue. On the way home from Chicago I burst into tears because I felt that my life as a valuable member of the Bar was over. My work had been my life and the fear of losing it was unthinkable.

However, I knew that my life needed to change. The day after I returned from Chicago I spoke with the judge in whose court I had done a significant amount of work, and explained that I could no longer be available to perform those services. Before that talk began I knew exactly what I wanted to say and how I wanted to say it. But when it came time to actually admit that I could not do the work because I was not physically capable of it, I simply cried. This was the first time I had been required to verbalize this fact, and hearing the words spoken gave them additional power to enter my consciousness. I had been resistant to the idea of giving up social engagements, political activities, and evenings out simply because I would be too tired to do what I wanted to do. Now I had to face the trauma of giving up a part of my work, and I felt totally overwhelmed.

My self-esteem was shattered and I began to experience a significant amount of depression. I did not want to admit that I was depressed, because I had always considered myself to be a person who is not susceptible to such a thing. But one day in early January in the year following the diagnosis, the depression hit me severely, and I was able to recognize it for what it was. I could not understand how I could have been diagnosed with MS for almost one full year, and I still didn't have it figured out and under control. I recognize today how foolish this belief was, but at the time I simply felt defeated. In response my doctor quoted Rollo May to me, telling me that "despair is a catalyst for change." I held that thought in my heart in the following weeks, as it made sense to me and gave me hope.

I had not really worked through the despair that I was feeling. Perhaps because of it, about a month later I lost consciousness as I arrived for work one morning. I was admitted to the hospital. During that stay I came to terms with the fact that I needed some relief; that if I was to continue to work at all, in any form, I would need to change my lifestyle to give me maximum energy and efficiency. Earlier, I had visited the couple who lead the local MS support group, and I discovered that while the spouse with MS is in a wheelchair when she is out in public, she guides herself with furniture and objects in her home to get around without the use of the wheelchair. This was a profound lesson for me. It allowed me to think of mobility aids as something less than an all or nothing proposition. I thought about this while I was hospitalized, and when I was released I talked to the neurologist about his willingness to prescribe a three-wheeled vehicle. I had met a woman who had such a vehicle, liked it, and began to think of it as a way to enhance my mobility, and more importantly, my energy level. The neurologist did write that prescription, and I was hopeful that relief was in sight. Eventually I was able to purchase the three-wheeler with the financial help of a friend. That machine has been a valuable tool to me, and I believe that without it I would be unable to work at all.

Learning to navigate with the three-wheeler has not been an easy process and, in fact, has caused me profound embarrassment on many occasions. But this struggle and insecurity has caused me to realize that I have learned a great deal from MS. MS has taught me that I am not really in control of all aspects of my life, and more importantly, that I do not need to be in control to have a satisfying life.

I have learned that what I once thought was of the utmost importance is not, in the final analysis, what is most important at all. What is important is being of service, whether that be as a judge, as a lawyer, as a wife and mother, or as a friend. MS has taught me that I may not know what is in my best interest, and that my being open to the unexpected and often baffling symptoms of each day with this illness will cause me to grow in ways which I could not have otherwise realized.

MS has taught me in a very personal way that Christ's admonition to his disciples is correct: that fear is useless, and what is needed is trust. It has taught me to accept those things which I cannot change, and to rejoice in overcoming physical challenges which before this illness were no challenge to me at all. MS has taught me patience.

MS has taught me to rely on my internal strength and to honor the messages which my heart, and my physical body as a whole, are telling me. It has taught me the value of allowing others to be of service to me, one of the most difficult of lessons for me to learn, and I have learned to rejoice in others' joy as they help me. MS has taught me the necessity of being open and aware of the present moment, here and now. On those days when I am particularly unstable when I cannot walk without being off balance and in pain, or when I cannot even eat a grape because I cannot hold it, I lose the illusion that I can control much of anything.

After saying all of this, I do know that I have not as yet by any means come to terms with the enormity of this disease. I am sometimes sad that I cannot even walk without great effort, that I experience significant pain most days, that on days when I am feeling strong and can forget for a moment that I am disabled, other people will look at me and be aware of my disability, regardless of how strong I may feel at the moment. I still cannot join a group of people without being self-conscious. I still suffer embarrassment each time I must be treated with special consideration because of my disability. I feel "different." I feel intense hurt that my son, who is dealing with his own pre-teen sensitivity, is embarrassed by his disabled mother and that he continues to feel insecure about my health, even though I am active and productive. I remain angry some days that small things demand such effort. On my worst days, I don't care about the lessons MS has taught me; I am furious that such effort is required of me.

I periodically push my body beyond the limits of its endurance because I don't want to acknowledge the limits this illness demands of me, and I want to forget about those limits. I hate the physical and cognitive disarray MS has caused in me. I hate the emotional turmoil it has engendered in me and in my family. I resent the attention it demands every waking and even non-waking moment of my life.

Those of us dealing with MS must ultimately deal with it in our own individual way, and we are called, I think, to respect the ways of others in dealing with this illness. My way is to see MS not as an enemy who has invaded my body which I must conquer. I choose to see MS as a part of me which must be acknowledged, accepted, and accommodated. My way does not involve fighting with MS. I feel most comfortable working with it, not against it, as this is my way of taking control of my life.

I remind myself that I am responsible for making any adjustments to my life which MS requires. It is not up to a doctor to make me better, not up to a psychiatrist to make me feel good, not up to my family to take care of me, not up to my religion to heal me. It is up to me to seek the professional help that is available, to utilize the resources at hand for my well-being and comfort, and to maintain an attitude toward life which allows me maximum energy to be of service to others, and to make a contribution in this little piece of the world in which I find myself.

A favorite quotation of mine is taken from Matthew Fox's commentary on the sermons of Meister Eckhart: "Humility is facing serenely all that one is able or unable to do."

This is still a challenge for me; serenity and humility are not my strong points. But I cannot look upon MS as an unmitigated burden because of the impact it has had on my spiritual, psychological, and emotional development. I have gained an awareness of, and a respect for, the dignity which I possess simply by virtue of my humanity. I have learned that it is not what I *produce* that is of utmost importance. Rather, it is discovering who I essentially am, and with that discovery, making use of those talents which I possess to give honor and glory to God in whatever circumstance awaits me. No illness can detract from this basic truth. While I often struggle, it is my hope that each day will bring me a step closer to "making the most of life and the least of MS."

After the Dream Comes Reality

by: Neal L. Stoffers

My dream actually began in 1978. Prior to then my dreams had only been those of a child or teenager. In 1978 my vision of the future began to revolve around the attainable dreams of an adult. In June of that year I was appointed to the Newark, New Jersey Fire Department. I was young, 20 years old, and healthy; both were important attributes for a physically demanding job. My first two weeks as a firefighter were spent in training. In early July, we were sent into "the field" to help the city deal with a worsening fire problem.

For the next six months, I was either in training or temporarily assigned to companies whose members were on vacation. It was not until January, 1979 that the department gave me my first permanent assignment. No longer "roving," I was now stationed on "the hill" in Engine Company Six, the busiest engine company in the state. I was ecstatic. In those first months as a firefighter I had already begun to suffer from "adrenal addiction." The challenge and excitement of going into burning buildings to fight fires had become addicting. The satisfaction of helping people in need cannot be put into words. I became one of the fortunate few. I was young, healthy, and loved my job.

Shortly after being assigned to Engine Six, we responded to a fire in a four-story brick apartment building. The building was located just two blocks from the firehouse. It was a night of record cold. Within half a minute of the bells rousing us out of our warm beds, we rolled out of our quarters into the biting winter wind. The captain called in a heavy smoke condition as soon as the overhead door went up. Thick gray smoke covered the neighborhood like a dense fog. When we arrived on the scene, our first priority was rescuing the residents of the involved structure. Ladders were thrown up to windows that did not have fire escapes. Fleeing residents were coaxed or physically assisted down fire escapes. It was not until after this had been completed that hoselines were stretched into the building. The fire had been set in the stairwell. By now all four floors were involved.

The members of Engine Six stretched two hoselines into the building and fought to gain control of the stairwell, one floor at a time. We succeeded in limiting the fire to the stairwell on the first two floors. By the time we reached the third floor, the fire had spread into one of the apartments off the stairwell. When we made an attempt to advance a line to the fourth floor, we were driven back by the heat. I spent the next few minutes lying at the top of the stairs between the third and fourth floors. The fire in the third floor apartment had yet to be extinguished, so I could advance no further. I watched in frustration from my precarious perch as the fire took control of the floor above me. Before any serious attempt could be made to attack the fire on the fourth floor, the third floor fire had to be controlled. It became obvious from my burning ears and neck that the fight below me was not going well. I remained where I was, fighting back fear while playing water into the fourth floor. My battalion chief then ordered us off the stairs because our line was needed more on the third floor than at the top of the stairs. The top floor had to be conceded to the fire for the moment. It would be a couple of hours before another attempt would be made to push up to the fourth floor. When the attempt was finally made, the stairs collapsed beneath the captain. The sun was rising when he was taken out of the building and transported to the hospital. Before the fire was brought under control, three alarms had been transmitted. Twenty-one companies with 84 firefighters and officers helped extinguish the blaze.

As Engine Six was the first due company at the scene, we spent the entire night either being burned inside the fire building or trying to stay warm outside. It was an exhausting night. My entire body ached from both the physical strain and from shivering. When we finally got back to our quarters my left calf felt strange, as if it had fallen asleep. A few days later, I went to my doctor for a physical. The visit had been planned prior to my suffering the loss of sensation in my leg. I had just changed doctors, and wanted to get to know my new physician. In the course of his exam, I mentioned the loss of sensation in my leg. The doctor first used a pin to determine how much sensation had been lost. He then told me that the nerve that ran up the inside of my leg had probably been bruised. The problem was forgotten when the symptom went away of its own accord. Life was too busy to pay attention to such a minor complaint.

Even though my life at work was busy, I still felt the need for more. My job was both exciting and rewarding, but I knew firefighting was really a young man's occupation. It was important to look beyond the moment. Firefighting was not, after all, part of my teenage dreams. I had dreamt of a job that would allow me to see more of the world, with all its diversity. Foreign affairs had always interested me. A career in the Foreign Service had been part of my young dreams. When diplomatic relations between the People's Republic of China and the United States were established in January, 1979, such a career appeared attractive once again. I did not want to leave the Fire Department at the time, but wanted to begin acquiring marketable skills in case an opportunity presented itself some day.

My work schedule gave me a lot of free time during the day. I began to put this free time to use in the summer of 1979. My interest in foreign affairs, coupled with recent events, led me to begin the study of Mandarin Chinese. I studied at a small language institute in New York City for a year. During that year my interest in the Chinese language and the culture that had produced it grew. By September, 1980, China had become an obsession with me, and I had begun studying at Seton Hall University for a degree in Asian Studies. Free time became a thing of the past. Meanwhile, the problem with my left leg had returned, and had spread to my right leg. My doctor, however, could find nothing wrong with me. With the supreme confidence of a healthy 23 year old man, I decided the blunted sensation that was traveling up both my legs was my reaction to a stressful life — a life that was too busy for me to slow down.

For the next four years my entire life consisted of work and school. If I wanted to successfully complete the program at Seton Hall I would have to devote myself almost exclusively to my studies. My social life was put on hold while school was in session. I moved into my own apartment because the time lost to the interruptions that went with living at home was too dear. My roommate in the apartment was my younger brother. After he got married, my best friend took his place. Both of them let me study in peace. The time between runs at the firehouse was used for study. If we spent an entire night at a fire, I would drag myself out of bed the following morning and go to class. I was living life in the fast lane, using my vacation time from work for school. There was no time for anything other than my obsession with China, plus fighting fires. This period was a very satisfying time for me. I enjoyed the excitement of my job, while indulging my obsession. As for the blunted sensation, it would spread and recede with the ebb and flow of the school year. By then I was certain it was just my body's reaction to stress, a small price to pay for such a full life.

In my senior year in college, I met a young woman from Taiwan in my economics class. I became her tutor after doing well on the economics midterm exam. The economics professor would waive the final exam for anyone who tutored a classmate, so becoming a tutor would free up much needed time for other studies. During our first tutoring session, Miaoli told me that she already had a boyfriend. This suited me, as I still held myself to the rule of no social life during a semester. It seemed like the perfect match of tutor and student. I could speak Chinese, and was not interested in any romantic complications. Her English needed less work than my Chinese, and she already was involved in a romantic relationship. This was a fail-safe liaison. It did not, however, work out that way.

I found myself spending an enormous amount of time tutoring Miaoli. She wanted me to help her with economics, with her English, and even with her piano class (and I could not even play the piano). During the winter break, she went back to Taiwan, and I tried to get back to reality. If I wanted to graduate the following May it would be necessary for me to take 18 credits, plus write a 50 page thesis in my last semester. I also wanted to take the GMAT exam, and apply to graduate schools. My dream of the Foreign Service was gone. Instead I planned to study for an MBA in international business. Time was never at more of a premium than during that final semester. I could not afford a romantic involvement in my life. Things had to return to the way they were before Miaoli entered my life. Yet, when she returned from Taiwan, I met her at the airport with a dozen long stemmed roses.

By this time the blunted sensation had spread to my hands and arms. My bladder was beginning to bother me, and the vision in my right eye was slightly blurred. There was no time for me to slow down and ask why these things were happening to me. My life was building to a crescendo. A Chinese obsession had been added to my obsession with China. My hours at work were spent studying, fighting fires, and fending off playful inquiries from my colleagues about Miaoli.

I graduated with honors from Seton Hall in May, 1984. The following month Miaoli accepted my proposal for marriage. While we planned our wedding over the summer, she stayed with my parents. In early October, Miaoli's parents arrived in New Jersey for the wedding. We were married on October 14th in the chapel at Seton Hall. Because of the wedding, my studies were put off until the spring semester. In January, 1985 I began my studies for an MBA at Pace University in New York City. The familiar grind of work and school had returned, with the added pressures of adjusting to married life. My eye problem had sent me to an ophthalmologist a month after we were married. The loss of sensation had now spread from my arms and legs to my torso. My bladder problem was becoming harder to deny. Life was, however, much too busy to worry about these problems. I had a wife, school, and work to concern me.

The spring semester at Pace began smoothly, but by mid-February my problems became impossible to ignore. I suffered a severe case of vertigo which was diagnosed as having been caused by a middle ear infection. My bladder problems became so pronounced that it was necessary for me to see a specialist. When my wife mentioned my other symptoms to the urologist, I told her these problems were not related to the reason we had come to see this doctor. The doctor corrected me, saying that sometimes all of these symptoms can be tied together in one diagnosis. He went no further than that. A few days after seeing the urologist, I woke up and found myself unable to void. Miaoli called the urologist, who suggested some at-home remedies. When these did not work, we went to the emergency room. A catheter had to be used to relieve my bladder after eighteen hours of being unable to urinate. I was admitted to the hospital for tests. The urologist could find nothing wrong with my bladder; our family doctor was baffled by my symptoms. He finally decided to send me to a neurologist. By this time, I had spoken with my professors and explained my health problems. When they asked what was wrong they were told that no one knew; it was a mystery illness. An attempt was made to continue attending classes, but this only partially succeeded.

In April of 1985 I went to speak with a neurologist. After spending a few minutes describing my symptoms to him, he told me he thought I had a "form" of multiple sclerosis. I was devastated. I had worked so hard, and now this. My only hope was that he had said I had a "form" of MS. He had not said I had MS, just a form of it. I was determined not to give in to this disease, whatever it was. I completed the semester at Pace and returned to the firehouse.

That first day back at work, I found myself sitting at the kitchen table hoping we did not have to go out. Even though I was only driving, the strength needed to fight a fire was not in me. I was explaining to my friends around the table what the doctor had said. They could not understand why I had come to work, and I couldn't verbalize the frustration felt, or the need to prove I could still do what I had done before. As we were sitting talking, an alarm came in. We were first due engine. As we pulled out of quarters a column of smoke was clearly visible nearby.

The fire was only a few blocks from the firehouse. I stopped the rig at the corner before the building that was on fire so we could stretch a supply line from a hydrant. It was only a matter of two or three hundred feet from the hydrant to the front of the building. After engaging the pump and getting out of the cab, my duties consisted of attaching the supply line to the pump intake, and getting water to the men fighting the fire. I may have had to move a hoseline or two, but this was not difficult. After water is flowing, a pump operator's primary responsibility is to monitor the pump pressure. Under ordinary circumstances, there is little else required of him. Even though two alarms were sounded for this fire, and fifteen units with 54 firefighters responded, I did very little that could be thought of as strenuous. Yet, just standing in front of a burning building was physically draining. Once I had found the rush of adrenalin on a fire scene rewarding. That day it only sapped me of what little strength I had. I knew then that I could not continue to do what I had done before.

My condition was obvious to everyone on the scene. Both my battalion chief and my deputy chief asked me how I felt a number of times during the course of the fire. After the fire was brought under control, we began to reload hose. This required me to climb up to the hosebed on the rear of the truck. My chiefs again questioned me about how I felt. I responded with a simple "okay" and continued to load the hose. In truth I was exhausted, and was praying to God for strength. My deputy finally took matters into his own hands. He knew I was too stubborn to admit I had a problem, so he ordered me off duty. A battalion chief drove me to my parents' house, because I felt too weak to even drive my car.

The questions that came to my mind were innumerable. All our plans for the future had become meaningless. The restrictions the doctor gave me effectively put working in the field of international business out of reach. I was on sick leave for six months, and spent a week in the hospital after the left side of my face went completely numb. Fatigue was now my constant companion. After spending six years living life in the fast lane, I had hit a brick wall. I was no longer living; existence was all I could hope for.

I began to hear stories of the devastating effects MS could have. There were stories of spouses leaving as soon as they heard the diagnosis. Would my wife stay with me? She had never heard of MS. The disease is all but nonexistent in Taiwan. Her life in America was centered around me. She had no family in the United States, and so was faced with an extraordinary challenge. Was her love for me deep enough for her to deepen her commitment? Especially when that commitment promised to go beyond what would normally be expected of a newlywed wife? Ours had been a whirlwind romance. We had been married a year after we had met. Did Miaoli have enough invested in our relationship to want to make the heavy emotional investment required of a "well spouse?" Or would she simply cut her losses and return to her family in Taiwan? What about having children? How could I be a good father? The summers would be too hot for me to play baseball with my son. There would be no family outings to the beach. During the winter months we would be haunted by fears of catching a simple common cold. In the end, would it be fair to my future children to have a father with MS? The question of children had to be answered quickly. We did not know if or when the spread of the blunted sensation would rob me of my ability to be a father. Would the fire department want me to remain on the job? Fighting fires was out of the question. At the beginning of 1985, I was a man who felt he was in control of his destiny. By the end of that year I felt I had lost control of my life. After the dream comes reality, and reality proved to be a bitter existence.

The adjustment period for me lasted until January, 1986. By then we had moved into an apartment in my parents' house, so we could be closer to my doctors. I returned to Seton Hall that semester to begin studying for an MA in Asian Studies. My wife proved to be a strong and loving partner who kept me "honest" when I tried to cheat a little and deny my limitations.

⊷⊶⊷⊷

On April 13, 1987 our son Will was born. His sister Joy entered the world on December 16, 1991. The fire department proved true to the axiom: "It takes care of its own." I was assigned to the training division, where my experience and education could be put to use training new firefighters. In May, 1991, I graduated from Seton Hall with an MA. Now I am thinking of continuing on for a Ph.D.

I have adjusted as best I could to my disease. Feelings of guilt at my weakness sometimes surface. I can, however, still walk, and in fact have suffered only sensory impairment. I am one of those "but you don't look sick" MSers. I do not go near fires or other emergencies. The frustration is palpable, and can bring tears to my eyes. I only infrequently go to firehouses. The atmosphere brings back too many memories of life in the fast lane. These are best left buried. Life goes on after MS. In some ways it is richer, because the disease has given me the ability to better appreciate what is left of a normal existence. In order to survive emotionally, however, I avoid thinking of past dreams. For surely after the dreams comes a reality that often does not resemble the dream. When this happens, the dream must be forgotten. Emotional survival requires me to build new dreams on the reality I now face.

The Dream Stealer

I had found happiness
After searching so long
I had discovered new meaning for life
And a new harmony for its song

Based on love
With dreams beginning to bloom
A new partner to share with
But all was ended too soon

By the Dream Stealer

The thief does not come from without
But dwells within
Waiting expectantly
For the dreams of the young to begin

Shielded only by a new-found bitterness
No other defense against the attacks
You are robbed of your strength to resist
While the world shows you all that your life lacks

Because of the Dream Thief

Others look at you
With questions in their eyes
Knowing not how to deal
With one whose dreams have died

The world has little pity
Needing only productive work
No others can understand the frustrations
The questions of self-worth

Only its victims know the Dream Stealer

You are filled with a frustrated feeling
As if trying to grasp air
Like grabbing a fist of water
And few seem to care

You can only shield yourself in bitterness
Against the enemy from within
Betrayed by your own body
Fighting a battle you can never win

With the Dream Stealer

Thirty Years of Self-Diagnosis

by: *Caroline Paulson*

*"In all the cases which one may investigate it will be seen
that the upholders of the psychological theory have failed
to conduct their experiments with sufficient care."*

from: *The Principles of Psychology*
by: William James

⸺ ▨◆▨ ⸺

I was so excited I could barely breathe as I finished reading the
story. I was about 15, and had been reading a tale of the far north for
entertainment only — but I had found an answer — I thought — I
hoped. Surely this explained why I was so puzzlingly different from
the others — why my physical reactions to things just didn't go along
with the rest of the kids I knew.

The story was about a trapper wandering in the Yukon alone,
written in the stream of consciousness style. Although there was a fair
amount of action, most of the story was about the trapper's state of
mind and how he took care of himself. The predominant theme was
watching out for cold, heat, and sweat because an excess of any of
these would kill the trapper faster than the weapon of any enemy. The
trapper was constantly aware of his own body heat, because if he
sweat inside his clothes he would surely freeze to death. His own
perspiration would be the deadly ingredient which would seal his fate
in this frozen northern wilderness.

I was transfixed with the revelation! Now I understood why I had
never sweat — My father was Norwegian and yes, *my genetic heritage
must have equipped me for that life in the far north.* If I were to follow in the
footsteps of that Yukon trapper, I might have a chance at surviving

him just because *I did not sweat*. How understandable it all seemed to me then!

So I managed to find an explanation for one of my many physical irregularities at an early age. After all, I had already had many experiences that had proven out my feelings. When I was little, my Norwegian dad and I had braved swimming in cold Canadian waters that my Texas mom wouldn't even consider. I clearly recall watching my dad's skin turn utterly blue while I laughed, still quite comfortable in the cold water. It's that I was more of a Norwegian than my full-blooded Scandinavian dad. After all, I had been seeking out coolness even when I was very little. On summer nights I would leave my room and go down to the cellar to sleep on a cool pile of sheet rock. This habit made my mother very unhappy, so as I grew older I tried my best to fit in with what she and the bigger world seemed to require of me. But I could only do just so much.

My confrontations with my high school gym teacher stemmed from all this. Sit-ups outside in a field on a sunny day suddenly got to me, and I felt faint. Miss Metress said that I had to do ten more because I hadn't even worked up a sweat.

"I can't sweat at all!" I had very honestly replied.

The teacher's response was a quick kick in the back, "For lying," she said.

Since I had fainted, that kick finished me for that gym class, and all of high school gym. My family doctor gave me a perpetual excuse based on allergies.

It was clear to me that I was different from the others; if they understood "allergies" and didn't comprehend inability to cope with heat and sun, then allergies would be the reason I would give them.

In truth, I did have many allergies to dust, paint, animals, and different kinds of pollen. I yearned for an active practical life which these allergies and endless respiratory infections seemed to prohibit. Every time a school nurse insisted on taking my temperature, I braced myself for trouble. In elementary school I was sent home day after day because my temperature was "wrong", and this was always more impressive to these nurses than my feelings concerning how well I felt.

It was even more troubling that I never developed any real menstrual cycle during my entire teenage years. My parents took me to doctors to find out why, but we never got anywhere. And also, my younger brother was seriously ill with ulcerative colitis, and my parents had to give him a great deal of their time and attention.

Little did I know that all my many differences would eventually be explained by one diagnosis — multiple sclerosis. But, it would take endless research and 30 years for me to get this answer. In the meantime I would have to sustain myself with my own explanations and my own methods of dealing with my situation.

I was not going to read any printed material with any greater sense of revelation than that *Far North Story* until I reached the age of 42. Finally, after visiting hundreds of M.D.s, reading countless books, and going through entirely too many hospital visits due to mystery symptoms, I spoke with an ear doctor who mentioned the possibility of MS to me. I called the MS Society, and they sent me a package of pamphlets.

At a page with a picture of an MS person's hand shaking out of control I stopped reading, transfixed — the sense of recognition was overwhelming. Those erratically banging hands that had caused me to give up my piano studies — that had embarrassed me at meals so often — there they were, drawn cartoon fashion in a little pamphlet — *About Multiple Sclerosis.*

—+—✖✦✖—+—

During those years between 15 and 42 I spent my time getting well educated, creating an interesting career in international business, traveling, and restoring my country home in New Paltz. And always, with any time and energy I had, I pursued my quest to find out what was wrong with me, whether I was acutely sick or doing better. I would ply strangers with questions about the way their bodies regulated temperature, how their eyes and ears worked, whether their limbs suddenly jumped at times, or if they had ever seen their own internal energy arcing, as I had. It was safer to ask strangers since they would simply stop me if they thought I was going too far, and that would be the end of it. If they had had any unconventional experiences similar to mine, they felt freer to share them with a stranger, secure in the knowledge that I would not tell others they were crazy, since I didn't know any of their acquaintances.

But even at the age of 15, I had many other puzzling physical events to explain away to myself. Fortunately for me, my father was a master electrician who worked daily at CBS fixing the most difficult of all electrical malfunctions, erratic electronic failures in the network's complicated broadcasting equipment. Every night at dinner we would hear about it. Well, not quite every night, but frequently. My father found tracking down that elusive loose connection or frayed wire in a huge mass of wiring just as satisfying as any Sherlock Holmes mystery, and was surprised that we did not share his enthusiasm. I did learn from him about the nature of electricity, and how this mysterious current coursed through all living things. As a teenager my dad had suffered a bout of arthritis, and had used a primitive electrical battery as therapy. He would wind it up and then give himself shocks to relieve the pain. The process fascinated him, and understanding things *electrical* turned into a lifelong pursuit. He never seemed to wince at shocks as he worked. I recall touching wires he was connecting bare-handed and being blown across the room. Perhaps his early "therapy" had blown out his nerves — or maybe he was just *the Electrical Man.*

Whenever anyone touched my thighs, I, too, was an *electrical person*. But it was a fairly easy thing to avoid. The biggest risk was when kids decided to tickle each other. My sides were numb, so I would let them tickle me there as I sat, stone-faced, praying that no one would ever decide to attack my thighs. In general, this ruse worked.

One day I was investigating a hide-out the boys had built in the woods when I found myself surrounded by the gang of male 10-year-olds. In the ensuing territorial battle, they grabbed me by the thighs and the most public of my early internal electrical storms started. As the shocks abated I saw the whole bunch of them, eyes wide and mouths gaping, half of them running away.

"She's crazy!" they yelled.

I really didn't understand why they reacted that way for a long time, but I did understand it was important to keep my thighs to myself.

It was at Syracuse University that my battle with physical education resurfaced. It wasn't until I got there that I realized all candidates for the B.A. had to complete 4 semesters of P.E. with a B average in order to get their degree. The first semester was an introduction with exercises, instruction on hygiene and diet — in short, activities I could handle. I got my B.

After that, it was all downhill. Every course involved team sports and balls coming at me. I had never been able to distinguish where a ball was coming from or where it was going. In elementary school, balls had crashed right into my face as I stood there trying to see them, feeling blind and helpless. I told them all I couldn't see the ball, but always, the reaction was the same.

"Paulson, you're just not trying."

I wondered if these people thought I would stand there and let a hard ball smash me right in the eye rather than "try" when I got a big shiner from one of these mishaps.

So here I was at Syracuse University coping with a slightly more adult version of that same situation. I registered for bowling, which seemed to be the least demanding of the courses offered, and hoped for the best.

I was a student aide to the Liberal Arts Dean, and had evolved into a special assistant to the blind students. I had achieved this by doing a particularly good job guiding them through the registration process. The Dean decided it would be a good idea for me to maintain contact with these students during the year, monitoring their progress and seeing what types of special problems they would encounter. I therefore had his ear. One day I braved speaking to him about my "deficit" and how I was worried that the University's P.E. requirement would mean that I would never graduate. He was not sympathetic. He said anyone could hit balls with a baseball bat — all they had to do was try. How frustratingly familiar that sounded to me!

Things weren't going well in bowling class. I simply couldn't direct and release those heavy balls smoothly. After a few attempts, my arm would start yanking around. It burned and sparked of electricity. The teacher considered me a troublemaker and seemed convinced that I was disrupting her class for the fun of it. My fingers cramped inside the little holes and wouldn't let go of the ball at the proper time. As a result, the ball would fly across the alleys. My standards for a successful throw were so low I considered a gutter ball a triumph.

Everyone would say, "There's nothing to it. You just try, and then you get the hang of it."

As the spring semester wore on, the temperature in the University's bowling alley went up, and my throw got even worse. Showing up at class was humiliating, but I didn't want to give the authorities that simple excuse to say it was all my fault that I wasn't learning. Twice a week I tried and tried to no avail, my right arm burning and flopping crazily after each session.

My final grade in Bowling was a D-minus. I was despondent. I knew that my performance in the other activities offered, tennis, volleyball, basketball, softball, etc. would probably be worse. I looked into the possibility of a doctor's excuse like the one I had used in high school, but this was college, and no doctor would go along with me. My upperclassmen friends introduced me to a woman who had completed all requirements for her degree except P.E. last year. She was still tied to Syracuse University, taking P.E. courses, and hoping to get her B.A. soon. She warned me not to assume I could "get around" the P.E. menace. I appealed to Dean Cope again. He rebuffed me again.

By the beginning of my sophomore year I felt that an impossible obstacle stood between me and my degree. It confirmed the strength of my desire to go to Norway to find myself. I felt I would discover my true nature there. I stayed at Syracuse my second year of college, and then went to Scandinavia in the autumn of 1966.

⊷⊷⊯⊹⊯⊶⊶

I spent my 20th year fulfilling my dream of studying in Norway. I went to a small state school that offered students a review/ reinforcement of a traditional Norwegian high school education. Young Norwegians who had left school early to work or travel attended these "folkehogskules" (people's high schools) to refresh their minds and possibly to prepare for further vocational training. The value of attending this particular school was that I would be culturally immersed. During my time at Voss Folk High School, no one spoke English to me, and all the students tried their best to make a real Norwegian of me.

It took three months of struggle before the language started to come easily to me, and I no longer had to mentally translate everything that came in or went out of my head. I learned the Norwegian approach to housecleaning, cooking, needlecraft, skiing, knitting, and using silverware. I surveyed Norwegian history and literature. I also survived several medical and dental treatments "pa norsk."

I learned that many of these people rarely sweat, whereas others sweat copiously. All felt that a thorough sweat was important to one's health. Even small towns had beautiful swimming pools with saunas, and most Norwegians went twice a week to rinse and steam-clean their systems. I also found out that many of these people had allergies, but these problems hardly stopped these young Norwegians from doing anything and everything they wanted to pursue. The smartest students in the school were in the "idroitligne", a course that prepared them to attend a licensing school for gym teachers. There wasn't much interest in balls or team sports here. The emphasis was on developing endurance for treks and skiing, strength and quick reflexes — all of which I respected. I did my best to participate, but I had endless respiratory infections to hamper me just as in my childhood. I was also a gringo, and no one expected too much of me. I would manage to keep up with them on an all-day hike, but the next day I would lie groaning in my bed while the rest of them got up and skied up the mountain, herringbone style.

I had plans to top off this experience by hiking about in the summer's perpetual sunshine in the almost Arctic tundra of Norway's far north. I took a fjord ship up to Tromso, and became acquainted with the staff at the local natural history institute. There were many interesting field work assignments for students during the summer months, but unfortunately, they had all already been given out to others.

I hiked around the outback, with the support of a system of huts and inns designed with the trekker in mind. The sun shone all the time removing any fears of being caught on the trail in the darkness. The only problems I encountered initially were some drunk but harmless Lapplanders. After a week things changed; the problem was within myself.

My vision was blazing white and then darkening out, which had frequently occurred previously during the heat of August. This had seemed very normal to me. After all, that was vacation time from school and I guessed that was one reason why we got summers off, because it's so hard to read in the heat. But now, in Norway, it seemed much worse. My bladder burned and stung, with sudden explosions of urine running down my legs. And my legs! How can you hike with legs that seemed to uncontrollably collapse? I grabbed the backcountry bus back to Tromso and went to see a doctor.

I guess that was my first MS consultation. For those who found their talks with their doctors regarding MS difficult, imagine *my* discomfort at confronting a leathery-faced old Norwegian man with my problems "pa norsk." He did not speak English, and my Norwegian, while very good for ordinary situations, was hardly up to expressing my symptoms or understanding his medically oriented responses. He prescribed pills for a bladder infection. I checked into a hotel to rest up.

I found it hard to rest with the sun shining all the time . I felt too weak to do much of anything and too restless to relax. I was too stimulated by the incredible beauty of this Northern summer with six hours of sunset-sunrise light effects and snow falling on the mountain above me, while the temperatures soared down at sea level. For ten days I tried to rest, hoping the pills would work, and I'd be able to resume my trek. Instead of improving, I found myself collapsing on the street. Now I was sure that *I had to just get myself home.*

I phoned my parents, got my ticket, and flew from Tromso to Oslo where I had to pick up my passport from the Russian Embassy. I had applied for permission to travel to the USSR with a group of Norwegian teachers. I was at the Russian Embassy, and things weren't going too well — there was some delay — I fell ill, and later wound up in a hotel room with an SAS hostess — I remember wondering whether I'd make it home on my own, and I visualized going through JFK airport on a stretcher. Fortunately, that was not needed, but on my arrival in New York my parents did take me directly to a small hospital where I was treated for gastrointestinal and bladder infections. Our trusty family doctor did not really know what to make of some of the other symptoms I reported. They decided I was stressed out from my adventuresome year in Norway. Indeed, when I got to the hospital, I was clumsy at speaking my own native American-style English. For a year I had barely uttered a word of English, and when I did speak it was with a foreigner who was using British-style English.

I left the hospital and applied to Columbia University to finish off my 2 years left on my B.A., after carefully checking to make certain there was no P.E. requirement. I started to work part time at the local mental hospital in the children's wing. I seemed better for a while. Then while at Columbia, I got worse. I would be walking down the street and suddenly, feces would drop out of my anus as though I had nothing to do with it. I suffered through three severe bouts of pneumonia during my junior year, and had constant bladder infections. That spring of 1968, Columbia University suffered through a student strike and suspension of classes. There were bloody marks on the sidewalks, leftover from the many confrontations between policemen on horseback and the students. At that time, a crack on the back of the head with a paddle was considered the proper way to spank a rebellious 20-year-old. I had only just arrived on campus, and didn't even understand what the issues were. The whole situation horrified me.

The doctors I visited for my physical problems were suspicious of any young person studying at Columbia. One doctor refused to see me again. He believed that if I truly had taken the pills he prescribed, my bladder infection would have cleared up by now. Since I still had the infection, and I claimed I had taken the pills as he directed, he was certain that I was incapable of telling the truth about anything. I was sent to a psychiatrist to work out my emotional problems. During the next summer I collapsed on campus three different times. The infirmary said it was heat stress and told me to take salt pills.

I found other doctors to keep me going on antibiotics. My insides burned. My vision was foggy. I suffered severe chest pains. I found it difficult to exercise. I gained weight. My bladder and my anus had minds of their own, and constantly presented me with unpleasant surprises. My parents checked me into Columbia Presbyterian Medical Center for a complete work-up, but despite the time and effort, no real conclusion was reached. Psychiatrists did their best to convince me this was my hysterical reaction to fear of sex. Sigmund Freud would have been proud.

No one seemed to realize that a woman fighting electrical shocks in her thighs and constant bladder infections would be unlikely to have a very satisfying sex life. I was to discover later that having sex when your spastic bladder retains urine is a good way to hasten infection. This resulting bladder infection often stirs up MS symptoms. So an untreated young woman would have a very real reason to "fear" sex. But the truth was, I had enough fear of the symptoms themselves to occupy me.

My bladder continued to worsen until I found I could barely pee at all. A pair of urologists sent me to The French Hospital as an emergency case, and did a thorough work-up. Repeated infections plus spasms had blocked my urethra, so they cut it open — just enough to insure that my bladder would not block up again. I read Linus Pauling's ideas about megadoses of vitamin C preventing infections and increasing your vitality. When I tried out his ideas, they seemed to help me. I also learned that squatting in the shower seemed to force the urine out. I was feeling better. I had accepted my ongoing incontinence problem as just a fact of life and one that I could handle now with the help of baby wipes and a lot of female paper products.

I had given up on my ambition to be an anthropologist. I could certainly understand that isolated, poorly-paid field work wasn't an appropriate career for me. I just wasn't hardy enough. Others didn't understand. So be it—I could hardly be expected to explain all these physical problems to others, particularly since many people simply thought they proved I was mentally unstable. The best thing was to say as little as possible about it, and get on with learning how to live in Manhattan on my own.

I took an apartment, got a beginner's job on Wall Street, studied for an M.B.A. at N.Y.U. in the evenings, and fell in love with a tall, dark, handsome man in the real estate business named Jerry. We enjoyed a very good sex life, and surmounted my physical problems. I felt like a successful young adult who knew how to earn a living, maintain an apartment, and have a good "relationship." It seemed to me I was safe. After all, those many physical problems during my Columbia years had left their mark on me, but the hard times seemed to be over.

I was busy creating a life in which my weaknesses would not inhibit me too much. Manhattan freed me from having to deal with cars, which was important to me. My depth perception had never been much good and was worse when I was tired. It was important to not have to drive to a job. It was also important to have a job which used my fine education, my appetite for data, my memory, and my research skills, since these were my strong points. I had to battle for my jobs. Every interview focused more on why I didn't just go get married far more than my ability to do the job at hand. I could hardly tell these men about my problems, which seemed to indicate I was not physically up to mothering. I knew that I needed my rest, and I did not really think that I would handle the demands of motherhood well, even if all my other problems were finally diagnosed. I put the thought of children out of my mind.

I still had no proper female menstrual cycle, and also had bizarre erratic patterns in temperature, blood sugar, bad allergies, and other symptoms which I now decided were not symptoms. They were just *me*, and I was a Norwegian. I would not let myself or anyone else forget that. After all, human beings are a diverse bunch. Being different seemed more normal to me than fitting into those narrow stereotypes that doctors seemed to believe in, I decided. I was slim, physically active, and very attractive. Trying to make headway in my career became my big preoccupation during most of my 20s.

⸱⸱─ ⸱⸱ ≭✦≭ ⸱⸱─ ⸱⸱

I was about 26 and working as Financial Planner for the Literary Guild when I went on a four-day trip to Iceland over Thanksgiving weekend in 1973. Volcanoes had recently erupted there, building a new island in the Atlantic. This fascinated me. The fire and ice theme of this little trip reflected my own inner sense of myself. I had learned that sudden changes of ambient temperature in pools of water were called thermoclines. I felt I was like a churned-up series of pools of water with different parts maintaining different temperatures. Internally, I had experienced volcanoes, spouting geysers, and burning flows of lava. I felt it was time to see the geological expression of these phenomena. Iceland fit my mood.

We landed in darkness and toured Reykjavik the next day in that sparse, indirect twilight of Arctic winter days. It was about 20 degrees, and most of the group complained bitterly of the cold. All to be expected. The surprising element was the ample hot water everywhere. Icelanders happily sat in big outdoor pools of water pumped up from hot springs below.

Just a few generations ago Icelanders had nothing but peat for fuel; no trees grow in Iceland. The immigrants from Scandinavia slept piled together in tiny huts, freezing. Now, modern plumbing had supplied them with something any U.S. citizen would envy — plentiful, cheap energy.

At that time OPEC had just been organized, and oil prices were beginning to escalate.

We toured on to the agricultural area outside the capital where huge vegetables were cultivated in hothouses heated by these same boiling spring waters. The earth's crust was so unstable there that you had to watch each step. Hot springs would open up and close down overnight. The homes seemed to float along on this crust. We saw one house with an open hot spring right at the front door.

"What will they do about that?" I asked.

"They'll just wait, and at some point things will shift and it will fill up again," answered the guide.

The New Yorkers were utterly horrified by the situation, but I noticed the Icelanders took it in their stride.

On to the biggest treat of the trip — an extra plane ride to tour Heimy and Surtsey, the location of the recent volcanic explosion. The plane was small and the views were breathtaking. Once we landed, the fishing village that had been covered in volcanic ash was a pitiful sight. I thought of the people who lived here, and knew that most of them had barely been aware of the outside world before this catastrophe. How frightening to live on a little island world and see it disappear under ash. These people had been compelled to leave everything! The wind froze my face while my feet smoldered inside my boots. The earth's crust was still boiling here. We tourists had difficulty tolerating these hot coals.

When I returned to Manhattan I had a very hard time explaining to my skeptical urbanite friends why my trip had been enthralling and wonderful. "Why didn't you go to the Caribbean or Bermuda and catch some rays?" they would ask. I knew I couldn't really expect anyone to comprehend my unusual travel tastes.

My trip had expanded my knowledge of my precious Scandinavian heritage and also stimulated my interest in the developing energy crisis. I delved into the topic of energy, and found it utterly fascinating. Little did I know that developing this interest was going to pay off very quickly. I was soon to land an entry level position in the international oil business. This was the lucky break I had been searching for over the last six years.

—•—⚓—•—

By December, 1974, I found myself beginning the new job of my dreams. I was now a management trainee at Asiatic Petroleum, a small subsidiary of the large and powerful European Royal/Dutch Shell Group of companies. I had brazened my way in.

I had gone for an interview not knowing anything about the company. The young British personnel man had scanned my resumé, asked a few questions, and then asked me to tell him more about myself.

I quickly retorted, "Since you have my resumé you already have quite an advantage. Why don't you tell me about Asiatic before this goes any further?"

He was surprised and somewhat taken aback, but he did proceed to fill me in on the company. As he talked, I recognized that he was describing the type of opportunity I'd wanted for years — now possible. Asiatic marketed fuel oil to east coast utilities and conducted other energy related enterprises. This small company reported directly to a large European parent, and it seemed that an employee there might enjoy small company camaraderie plus big company stability and sophistication.

I was so sick and tired of being slotted into what I felt was trivial business. I had always been interested in commodities, things that were critical to a nation's economy — lumber, wheat, minerals, and yes, petroleum. The fact that I was a woman didn't mean that I would be content to use my M.B.A. to calculate profit margins on lipsticks and soap powder.

The young man started to wrap up the interview saying, "We'll be speaking to a great number of candidates."

Not willing to be dismissed, I blurted out, "No matter how many you interview, you won't find anyone with a greater interest in the energy business or more highly suited to joining a European company than me."

I quickly and assertively made a strong case for myself. The young man had been impressed. I had virtually demanded the job, and I got it. It was the best thing that happened to me during all of 1974, which had been a very difficult year.

—·—⟨•⟩—·—

It was strange to me how this assertive approach worked so well in business, but got me absolutely nowhere with that other group of professional men I was always having to deal with — M.D.s. Over the summer of 1974 I had been falling down a lot. I distinguished between regular falling, which happened without any blank spaces or electric shocks, and *the strange falling*, which seemed like a blacking out, followed by finding myself in a crumpled heap. In August I had been experiencing this *strange falling* almost every day. One day I was walking down the subway stairs, the blackness came over me and then I was at the bottom, bruised and bleeding from crashing down 16 steps. I had even knocked down two people, and they were angry, yelling at me along with many others. My ankle was very badly sprained. My doctor questioned me and sent me to a neurologist.

I had been looking for a new job for a while when I finally saw the nerve specialist. It was very difficult, holding down my financial job, going for interviews, coping with my frequent falls, plus seeing doctors for my ankle, which was healing slowly. It was October, 1974 when I visited a neurologist for the first time. He asked me about myself and examined me; then I asked him what his opinion was.

He said, "Not so fast." He indicated that he was the doctor, and he would ask the questions.

I replied, "Maybe you don't understand why I'm here. I'm a working woman. I have to go to an office from 9 to 5 every day. I can't be falling down all the time, and continue to earn my living. I expect you to help me function."

He laughed at me and said my job couldn't be all that important.

He suggested I should go to the hospital for tests. I asked why. He said, "You should trust your doctor. You shouldn't ask so many questions."

I explained to him that I wasn't in the habit of going to the hospital just because a doctor suggested it. I had to be convinced it was needed. I'd already been in and out of hospitals eight times during the last nine years, and I couldn't see that any of it had done me any good, but I didn't volunteer this. I did get him to explain about a myelogram, one of the tests he recommended. His description of injecting dye into my spine terrified me.

"Why would that be necessary?" I queried.

"Oh, It might prove interesting," he replied.

"Is that the only reason you can offer me?" I asked.

He shook his head in reply, obviously unwilling to explain further. I told him I couldn't make a decision at this time.

As I was leaving, he said, "Call me when you get serious." But I had already decided against dealing with this mystery man again.

As the weather got cooler, I was falling less and feeling better. I got my offer from Asiatic in November just as my old employer was losing patience with my many absences. I had expressed an interest in rotating out of the dead end number crunching job I was in, and they had slapped me down very roughly. Therefore I was surprised that they were astounded by my determination to leave after my two–year stint. But everywhere it was always the same; I was the unusual woman working in a man's world. At my 1972 graduation there were 377 M.B.A.s, and all but two of these were men. I never met that other woman M.B.A. She majored in marketing, I in finance. Despite this advanced degree in business, managers didn't expect me to go after opportunities like a young man would. Doctors never appreciated my career orientation either. So, I wondered what to expect as I entered yet another male domain. This time it was the world of the international petroleum business.

I was pleasantly surprised to find female colleagues in this small firm. One in particular was personally special to me. She reminded me of my father. Like him, she was a Norwegian–American. After a few weeks I asked her my Norwegian question.

"Ruth, do you have a normal body temperature, or is yours lower than other people's?"

She didn't really understand me. I explained to her that I had been puzzled by my lack of sweat and abnormal body temperature patterns my whole life, and I thought it had something to do with my Norwegian genes. Ruth said she couldn't help me on that.

I said, "Well, maybe I'm just a human lizard and that's the problem." We chuckled and didn't speak of it again for many years.

I was quite happy that winter. I was working with a diverse international group of people. I had four likable female peers in the company. I was learning oil economics from distinguished English gentlemen who also happened to be my superiors. I had broken off with Jerry, so my romantic life was not so pleasing, but in every other respect, things were definitely looking up. My greatest worry was my health. I had to come to work regularly and make the most of this wonderful opportunity. *Please, please no falls, no pneumonia, no urinary infections, no eye problems. Please, body, don't betray me.*

One day, I was out to lunch with some of the executives from the company. I was walking up the stairs with them when suddenly, the white light flashed and I came down, full body weight on my right kneecap. It was the flash attacking me again.

The marketing vice president was flabbergasted. He was gimping about on crutches due to a recently broken leg. "Strangest fall I've ever seen," he kept muttering. I play-acted like it was nothing as best I could. I knew what happened if the bosses caught on to the fact that I was physically *unusual.* I hoped that if I minimized the incident, less would be said. As far as I was concerned, the less said the better.

I had been at Asiatic three and a half months when it happened. It was March, one of my worst months. The external weather turbulence would often set off thunderstorms, both internal and external, that I dreaded. Sometimes I was so confused that I did not know if a particular lightening bolt was inside me, outside me, or both. It was always a time to be cautious, like August; a time to survive, not a time to really live.

This particular March evening I was alone in my new brownstone walk-up apartment. I had finished my evening stretches and was on my way to the bathroom when a blinding flash of light knocked me down. *Had the lightening finally struck me directly?*

I was on the floor surrounded in that special blackness that I knew comes from the inside. It took a long time to come to my senses and look around. The lights were on. Nothing appeared changed except that the view from the floor has a rather different perspective from my normal point of reference. I tried to move — horrible blinding pain — then blackness descended on me again. After awhile, I awoke again and looked at myself more closely. *What could be wrong?* I couldn't see anything, no blood, no twisted limbs. I tried to move — shock and blackness again.

Finally I saw it. My right leg — the knee did not look right — there was a large lump on the right side of the leg. Then I realized that my kneecap was in the wrong place. *My God, that bolt of lighting had jerked my kneecap right out of its socket! But why? I wasn't doing anything. I wasn't jumping, twisting, or stretching. How could a walk across the living room floor do that? I had to get to the phone.*

My attempt to get to the phone three feet away had the same result as my other attempts to move. When I started to come to awareness this next time, my mind was cool and calculating. This was not a good situation, and I couldn't expect anyone to come to my aid. I had recently moved here and had just gotten new locks. I hadn't given anyone else an extra key yet. And besides, the building was new and still half-empty. Simply yelling would get me nowhere. What to do? I lay there and let my mind work.

It was strange. As long as I was absolutely still it wasn't particularly painful. However, the slightest movement would blast all my senses with unbearable pain. As I lay there, I began to remember things, and finally a memory came which suggested an answer.

I was back in Norway, hiking along the top of the mountain with a young fellow from Kansas who was living in the town. I had met him just as I was about to go mad from English deprivation. We enjoyed trading tales and taking walks together very much. As we walked along, his face suddenly turned white and he grabbed a tree trunk to steady himself.

"What is it, Harry? What's wrong?" I asked him. But he couldn't speak. He fell into the snow. I tried to pick him up.

"No, no!" he screamed.

Shocked, I let him go and he fell into the snow again. I dropped down into the snow next to him and quietly whispered, "Tell me what to do."

Gasping, he said, "Lift my right arm." I did so and as I did I felt something drop, and saw a look of relief on his face.

He explained to me that his shoulder had dislocated, and by lifting his arm, I had helped reposition it. He told me this was an old football injury, and that it had happened several times before, but always under heavy stress. This incident seemed very different from the others. Within a month, Harry returned to his Army family's home in Germany for surgery to stabilize his shoulder.

Judging from what I had seen then, relocating the kneecap myself was the only course of action that seemed open to me. I moved my arm down to the cap still throbbing on the right side of my right leg, trying not to move the leg until the very last minute. In one great effort I shoved it to the left and passed out.

⋯⋯✦⋯⋯

Time went by. At first you black out totally. Then you become aware, but are still surrounded in a blackness — almost disassociated from your body. It takes what seems like a long time to really come back. While you lie in that blackness your mental defenses are down and the thoughts that cross your mind are apt to be scary. If your subconsciousness isn't on your side, it will push you into a panic. You battle to stay rational.

Finally I came back. I had hoped my big effort would solve the problem. But now I looked, and saw a twisted right leg with a kneecap sitting higher than it should, still out of its socket. *I would have to do it right this time.* I prepared myself, and in one movement I raised myself up, straightened the leg, and pushed the cap down. I heard a crunch as the white light blasted me, and I once again passed into unconsciousness.

When I awoke this time, the kneecap was in its proper place. I left the leg straight and scooted around on the floor on my butt. Just like Harry, I was now damaged but able to function. I mentally thanked him for giving me the information I needed to cope with this crisis.

I had been heading for bed at about 11:00 P.M. It was now 3:30 A.M. I didn't see much point in calling anyone at that hour. I dragged a straight chair to the door and unlocked all the locks. By dragging the chair to the refrigerator I was able to get up on it and get some water, food and ice. I then scooted on my backside to the sofa and tried to rest, despite all the pain and swelling, despite the many tears I was shedding.

The next day I called my doctor and some friends to get help. I had cried my eyes out through the night and had no more tears left that day. I guess that's why no one reacted that strongly to my situation. I guess I didn't sound upset enough. Towards evening I wound up in a lower east side emergency room. I described the accident to the resident doctors who openly sneered at my story.

"If your kneecap did dislocate, you should know that only qualified medical personnel should ever touch such an injury.

Moreover, we have never heard of anyone relocating their own kneecap."

"It's highly probable that you merely sprained your knee, and this is a hysterical reaction."

"We really don't believe it was that bad."

"Since we can't see the dislocation, we really can't say that it ever happened."

Several teenagers who had been involved in a street rumble were dragged in on stretchers. I saw them lying near me, their chests, legs, and genitals soaked in blood. I lay quietly while the emergency room staff attempted to save their lives. By 3:00 A.M. one of them had died and the others had been treated. I felt that now it should be my turn.

The orthopedic resident put a large plaster cast on me from hip down to my ankle. I had a little bit of motion in my ankle, but not much. He then told the orderly to get me a pair of crutches and told me to get out. I was astounded. I was a single woman, living alone in a 75 step walk-up. How would I even manage to get down the hospital stairs? The doctors yelled at me to get out and stop bothering them; they had lives to save.

A young black orderly sat quietly in the corner and shed a few tears for me. These residents said they had to clear the emergency room to get some sleep — that they hadn't had any sleep for 40 hours and they weren't going to be further deprived on account of me.

One of them screamed at me, "I suppose you think we shouldn't have worked to save their lives. I suppose you think your hysteria is more important than them!" They screamed at me, "Get out!"

The young black man went out and came back sometime later.

"It's all right," he said in a low tone. He rolled me out into a hall, a type of canteen.

"If you are very quiet, you can stay here until 7 o'clock this morning. If you feel up to it, I'll show you how to use those crutches."

He gave me crutch lessons, and called my friends Debbie and Bill. They came for me near 7, and I crashed in their apartment.

I wound up convalescing with my parents in their upstate home. I was in that huge immobilizing cast for seven weeks. I returned to work with a right leg that was stiff as a board, grateful that Asiatic hadn't fired me, grateful that the vice president I reported to had seen me fall, and had recently had a broken leg himself. Due to these circumstances, I could probably still make good at the company. I led a painful and disciplined life, trying to heal my leg, do my job, exercise, and get my laundry done. I thought the worst was over.

By the beginning of June, my leg was bending again, and I felt optimistic. By the end of June all of my optimism was gone. My knee had loosened up too much. Now it was nothing but a broken hinge. A huge brace held me up. I found a surgeon who said this was predictable given the severity of the dislocation. The tendons were so stretched out that the kneecap sloshed around under the skin. Fixing it would require a total patellar transplant. That is, they would bisect up the knee and the cap, and then re-attach the parts in such a way as to re-create a stable hinge. It was a long and arduous procedure. They would not even guarantee it would help. My surgery was scheduled for early September, 1975.

That August was particularly terrible. Black spots appeared in my vision and wouldn't go away. I wasn't doing anything but dragging my dead legs to work. My kneecaps burned because they weren't sitting in the correct places. Moving abrased them. They were both crunching and snapping with every step. My left leg started to twist and drag. Even though I was moving slowly, I was still falling down maybe three times a day, brace, canes, and all.

Was this stress?, I wondered. I both dreaded and longed for the surgery. *Would I be able to hold on to my job through all this?*

I didn't speak to anyone about my circumstances. After all, July and August were always horrendous times, only to be survived. And my thoughts were never very sane or fit to share with others during the heat of the summer.

⊷·⊷ ⬛◆⬛ ⊷·⊷

The following January, in 1976, I returned to my job at Asiatic, pain–wracked and hobbling, fearing that I would barely be able to perform my duties. My immediate supervisor seemed to feel that I had been taking advantage of my situation. My surgeon would never say anything about the time it might take me to get back to normal. He would never comment on how long it might take for me to go back to work, either before or after the operation. In the absence of any information, my colleagues at work had drawn their own conclusions.

At this time, Joe Namath was astounding the world by returning to football after knee cartilage surgery. No one really understood that the five-hour operation I had was much more serious and much harder to recover from than cartilage surgery. Everyone assumed my injury and operation were much the same as Joe's. I myself didn't know that much about it. On my return to work I was greeted with suspicion and formal civility. I was obviously having a great deal of trouble walking, and this softened people's attitudes somewhat. My balance was non–existent. I was exhausted all the time. The nerves in my legs sparked and jumped. My damaged kneecaps burned and crunched as I dragged about on crutches, then on canes.

As always, I did my exercises religiously. I found a holistic physician, Dr. Rosenberg, and enlisted his help in building myself up. This doctor was a D.O., a Doctor of Osteopathy, and not an M.D., which seemed to give him a different outlook than the M.D.s I had previously consulted. He had also written a book, *The Doctor's Book of Megavitamin Therapy* which I read and found very interesting. Under his guidance, I ate a clean, varied, and nutritious diet and took megavitamins. For an entire year my life was about desperately holding on to my job while improving my legs and my general health. The more my leg functioned, the worse other things seemed. Nerve pain, falling down, and fatigue became the accepted features of my daily existence.

The expression on my face was unpleasant, and my new supervisor at work refused to accept my explanation of constant, chronic, burning pain as the root cause. He felt it showed my distaste for him. He was an alcoholic, and not a very desirable character. Due to my prolonged physical problems I had fallen off the management track, and was actually functioning as a high-priced statistician in the Economics Unit. Every night my legs twisted and snapped violently. I would repeat yoga mantras and try to rest the part of myself that wasn't engaged in constant motion. Towards 4 A.M. I would usually, finally, fall asleep, only to rise at 7 to face another day working with people who thought I was a hysteric or a fake.

I asked my surgeon why things were taking so long to straighten out. He replied that many people take a full year off just to recuperate after that type of operation.

"Why didn't you indicate this before?" I queried.

"I didn't want to discourage you," was his reply. "Your knees are badly damaged from everything they've been through. You can expect things to stay as they are. It's been a year. There won't be that much more healing from here on out."

I didn't believe him. I couldn't believe him.

After all, I reasoned, that was probably just his way of saying, "I don't think I should see you anymore. There's nothing more I can do."

I kept on hanging on to my job for dear life, eating well, and exercising. I went for acupuncture and rolfing treatments, and learned invaluable lessons from these alternative body workers. The network of nerves and muscles that seemed to operate poorly for me was also important to them, unlike the typical M.D. who seemed to ignore the nerve and muscle part of the body entirely, emphasizing emotions and sex instead.

I began to feel that I was a little like a baby. Babies have to be willing to fall down or they won't ever learn to walk. So, just like a baby, I, too, had to be willing to fall in order to walk. I found myself surprised if a day went by without a tumble. At least they weren't that scary falling-down-in-blackness-type fall I'd experienced before. It took many years, but I was getting better.

In the future I would tell people that healing is possible over a very long time frame — 4 to 5 years — and that doctors were wrong when they expected quick healing.

It wasn't until 15 years later that I heard from MS doctors that remyelination is possible, but only over a 4 to 5-year span. I also met others with MS who told me they too had suffered a sudden, violent, unreasonable dislocation of the kneecaps before being diagnosed. It took me all that time to get a diagnosis of MS, and learn that this accident was in fact an MS-induced injury plus an MS attack.

So, by the age of 30, I had struggled my way through two severe three-year bouts of MS without recognition. The first had openly been a mystery, but was ascribed to a young woman's hysteria. The second was masked by a bad leg injury during an era of medicine when many injured simply accepted their maimed leg as their unfortunate fate in life. Sports medicine was invented only after Joe Namath proved that injured people can recuperate.

I was now coping with incontinence, bad legs, eye problems, nerve pain, and fatigue every day as a matter of course. My female cycle was still either non–existent or erratic, along with aberrations in all the other body indicators, such as temperature, blood pressure, and blood sugar. *By this time my abnormalities had become my normalities.*

⋯ ⚎⚎⚎ ⋯

One spring day I woke up and the pain was gone. The relief showed on my face immediately, and everyone in my world was quick to react. At the age of 32 I was suddenly promoted to the position of Manager of Planning. My alcohol–besotted boss was being retired with a generous pension. I was back with my beloved Jerry. In short, my life was moving along full speed on all fronts. And I was pushing it along, trying to make up for those years I looked back on as lost and miserable.

But this time, I knew it wasn't over, and I didn't feel safe. I started my own insurance program, with an emphasis on disability income insurance even though Asiatic had rather generous disability benefits. This time, I was certain it would happen again.

⋯ ⚎⚎⚎ ⋯

I was on a wonderful vacation with Jerry when it started again. I had persuaded my city–bred man to take a ten–day drive with me down through the Blue Ridge Mountains of Virginia to the Smokies in Tennessee. We were having a marvelous time.

Jerry was basically a man who enjoyed the sun and the beach — both lethal to me. He'd seen me suffer from horrible burns after ten minutes of sun at high noon that had no effect on him. He had adjusted, somewhat, to vacationing away from the shore in order to suit me, but now he seemed to really be enjoying himself, not just there to please me. The little inns were more civilized than we had expected. Everything was going well until we arrived at Gatlinburg, Tennessee, the entrance to Great Smoky Mountains National Park.

We checked into the motel at 2 P.M. I ran to take a dip in the pool. I dived in, and then noticed that the water seemed a little dirty. The heavy scent of chlorine I expected wasn't there either. Jerry took a sunbath and didn't swim. That evening as I was dressing for dinner, the flashes started. Jerry saw me falling through the blackness, and ran to catch me.

"What was that?" he questioned with a worried face.

"Oh, you know, sometimes those things happen to me. Don't worry about it. I'm all right," was my automatic defensive response.

The next few days showed that something unusual was happening, both to me and the motel. The place seemed deserted, and service was barely provided. You expect a motel to be 95% empty at 2 P.M., but not over a weekend at the height of the season. I wondered if poorly maintained pool water had made me sick. I was suffering severe stomach cramps accompanied by more and more frequent falling episodes. I tried to minimize their importance, play act like I was OK, but Jerry's watchful, concerned eyes were always on me. This was a new and not altogether welcome situation. I was accustomed to a lot of privacy when I suffered through my little break-downs.

After three days, we decided to cut the trip short and head for home. Jerry was very concerned, and I kept getting worse. I seemed to be disappearing into a cloud and then coming back again. My coordination vanished. I couldn't button my blouse or open my handbag. Jerry wanted to take me to a local hospital, but I wouldn't hear of it. We weren't that far from NYC. He drove straight home — straight to Dr. Rosenberg's office.

At first the doctor didn't seem too concerned. He drew blood and then examined me. He thought I looked sick, but not too bad. Then his technician ran in with my blood count. These three men left the room to confer. Jerry came back in and announced we had to go straight to the hospital. I asked, "Why so fast?" and didn't get much response. I felt very weak, not up to fighting them. In the car on the way to LeRoy Hospital, Jerry finally told me that my blood count was very bad. It seemed that I had some type of massive infection. In the hospital they would find out what it was and determine the proper therapy.

I stayed in this small hospital for several days, going in and out of this strange white cloud. Sometimes I was able to walk or pick up a glass of water; sometimes I couldn't. Other than vitamin shots to build me up, I was not taking any medication. Jerry brought me a flower arrangement which began to wilt and die immediately. I would look at those withering cut flowers and wonder if I was also dying.

My mother came down from upstate to be with me, and she felt uncomfortable and left out, too. She didn't know Dr. Rosenberg, who was conferring with Jerry as though he was my husband, despite the fact that there was no such legal bond. The other doctors were also strange. None of them would answer any questions from us females. One day my doctor looked at my chart and did a double-take.

"What is it?" I asked. He shook his head and left the room.

Later, Jerry came in and found me crying. It was his turn to ask, "What is it?"

"The doctor won't tell me, but I know that something is very wrong," I responded.

After all, it had been days and many tests, but no therapy had been started. My doctor returned and asked to speak with Jerry in the hall. While they were gone I cried some more. I thought about the laughable notion every psychologist, M.D., and psychiatrist in Manhattan had seemed determined to sell me — that *love would heal me and make me well — that a good sex life with a good man would cure me of my hysteria — that it was all in my mind.* This time round, all those theories seemed disproved. *Sorry, it's just not that simple,* I sadly said to myself.

Jerry and the doctor returned. They were nervous.

Jerry started, "There's some thought that maybe this isn't the best hospital for you to be in. This is a small place, and there's not that much they can do here."

"What do you mean?" I yelled. "What is it?"

The doctor explained, "Well, for now, we have reached a tentative diagnosis of mesenteric adoneosis, but we're not at all sure that's the problem."

"Where do you propose to send me?"

The answer came back: "Sloan–Kettering."

"No, *why?*" I knew no one goes to Sloan–Kettering unless cancer is suspected.

"They would be able to make certain we have the right diagnosis there. Possibly a stomach operation might be called for."

"Exactly what are you saying?" I demanded. They fluttered about in some confusion.

I made up my mind then that I was not having any surgery unless I had all the details. The conversation went downhill from there, me demanding "full disclosure" and the two of them shilly-shallying around.

—·——·—

My doctor came back the next day. I began accusingly, "Are you going to tell me what's going on today?"

He held up his hand protectively. "Look, don't start with me. This is hard on me too. You realize, most doctors would not take the blood tests I do. They would simply have dismissed you as a hysteric. You must understand that I am doing the very best I can for you."

The remark softened me some, but still I resented the feeling that I was going to be the last to know the facts of my case.

"Look," my doctor explained. "There are two ways we can go in a case like this. Minimal or maximal medical care. We're going to have to make a decision."

It didn't take long for me to decide. "Minimal, please." The doctor was still being evasive, but at least we were communicating.

⊷⊶ ☲◆☲ ⊷⊶

I stayed in the hospital another week. I got better. I walked out, and on my way the gastroenterologist offered me his card and said, "Call me when you feel worse."

I replied, "I think I'm doing OK."

He cheerily said, "It may not last long. Please do come to see me."

I never did.

Later Jerry and my doctor admitted they had been quite certain I had rapidly growing stomach cancer. My recovery had proved them wrong. If they had been correct I would have quickly died, regardless of whether I had been receiving minimal or maximal medical treatment.

I thought that the whole thing seemed rather like my Norwegian sickness. My mother had always had this pet theory that bad water had caused my illness, which meshed well with my Gatlinburg dirty pool theory.

So in my mind these two mysterious illnesses became linked by symptoms and possible cause. But of course, just as in the other cases, there really was no diagnosis, no treatment, no explanation.

━·━·━✠━·━✠━·━

Jerry and I went on with our relationship for awhile. We continued to care about each other, but we just couldn't move ahead to a final, lasting commitment. My frequent illnesses didn't help. We were incompatible on a very basic issue — room temperature. He wanted it 76 degrees; I wanted 65 or lower. I held on to my brutally chilly upper brownstone apartment just because it was cold and quiet. Staying in Jerry's apartment for very long seemed to make me sick. At one time, Jerry said that he would spend the rest of his life in long johns if that's what it took to be with his favorite Norwegian. Unfortunately, it's much easier to say such a thing than to actually do it.

I needed to create a home for myself. A year after my forecasted demise from stomach cancer I bought my little cottage in New Paltz on my own.

━·━·━✠━·━✠━·━

I'm 45 years old now. I have been legally disabled for 6 years, but the decision was only reached 3½ years ago, since my case was so difficult to assess. I sit here, sorting through old records which seem to be little else but bills for pointless medical treatments and consultations. I look through the checks for the last 10 years, so many checks to health professionals, so many arduous trips to see people who refused to answer my questions, people I had grown to hate for endlessly stringing me along. People who promised help and then delivered nothing, not even my records.

I had to hire a disability lawyer to sort it all out and protect my benefits. Even he could not get a straight answer from most of these bizarre "professionals."

At my disability hearing, the administrative law judge snickered and laughed at me for a full hour, and then seemed to have some sort of realization. His attitude towards me changed suddenly. Two months later, he sent out an eight page decision ruling me disabled due to seizures, incontinence, and brain damage. His text mentioned different symptoms culled from my medical records which we later realized fit an MS profile precisely.

It was only after this ruling that a young ear doctor mentioned what 20 neurologists had never mentioned, the possibility of MS. He had proven that both my auditory nerves were damaged. The left one was so bad that it delayed all its transmissions — a scientific explanation of the confusing and painful private echo chamber that I had complained of for years. I knew now that auditory lesions do not necessarily show up on brain MRIs. Mine remain normal to this day, despite memory problems and continuing nerve problems on the left side of my head, including both the left eye and ear.

I've been trying to write the rest of my story of my 30 year journey to diagnosis, but it doesn't come very easily. Things got a lot worse before they became better. In my 30s, my MS started to progress. This means that I kept feeling poorly and never really seemed to improve, only to worsen. After the age of 33, I was not to meet a genuinely helpful M.D. for eight long years of endless searching. If my experience is any guide, doctors find it easy to take an abusive attitude towards a chronic "complainer." *My relationship with the medical profession moved from poor to outright bloody combat, with me suffering most of the blows.*

⋅⋅⋅—■✦■—⋅⋅⋅

The M.D.s literally harassed my D.O., Dr. Rosenberg, out of business, so he wasn't there when I fought my next rounds with MS. When he told me that most M.D.s would not have taken my Gatlinburg disease seriously, I didn't believe him. Unfortunately, it turned out that he was totally correct. Most M.D.s constantly insisted that what I needed was "a good sex life." A few M.D.s told me that I would never be diagnosed until I was dead. They claimed that an autopsy would be the only way to finally decide the issue.

I have written many notes about it, but I'm suffering too many nightmares to push forward with this chronicle right now.

⚊⚊❈✦❈⚊⚊

I have lived full-time for three years in that upstate cottage I bought when I was 32. I do what I can each day, and enjoy my beautiful view of the mountain with its cliffs. I enjoy living in New Paltz. It's an informal community, so I can go about in sweat pants to protect against incontinence accidents without appearing strange. My preference for cool temperatures works out well here too. The people of Ulster County seen to have some knowledge of MS, unlike Manhattanites living in a different world just 90 miles to the south.

My parents live about 15 miles away, which is nice for us all. My 83 year old dad comes here and works on my place with great energy and dedication. Even though he does all the work, just having him here wears me out totally for the next 24 hours. He has always been able to work me into the ground, but one would think that by this time, I'd be able to keep up with him. If I didn't have MS, I'm sure I could turn the tables on him.

I walk quite well in short spans, before my leg spasms yank me up and my left leg twists around. My neck also gives me trouble. Sometimes I can't get my head up off my left shoulder for days. It seems to me that people ought to be able to understand that trouble with a neck is just as much a possible variant on the MS theme as trouble with any other joint. I can't understand how this image of the MS patient as a person sitting in a wheelchair got so entrenched in everyone's minds. The text below was published just as I was recovering from my first severe bout with MS. I will leave it to the reader to judge whether medical science had the expertise to recognize a case such as mine during the 1970s.

From *Neurological Pathophysiology* (a text for medical students), edited by Eliasson, Prensky, & Hardin (all M.D.s), Oxford Univ. Press, NY, 1974: "The term 'demyelinating disease' has been applied to a diverse assortment of acquired illnesses in which there is a loss of myelin from the nervous system, while other elements of nervous tissue... are relatively well preserved in the diseased areas... multiple sclerosis is the most common demyelinating disease... the disease should be diagnosed only when the signs and symptoms indicate that lesions are 'separated in time and space'."

"Typically a young adult develops periodic attacks of central nervous system dysfunction resulting from lesions in various locations. Common symptoms are blurred vision, diplopia (double vision), vertigo, imbalance, numbness or tingling in the limbs, trunk or face, focal weakness or incoordination, difficulty with urination... Characteristically, the initial symptoms are present only for a few days or weeks, followed some months or years later by different transient symptoms. Multiple symptoms and signs occur later with less complete remission.

"Another interesting feature of the disorder is the occurrence of symptoms lasting only a few minutes. This pattern is frequently seen in patients who have had attacks involving the optic nerve. There may be a brief reappearance of a central scotoma when the body temperature is raised, as by a hot bath. Other focal symptoms (extremity weakness or numbness) may also be present during this temperature-related exacerbation. Another type of 'mini-attack' involves spontaneous repetitive brain stem dysfunction (vertigo, nystagmus (spasmodic, involuntary eye motions), and dysarthria (speech difficulties due to problems with tongue and/or other associated muscles). These symptoms resemble transient ischemic attacks (or minor strokes)..."

"The tendency toward remission can probably be explained, in part, by subsidence of the inflammatory response... and possibly by some degree of remyelination of denuded axons. In many instances, however, the return of function is greater and more rapid than one might expect from the limited remyelination. This discrepancy suggests that axons denuded of myelin over short distances may still be able to transmit impulses... Experimental evidence indicates that axons retaining only a thin layer of their myelin sheath can still conduct normally."

"The brief reappearance of clinical symptoms under stress of body temperature rise suggests that axons in a demyelinated region have a reduced 'safety factor' maintaining their ability to conduct impulses normally. Damaged axons can be shown in the laboratory to be blocked more easily by temperature rise than healthy axons. The lability of function of damaged tracts in multiple sclerosis patients can be demonstrated also by the transient improvement in neurological deficits that results from lowering body temperature..." (Excerpted from pages 334–339.)

My question remains: *If medical textbooks of the 1970s described MS in such a realistic and complex manner, why do virtually all health professionals fail to recognize these symptoms when the undiagnosed patient brings his complaints to them?*

It seems to me that the modern emphasis on the MRI is just another way of avoiding a real issue in our society. We need an awareness that neurological dysfunction isn't any crazier than any other type of illness. If our own medical professionals constantly call our symptoms "crazy," we can hardly expect any comprehension from the general public.

It is also strange that today's doctors seem to have forgotten about the temperature aspect of MS. From my point of view, the old-fashioned hot bath test would have been far more helpful than an MRI. The hot bath test, or some modern variant on this theme would help a patient with sensory distortions review how to manage this important variable in day-to-day living. A scan does nothing to help clarify the issues of daily living. Diagnosis has to deal with problems that crop up in daily life if it is to help a patient who cannot be cured.

I am still inspired by the Yukon trapper I read about when I was fifteen.

By now I have turned him into an imaginary friend. Whenever I feel my symptoms are too confounding to tolerate, I mentally transport myself to the Arctic and discuss the situation with him. He reminds me of the multi-dimensional, self-monitoring an Eskimo must master to survive.

I take heart and renew my vigilance over the variables of balance, vision, sounds, and temperatures. My daily confusions are compounded by sensory distortions and coordination failures. But on reflection, my challenges don't seem that much worse or different than those a healthy Arctic dweller would face due to the erratic weather and light conditions up north.

My fellow New York State residents will never comprehend why I must pay such acute attention to aspects of life they never need to even notice.

But at least my Arctic friend understands.

There is a Brighter Side

by: *Harold Tilley*

It was early in 1939, at the age of twenty, that I realised that something was wrong. During the previous year I had spent two months in a hospital with a bacterial infection, and had only recently recovered completely. Now I was suffering from a tingling sensation and weakness in my legs, accompanied by bouts of double vision. Within a short time I had lost the use of my legs, and had no feeling in the lower half of my body. The following three months found me in the hospital again, receiving massage, electrical treatment, and large doses of vitamins. It was at this juncture that the girl to whom I was engaged to be married walked out on me, yet another blow which added to the ill fortune that was dogging me.

In retrospect, I realised that she could not be blamed. An active girl of nineteen with her whole life ahead of her, she must have been horrified by the prospect of spending countless years with a husband in a wheel chair. However, at the time, her decision was depressing to contemplate from a hospital bed.

Nevertheless, as no one told me I had multiple sclerosis, I never imagined I was suffering from an incurable disease. In fact, with the optimism of youth, I was certain that complete recovery was only a matter of time and will power. And recover I did. It began with a few shuffling steps down the ward, supported on each side by a nurse, and progressed to walking short distances with a single stick. Of course, it was not as easy as my narrative makes it sound. There were occasions when I had setbacks and my legs refused to move at all, but these were offset by times when I made heartening progress. As the months and indeed years passed, my legs grew stronger, so that by 1946 I was able to dispense with the walking stick, and bit by bit take up the sporting interests I had enjoyed in the past. I rode a bicycle, I swam, I played table tennis and cricket, although I always had to field near the bat because I never recovered my ability to run appreciable distances to retrieve the ball. I even ventured onto ice skates again, but after a few sessions decided that it was too strenuous for me.

In 1951 I married, and helped my wife raise three very lively sons, frequently taking them for four or five mile walks, as well as teaching them by example how to play soccer and cricket. I also maintained the garden and redecorated the interior of the house. Occasionally I was reminded of my mysterious illness, when the tingling in my legs returned and walking became an effort, but these bouts were over in a few weeks, and I could often continue working throughout their duration.

Then, twenty years later, in 1971, the illness appeared again in a more acute form. The symptoms were the same as before, but this time they were more severe, and while I did not lose the use of my legs, my walking was very restricted indeed, which caused my doctor to send me to a neurologist. When he diagnosed multiple sclerosis I was neither surprised or dismayed, for some years previously I had read a description of the disease in *Reader's Digest*, and had then told myself that if, as I surmised, I had MS, it was only in a mild form. After three months rest at home, during which time I began to receive the neocytamen injections which have now become part of my life, I returned to work, but found that I had not made such a good recovery this time. Although I could manage without a walking stick, I could only cover very short distances before my legs tired and felt as heavy as lead. My employers, the city administration in Southampton, were more than sympathetic, and went out of their way to make work as easy as possible for me. However, in 1974 a massive reorganisation took place, and I was offered early retirement, which I accepted gratefully.

Since then, with the pressures of work removed, there has been no marked deterioration in my walking ability, although in 1978 I suffered a cervical disc lesion, which apparently cleared up, but left me with tingling and weakness in my right hand. Medical opinion is divided on whether this is due to the neck trouble or MS.

So how have I occupied my leisure time over the last seventeen years? To start with, I had to discover my physical limitations, a decidedly painful process, for I would carry on with a task until completely exhausted.

This taught me to look for the simplest way of tackling every job needing physical effort. For example, if I want to weed a flower bed, I sit down on a piece of old carpet, which offers the advantage of putting me so close to the weeds that none get overlooked. I use the same technique for digging, a trowel taking the place of fork or spade. Admittedly, it takes longer that way, but time is not so important anymore. To make garden maintenance even easier, we have extended the grassed area, and a weekly session by my wife with a power mower keeps it trim. As for decorating, this too is a joint venture. I tackle those parts I can reach when either sitting on a chair or on the floor, leaving the rest to my wife.

I have not had to give up outdoor sport completely, having resumed one of my boyhood activities, namely freshwater fishing. There is nothing more pleasant than spending a sunny summer afternoon sitting in attractive country surroundings by a lake. Even if the fish refuse to bite there is an abundance of wildlife to divert one. Water voles, foxes, the occasional deer, and a bewildering variety of birds can be seen, wild flowers blooming amongst the long grass, and fellow anglers are ever willing to stop and talk.

Of course, there are many interests requiring less physical effort than those described hitherto. When I first retired from work, I bought a typewriter and taught myself to type (not as a trained secretary would), just two fingers on each hand, but fast enough to satisfy my needs. I then set down on paper all that I could remember of my life up to the end of the Second World War. I was prompted to tackle this task by recalling that when I was young, my father had told me much about his early life, and fascinating it was, too, but with the passage of time I had forgotten most of it, and I did not wish my sons to have similar gaps in their knowledge of me. As I relived my youth I remembered more and more events, so that I finished with a book of over two hundred pages. This whetted my appetite for writing, and for the next ten years I produced a monthly news sheet for retired staff from the city administration, as well as editing a quarterly magazine for the local fishing club. It was only a short step from there to selling articles and short stories to commercial magazines. Since then I have completed a full-length novel for which I am trying to find a publisher, and am well into a second. When the weakness in my right hand manifested itself, I acquired an electronic typewriter, which required far less effort, and now that the weakness is more pronounced, I have taught myself to type with the left hand alone.

I encountered a similar problem when playing the piano, in that depressing the keys required an appreciable amount of effort, and I tired rapidly. An electronic organ, however, proved much easier to play, both in the reduction of energy expended, and in the technical ability needed, so I am still enjoying music to the full.

There are so many interests I have developed in retirement that space prevents me mentioning them all. One such is recording radio and television programmes of particular interest while we are out of the house or entertaining visitors, and then enjoying them at a later date. I also give talks about music to local societies, illustrating my remarks with tape recorded examples. In this activity my wife acts as my driver, and also helps carry the equipment.

Having passed the three score and ten years, which the Bible describes as man's life span, I can look back over my own years, not with complacency, but with a certain satisfaction in that I have at least attained some of the objectives I hoped to achieve prior to becoming disabled. Not that I plan to live a relaxed and idle life from now on. There are still a number of projects I want to work on, and I shall no doubt find more to keep me occupied as long as I live. Happiness comes through being busy, so busy in fact that one can forget MS.

Now if you think that all I have written so far is an attempt at self-aggrandisement, I should explain that its purpose is to show how much MS sufferers can achieve with a little thought, and also that it may give some encouragement to newly diagnosed readers who feel that their lives are to all intents and purposes over. For them it could be the beginning of a new and absorbing chapter.

Like a Hollywood Stuntwoman

by: Toni R. Tate

I checked myself in the mirror one last time before I loaded my pockets with the "tools of my trade." My uniform looked presentable; it was white, it was clean, and it wasn't wrinkled. I proudly clipped my hospital identification badge to my collar and flung the bright red stethoscope around my neck. I reached for my walnut-toned cane, the mobility device which afforded me additional stability when walking distances greater than approximately 25 feet. "Baby, I'm ready to go," I said. My husband then rose from his position on the sofa to escort me out to our car, which was parked in the apartment complex's parking lot.

He asked his usual question with a look of genuine concern on his face: "Are you going to be all right, Baby?"

"Yeah, honey, I'm fine," I said, and I was telling the absolute truth. I'd had a few days off for the Independence Day holiday, and I was well rested. In fact, it was almost if I could still taste Randy's spicy-tangy-sweet barbecue sauce which had dressed pork ribs at our dinner table the previous night. I felt good, I felt strong, almost as if my neurological system had not been partially demyelinated by MS. I had the feeling that nothing could go wrong; my husband was my companion, my lover, my friend. I had two healthy, intelligent, and loving sons, and I truly enjoyed my work as an RN in a large, acute-care hospital. Not many people are fortunate enough to work where they feel as I did about my job: proud.

"Well," I thought to myself, "gotta go do battle against pain and suffering." I felt like a warrior in white.

Randy and I chatted as we made our way down the sidewalk. It was a beautiful July night, not too humid. I was hoping that these prime weather conditions would linger for a while longer, when I suddenly felt myself collapse. I felt an immediate sharp pain in my right ankle. My purse flew about 10 feet in the air to my left, my walking cane flipped high into the air to my right. The first thing that crossed my mind was the possible opinion of the stylish young woman who had come out to walk her professionally groomed dog." She must really think that I'm a klutz," I thought to myself.

When I looked up at Randy, he was kneeling over my clumsy body sprawled across the sidewalk. "Toni! Toni!" he called out. He looked panic-stricken. "Can you move?"

My pride hurt as well as my ankle, so I sat up and tried to knock debris off my uniform and get grass out of my hair. "I'm okay, Randy," I half-lied. I tried to stand, to no avail. I grabbed the nearest post of the split rail fence which bordered the sidewalk. I pulled myself to a standing position, but I could not take one step. I leaned against the fence and tried to compose myself. "How am I going to get out of this fix?" I thought to myself. Meanwhile, Randy had busied himself with gathering my belongings. He then put his arm snugly around my waist to assist me in walking back to our apartment.

I tried to walk while holding onto Randy's strong torso, but steps still did not come. The idea of maintaining some illusion of graceful-ness in front of the "Dog Lady" was proving to be impossible. The weakness and pain in my ankle would not allow me to bear any weight on my right leg. Just as I was contemplating getting down on all fours and crawling back home, Randy threw my hefty frame over his left shoulder like a sack of Idaho potatoes, and he then struggled back to our kitchen door and unlocked it. Once inside, I removed my shoe and noticed that my ankle had become enormously swollen. While sitting near the broom closet, I reached in and retrieved a large bucket, which Randy then filled with ice and water. He was correctly remembering the first aid techniques that he had learned as a Petty Officer in the Navy. Every bit of nursing knowledge that I recalled said that we were doing the proper thing: ice-down a sprained ankle. As my bare foot and ankle soaked in the uncomfortably frigid pail, I reached for the phone to call the 3–11 P.M. supervisor to inform her of my mishap, and to let her know that I would not be able to report for my 11 P.M. – 7 A.M. tour of duty. She sounded sympathetic; she knew that I had MS. My supervisors were always saying, "Mrs. Tate, you are doing so fine." Well, Mrs. Tate wasn't doing so fine now.

After a 30–minute soak in the ice, I was able to hop back to my bed with Randy's assistance. With his help, I elevated my injured extremity on pillows while placing an ice pack on my throbbing ankle.

"Do you want to go to the Emergency Room?" Randy looked truly concerned. He briefly lifted the ice pack to check on my edematous ankle.

"Nah, just hand me a nightgown." Randy and I managed to remove my uniform; we did so together in silence. I don't know what Randy was thinking, but I was commenting to myself that I was blessed to have a husband like Randy. He was probably wondering what he had gotten himself into.

After checking on me to see if I was reasonably comfortable, Randy drifted off to sleep. I lay awake for a while longer musing over my circumstances. I knew that we were a two–income family, even though I worked only three nights a week. I was also wondering how I could drive with my right foot incapacitated. I mean, I felt as though I was born with a steering wheel in my hand — that's how long I'd been driving. Then, I realized that I was probably blowing the whole thing way out of proportion. I remembered that when my brother sprained his ankle playing basketball, he was only disabled for a few days. "Just keep it iced and elevated, and you'll be up and at 'em by the weekend," was the reassurance that I gave myself. I fell into a fitful sleep.

The next morning, my ankle was still extremely puffy. I came to the realization that I probably should have it X–rayed. I informed

Randy of this, and he began getting the boys ready to take to his mother's house. I managed to get to my bathroom to throw some water on the essential areas and put on a pair of clam digger shorts, and then sat back to wonder how I would get out to the car.

The fact that I made it out to the car still surprises me. I vaguely remember limping while holding onto Randy as though he were a physical therapy assistant.

Once in the car, I let my mind wander. I was trying to remember why I fell in the first place. Did MS cause my feet to betray me? Or did I simply trip on an irregularity in the pavement?

I resigned myself to believe that I had tripped on a crack in the sidewalk. I couldn't face the fact that I could have sustained an MS-related injury. As I rode in the car, I hoped for the best, but expected the worst. The boys didn't appear to be too upset; they just seemed happy to be going to their Grandma's house. I could tell from Randy's silence that he was worried also, perhaps more than I.

When we arrived at the emergency room, Randy procured a wheelchair from the ambulance dock area. I transferred myself from the car to the Everest-Jennings wheelchair with minimal difficulty. The time that we spent in the waiting room seemed to fly. It appeared that as soon as we finished registering with the receptionist, the smiling nurse emerged from behind the "Authorized" door and called my name. I told her my "chief complaint", and she checked the obligatory vital signs. She then parked me in an alcove and told me that a doctor would be with me momentarily. Sure enough, an immaculately groomed physician promptly came by, looked at my ankle, and directed an orderly to take me to the X-ray suite. After receiving my assurances that I was not in the "motherly way", the X-ray tech shot the ordered films and told me that it would just be a few moments before he would have them ready. Almost instantly, he handed the films to me to take back to the E.R. physician. I immediately held one of the pictures up to the light to see if there were any obvious fractures. To my dismay, I saw that I didn't need to be an anatomy professor to detect what I had dreaded: a transverse fracture of the distal third of my right fibula. My heart sank.

After viewing my X-rays, Doctor "Clean" sent me to the medical office building adjacent to the hospital to be seen by an orthopedist, and to have my banged-up ankle set and cast. I rode in complete silence over the glistening, freshly waxed floors to my next destination. Randy had appointed himself as my morale officer, and he was busy trying to cheer me up. I knew that he meant well, but his humor left me flat. All I could think about was my job. I wouldn't be able to function in a cast, not as a floor nurse, anyway. The idea of paid sick time was laughable. I hadn't accrued sick leave for several years, not since MS weakness had forced me to change my status from full-time to part-time.

"Look at it like this. Now you'll be able to spend every night with me. I mean, I miss you at night. Besides, you need some time off." Randy then stroked my face lovingly. He really made me feel good when he said things like that.

While sitting in the orthopedics office waiting room, I was becoming more relaxed. I even became interested in the television program that was on. I thought about my current circumstances intermittently. "Well, no need to cry over spilled milk," I told myself. Man, I must've kicked over an entire bucket of it.

When the nurse called me from the inner office door, Randy and I made our way through the door. The nurse and I exchanged smiles; I hoped that hers was not fabricated like mine. She ushered us into a room which contained items that I recognized as casting supplies. I silently hoped that this would not turn out to be unbearably unpleasant.

Randy and I made small talk while waiting for the doctor. I was beginning to enjoy his company; it was rare that we could spend time together on a weekday. Randy had called his job to take an emergency vacation day to attend to my needs. I was glad that he was with me.

The tall, thin doctor soon made his entrance. He was courteous enough as he examined my X-ray films closely. "Mrs. Tate, your ankle is broken in two places." He showed me the break that I had already seen on the film and a smaller one on the opposite side of my ankle. I didn't realize that I had done such a thorough job of damaging it. He told me that he would have to set it and put it in a cast. My chart would probably state: "Closed reduction and external fixation."

Dr. "Bones" explained that he would have to manipulate my ankle to realign the bone fragments that were broken. I decided that this was definitely not one of my better days. I expected the closed reduction of my "bimalleolar fracture" to be an episode of excruciating pain. I wished that I had a bullet to bite.

Dr. Bones cradled my foot and ankle in his skilled hands and manipulated it ever so slightly. I gritted my teeth and clenched my eyes shut. When I opened my eyes he was through. I'd expected worse. In comparison, I found the whole procedure to be more unpleasant than a root canal, but not as offensive as a spinal tap. He then asked me what color cast I wanted. Since he didn't have black satin with sequins, I opted for a royal maroon color. It was a color that I could live with; plus it wouldn't show dirt readily.

After my cast was applied, I went back to have another X-ray done to make sure that my fragments were in a good position. The second film confirmed that my bones were properly aligned. After giving me a prescription for an analgesic and a pair of aluminum crutches, Dr. Bones told me to make a follow-up appointment, and sent us on our way. I took it easy and rode the wheelchair back to the car.

I must have been losing some of the anxiety which had plagued me all morning, because I was beginning to feel hungry. So, we picked up the boys and headed for a fast food drive-thru window to get some brunch. That is, if fried chicken and biscuits qualifies as brunch.

Getting from the car to our home was a major effort. I'd forgotten how uncoordinated and weak I'd become. Halfway to my door, I had to stop and regroup. I could see that crutches were not easy to maneuver, and I was not looking forward to wrestling with these instruments of almost certain mishap. For me, using crutches was akin to the average person trying to walk a distance of 200 feet on a tightrope suspended 100 feet high in the air. Simply stated, using crutches was difficult for me.

Dr. Bones had told me that I could expect to be in the non-weight-bearing cast for approximately two weeks, meaning that I would have to use crutches. Fortunately, my older son, Robert, was out of school on summer vacation, and he helped me to take care of my toddler son, Randall. Randy rearranged the bedroom furniture to put my side of the bed within three feet of our bedroom's half-bath toilet. During this time, with remote control in hand, I mastered the art of couch potato from my king-sized bed.

Family and friends stopped by on a regular basis to perform routine household chores, or just sit and talk. One day, my mother and mother-in-law came by to tidy the place up a bit. When they tackled our bedroom, I found it ironic that my mom made my side of the bed and his mom did the same for his side, as they worked in unison. My sister, Jackie, vacuumed and the like. Thelma, my best friend since grade school, was appreciated greatly for running errands, as only a friend of twenty years could do. My friends and co-workers on my floor sent a lovely card with enough cash tucked inside to buy groceries for two weeks. My brother-in-law, Lonzell, drove me to the doctor's office so that Randy could go to work freely.

It wasn't until these trying times that I discovered the true meaning of the old saying: "A friend in need is a friend indeed." My loved ones will never realize how much I appreciated their examples of human kindness and compassion; I truly needed friends at this time. Also, many additional displays of veritable friendship were received, but are not mentioned here. Just because other specific names are not noted does not mean that those acts were not greatly appreciated.

One particular group, the Mid-South chapter of the National MS Society, were life-savers because when I called and explained my dilemma, they promptly had a wheelchair sent over from the MS closet. I use the term life-saver because I fell more than once while trying to maneuver myself a few steps while using crutches. Once while Thelma was visiting, I lost my balance and fell against a piece of furniture and scratched my leg deeply. I'll never forget the look that froze on Thelma's face as she immediately rushed to my assistance. We had been through thick and thin together, but never anything this thick. I mean, we had always been able to get out of an unpleasant situation by relying on our wits alone. It had become apparent that no amount of quick thinking would be of much use now. I sat down on the bed after I had positioned myself so that I could easily pull up. After I situated myself, Thelma handed me the mercurochrome and bandages, and helped me to attend to the fresh scratch on my right thigh. It was then that I called the MS Society and asked to borrow the wheelchair. I could not have been more appreciative of that vehicle even if it had been a custom-made Rolls Royce.

For the weeks that I was forced to don that maroon colored cast, I learned two things. First, how to proficiently drive myself in a wheelchair. Second, I learned that reactions to people in wheelchairs are highly individualized. Some people try to ignore you as though they thought that you were Typhoid Mary, or perhaps someone carrying a dreaded disease, and by ignoring you, they could immunize themselves against the malady that had befallen you. Others make sure that they gain eye contact and flash you a warm smile. This reaction suited me fine because I have always been one of those genteel southern ladies who is not hesitant to greet passersby with a nod of the head and a heartfelt smile. Still others, the bolder segment of the population, come out and ask how you hurt your leg. I soon learned to accept all reactions in stride. After all, I figured out that it really didn't matter much what strangers thought of me; it mattered about as much as the price of a pork chop sandwich in Baghdad, Iraq. I didn't even care what the Dog Lady thought when she saw me.

I learned to perform many tasks, especially cooking, while in this cast-bound state, thanks to my borrowed wheels.

In fact, I could have hosted a TV cooking show called "Wheelchair Cuisine à la Toni." I learned that driving a car is *not* an absolute must. In fact, I became quite at ease with acting as though I were starring in a budget movie: "Driving Miss Toni." Taking a tub bath became a rare treat. Most attempts at personal cleanliness were limited to a wash pan of water and bar of soap, sort of like what we nurses call a "bed bath." Taking a real bath took quite some arranging. I had to wrap my entire leg in a doubled trash bag, and securely tape the whole thing to my skin with waterproof tape. But Randy had the hard part: lifting me into and out of the tub. I'm sure that this time was reminiscent of Thanksgiving to Randy, only he had to put this butterball in the tub instead of the oven. I also became quite comfortable zipping around in the grocery store in my "wheel-mobile." Over the past few years, marketing had become quite a chore for me because of the necessary walking, and I didn't stand or walk with ease anymore. As a matter of fact, grocery shopping had become pleasurable again, thanks to my borrowed wheels. In fact, even after Dr. Bones put me in a walking cast, I continued to use my wheel-mobile when shopping to avoid the pervasive fatigue that bothered me so often.

After approximately eight weeks in a cast, I was finally freed, but Dr. Bones could not release me to return to work. Sure, all of the bills were paid, and we were making ends meet solely on Randy's salary, but I was used to working, and I missed my job. Plus, I don't care how you look at it, two checks are better than one. "Oh well," I joked to myself, "if push comes to shove, I can always pawn my jewelry." Nope, better not try that. Ten-to-one odds that a suspicious-minded pawnbroker with an active imagination would think that I was a drug-crazed house burglar and call the authorities on me, and that would be too embarrassing. I guess that the pawnbroker wasn't the only one with an active imagination.

I again made contact with my supervisors and informed them that I would be off work for a few additional weeks. They didn't appear to be too upset. "Take as long as you need, Mrs. Tate. We have you on extended sick leave. You'll have a time card in the rack whenever you get back." I was glad that they had such a positive attitude. However, at this point I was just hoping that I wouldn't lose my nursing skills and my bedside technique. As a result, I reviewed certain articles in my nursing journals. My body was weak, but if I could help it, my mental abilities would remain strong.

I drove again for the first time with Randy serving as my coach. It was just like riding a bicycle; I hadn't forgotten how. I was able to make short trips, but I still was somewhat shaky. I wouldn't have trusted myself to drive cross-country at that point.

After about six more weeks, Dr. Bones gave me medical clearance to return to work. On my first night back with my ever-present cane, I was greeted warmly by my friends and co-workers. "So glad to have you back," seemed to be the phrase of the night. I replied that I was glad to be back, and I was genuine in my response. I felt like a nurse again. I was helping people who desperately needed my assistance. Even though I was only working three nights a week, I always left work in the A.M. with the feeling that I had helped someone, even if it was only by offering a pain medication, or simply holding a cup of water for a weak patient.

Things had finally gotten back to what was normal functioning in my family. I still used my cane when walking significant distances. As it had been in the past, grocery shopping was a tiring chore for me. I no longer felt comfortable using the wheel-mobile, since I could no longer hide behind my cast. I had to acknowledge that my MS–related problems were the only reasons that I found myself physically challenged at this time. I didn't want to face the fact that I could have an invisible problem which pervaded my life so thoroughly, so I persevered in my usual independent manner of doing things. I was able to maintain the status quo for a while.

Several months later on a Friday, I was performing household chores when another incident made me realize that I was not an average working mother. Randy had briefly paused in the living room to watch an interesting snippet on television while I was straightening the bottom of the linen closet. I was stooped over the paper products when I lost my balance and started to fall. I remember falling in (what seemed like to me) slow motion. It was surreal. It was eerie.

It felt like something straight out of *The Twilight Zone*. When I came to rest, I looked directly into Randy's face. His eyebrows were raised. He immediately asked me if I was all right, if I was hurt.

"Yeah, I'm OK." I was starting to become amused, and I began to snicker. Randy saw that I was not hurt and he began to smile also.

"Hey," he said as he helped me up. "You did that like you've been practicing. Kinda like a stuntwoman." I was in agreement. I felt like that fall was unlike all the others. It was like I had been expecting it.

I had not been fazed at all by that latest stumble. After Randy helped me up, I continued with my chores, only being more mindful of my balance problems. I noticed that Randy continued to cast dubious glances my way. He was looking at me as though I were a live hand grenade.

When I had finished with the linen closet, I parked myself on the sofa to contemplate matters. I had fallen more lately than I had during my entire childhood, with all the pitfalls that can trip a youngster up:

roller skates, jump-rope, and impromptu footraces. The part of the Serenity Prayer that states "...accept the things that I cannot change" stuck in my mind. Even though it had been almost four years since I had been told that I had MS, I had not accepted the diagnosis. I was still trying to live my life without making too many changes — things that might label me as "handicapped." I had always taken a certain degree of pride in hiding the fact that I was not the physically-altogether young woman that I appeared to be. I had resisted using a cane; I had stubbornly forsaken my wheel-mobile when I definitely needed it to maneuver myself while shopping. Instead of using these borrowed wheels, I tortured myself by trying to do my marketing on foot. I had to realize that things were not as they had been. Remembering that I had been charged with taking care of the sick and infirm, I must have thought that I could have no infirmities of my own. I sat there reflecting.

Realizing that I had become painfully tired, I reached for the remote to settle down for an evening of television with my family. After all, it was the weekend, and all we were obligated to do was "hang loose." Randy didn't have to go to work till Monday morning; I wasn't due to clock in until that P.M., and my sons always have "play and no work" on their minds.

The next morning, we went on to have our weekly, traditional, cholesterol-laden, Southern-style breakfast, complete with hot grits and red-eye gravy. Randy and Robert did their customary chore of clearing away the breakfast dishes, while I dressed Randall and myself for our biweekly excursion to visit family. As usual, we made our rounds to Randy's mother's house, and then to see my parents. As per routine, Robert and Randall "O.D.'d" on cookies from their grand-mothers' snack stash. After we had finished with our parental visits, I went to the restroom to empty my bladder one last time before heading to the supermarket.

After we arrived at the grocery store, we went up and down the aisles. Before we could finish selecting our foodstuffs and sundries, I had to head for the ladies' room. After making it to the stalls, I sat there for a moment to rest. I hated having to use this public washroom; it was probably a meeting place for all manner of pathogenic microorganisms, but I was at the mercy of my bladder, and the walking that I had to do while marketing didn't help matters much. At that point, I couldn't decide whether MS had done more of a disservice to my balance, stamina, or bladder. I guessed that my decision was determined by whichever problem was causing me the most difficulty at the time. There was no doubt that at that moment, as I pondered the pathogenicity of my surroundings, I considered my malfunctioning bladder to be a grave matter for me. But this was no unusual situation. I was knowledgeable of the location of every relief station in my quadrant of Memphis. In fact, it was true that my bladder had been a cause of concern for me for some time, and here I sat, disgusted by the apparent condition of my urinary tract. I believed that I must have had a bladder with the capacity of an eye dropper. Either that, or I was not completely emptying myself. I decided that the latter was my problem, and resigned myself to restricted fluids on shopping days. I thought it was that simple.

We did get finished with marketing, and I decided that we could have fish sticks for dinner, because they took little or no effort to prepare. My family had adjusted their taste buds to accommodate the "change de cuisine" that I was subjecting them to. Besides, they had no choice.

Autumn was a picturesque display of colorful finery. Temperatures were pleasantly balmy. It was the best Fall that I could remember. Robert went back to school in catalog-selected clothes because I had come to the conclusion that shopping malls were not my cup of tea, as I was feeling weaker lately. Randy and I took the boys on a few drives through the park so that they could marvel at nature. We, also, were observing nature's finery with wonderment.

Christmas turned out to be as bone-chillingly cold as autumn had been pleasant. Christmas Eve was so frigid that the kitchen pipes froze and burst, spewing water across the floor like volcanic lava (which would have been welcomed in our kitchen). Molten lava could have warmed the place up a bit.

That cold snap came and went leaving the remainder of winter to have only moderately chilly temperatures. Frozen precipitation was virtually nonexistent that year, and the groundhog did the right thing on February 2nd. However, I noticed that it generally rained cats and dogs every night that I had to go to work. In fact, the weatherman could almost predict rain by my schedule. Invariably, there was a downpour on the nights that I had duty planned. During that winter, I took an umbrella to work as frequently as I carried my stethoscope, clipboard, and cane.

Even though I was only practicing my chosen profession three nights a week, my job as an RN made me feel as though I were a positive force in my patients' lives. I was highly pleased with myself because I was a nurse for more than a paycheck. I truly cared about doing the best that I could for my patients. Plus, I realized that working these few shifts made me less susceptible to "burn-out." I wasn't jaded like a few of my counterparts. I could empathize with my hospital's customers.

I understood that comparatively few of my patients were MS clients like me, but I could relate to almost all maladies that people presented with. If I had not been affected similarly with a like problem, I imagined what it was like. People are different, but all groups are susceptible to some form of illness. I found this to be the case with MS. I saw people of all ethnic groups that had been affected: African-American, European-American, Native American, and Asian-American had three things in common with me: human body, human mind, and MS. Infirmity knows no form of segregation: racial, financial, or otherwise.

Whenever I went to work, I had to use my cane only when walking to and from the parking area and to the cafeteria. I could fare pretty well while on duty because I walked close to the handrail in the corridor. Secondarily, I had switched shifts to work midnights because the pace was far more relaxed; there was not as much walking, since there were fewer scheduled medications to be administered. Most of my night was spent sitting at the nurse's station desk charting. It was infrequent that my patients required procedures in the middle of the night. I can remember only a few times when I had to rush to assist a patient who was having difficulty. In those instances, I was probably running purely on an adrenalin burst; I couldn't rely on stamina any longer.

By God's grace, I continued to work for five years after I had been diagnosed, even though I had been forced by my condition to change duties, schedules, and frequency of work. I had altered my service from the trauma operating room with 12-hour shifts (full-time) to 11 P.M. – 7 A.M. general medical/surgical duty on a part-time basis. But no matter what, I enjoyed the work, even though I was becoming more disabled, and even this "light duty" was too physically challenging. An old friend of mine who had attended nursing school with me suggested that I might be more capable in a psychiatric setting. I pursued this option until the interviewer informed me that I would have to obtain a statement from my doctor verifying that I could participate in restraining a combative patient, should a "show of force" become necessary. After I heard that, it appeared to be a moot point to obtain the doctor's statement. I knew that I did not possess the physical wherewithal necessary to wrestle with a psychotic "Mike Tyson–type" patient. It was challenging enough just to walk down the corridor. Moreover, I didn't want to have to get stitches to show that I was a dedicated care–giver. I let the issue of psychiatric nursing come to rest. Working 11–7 med–surg wasn't too bad, anyway.

Eventually it got to the point where it was impossible for me to work at all. I have been forced to stop working and apply for Social Security Disability Insurance, as I no longer have many alternatives in employment. Several years ago, I applied for commercially offered disability insurance, but they denied my application and refunded my initial premium so quickly that it made my head spin. I guess I could understand their position. I suppose that they figured that it would only be a matter of time before I would want to make a claim. They were right. I wasn't a good risk. I was too volatile for them. I now like to consider myself "Toni R. Tate, RN, Staff Nurse Emeritus." It gives me more self-worth.

Ultimately, I realized that sporadic fluid restriction was not helping my urinary tract at all. I got fed up and asked my neurologist to refer me to a good urologist, so that my bladder needs could be attended to. I had urodynamic studies done before he ("Dr. Uro") could ascertain which medications to prescribe for me. Since I have had those tests done and have seen a urologist, I feel almost like my old bladder is back. I have been urologically emancipated. I take two different medications on a twice-daily basis, but the bladder control is worth it. Anything is better than wetting your pants in K-Mart. (I did that once. Luckily, I had on a pair of dark blue jeans, and it was not overtly visible.) I still wear a small-sized bladder protection pad for added insurance, but I don't have nearly as many urinary problems as I once experienced.

I have also become more used to employing the use of a wheel-mobile when necessary. I never use the expression "wheelchair-bound," because I actually feel liberated by this mobility device. I admit that it took some adjusting by the whole family, but we have worked out a systematic plan for even the most mundane of tasks. Our methodology rivals that of NASA'S. I suppose that it should — it almost takes a military operation just to go to the mall. I wheel myself out to the car, Robert governs Randall, and then Randy expertly fits my wheels into our compact-sized trunk while I situate myself in the passenger seat. We all buckle up, and *Boom!!* — we're ready to roll. We can go to places and events that used to be off-limits for me because of my lack of stamina and bladder control. We are even contemplating visiting some of the highly touted tourist attractions in the region. We are already preparing our Bermuda shorts, sunglasses, tennis shoes, and camera bags with neck straps.

Fifteen years ago, I would have never guessed that my life would be so full of changes that have been necessary because of my chronic condition. When I was newly diagnosed, I was sure that "Doctor Neurology" had made a sure but very unfunny mistake. Even though I had been licensed as an RN in the state of Tennessee, I didn't know very much about MS. Shock consumed me, as well as dismay, when Dr. Neuro gave me a diagnosis subsequent to all the testing. I was the first person of my ethnic group that I had ever known to be affected by MS. Now that I, too, am in that number, I realize that I am not rare at all. I just had never met any other African-American MS clients. It's not that we don't exist — I merely had met MS clients from other ethnicities. I now know differently. This bit of knowledge can be used to support the theory that even though we may vary slightly in appearance and customs, people are basically the same once you get past the superficialities.

Periodically, I think back to something that Randy said to me once about a fall that I had taken. I try to remember Randy's analogy and live my life as though I am a Hollywood stuntwoman. Even though I may not always succeed, I try to roll with the punches — my entire family does. Life is easier that way. We don't sweat the small stuff. We can't. We don't have the time.

Disabled Does Not Mean Unable

by: Glenn Liebensohn

Does disabled mean unable? Sometimes it does. Some people who find that they have a chronic, incurable disease become that illness. There may be little that can be done about the way a disease attacks us physically. The real issue, however, is the way we see ourselves in relation to our illness.

I was diagnosed as having multiple sclerosis in 1985. Six months prior to my diagnosis, I began having eye problems —blurred vision and slight pain behind my left eye. I was sent to an ophthalmologist by my neurologist, and was told that I had optic neuritis. My doctor then ordered a CAT scan. Next came the evoked response test. As the technicians attached electrodes to my arms and head, I was told to concentrate on the monitor as patterns flashed on the screen. It was like watching test patterns on television after the station has signed off for the night.

Two days later, while at work, I received a call from my internist. My worst fears had been realized. I had multiple sclerosis. I went into the men's room, locked the door behind me and started crying. I was 33 years old and I felt that my life was over. I was a newlywed with two sons and a good job. Suddenly, I felt like I had nothing.

When I told my wife about the test results, we hugged and I cried, but she never even shed a tear. She did not want to talk about my illness. When I made plans to attend a support group for newly diagnosed MS patients, she made excuses not to go with me. During the next six months, we had no relations and no relationship. We were married only on paper. Finally, I decided to move back in with my parents. When I told her that I was leaving, she gave me her wedding ring and asked for my apartment key. She never even asked where I was going.

Once I moved back into my old bedroom, I felt defeated. I had quit my job, and I now began to feel so confused that at times I didn't know what day it was. One afternoon, after waking from a nap and thinking it was early morning, I limped to the diner for breakfast. When the person next to me ordered meat loaf, I began to suspect that something was wrong. Once it grew dark, I knew for sure.

A couple of days later, I awoke in a panic, looking for my ex-wife. I shouted her name several times and dragged myself outside, thinking she might be on the front stoop. When I realized what I had done, I felt sure that I was losing my mind. Finally, I asked myself, did I want to live or die? Once I knew that I still had the will to live, I stopped blaming others for my misfortune, and started working on the things in my life that I could control.

Since I was having difficulty keeping track of my life, I had the *Bridgeport Post* delivered daily to help me verify the date of each day. I set up four calendars around the house and marked off each day religiously. I began to wear my watch regularly to enable me to have a more precise sense of time. These small rituals provided me with an important routine, and slowly I gained the courage to parole myself from my self-imposed prison. I vowed that I would leave my room every day and go somewhere. It didn't matter what I did, I told myself, as long as I did something.

At first, I was extremely self-conscious about having to use a cane to offset my periodic loss of balance. I wanted to be able to walk normally as I had always done for almost 35 years. I felt the stares of those who passed me on the street. But I also knew that using this support would keep people from mistaking me for some sort of substance abuser.

One day, I walked several blocks to my old grammar school. The building has been abandoned now for ten years. The doors and windows were boarded up and the concrete was cracked and pitted. Grass grew through the fractures. A large boulder blocked the entrance to the playground where we used to line up in the morning in single file by grades, awaiting the ringing of the bell to start class. As I stared at what looked like an ancient ruin, many memories entombed inside me flashed through my mind.

I remembered how I had once been a shy five-year-old, frightened of not fitting in with other kids. But, I remember overcoming those fears and making friends. I saw myself playing kick ball, my strong legs carrying me swiftly past the bases, after I had sent the ball deep into the field. I remembered, too, my first girlfriend and my first kiss.

Eventually, I moved out beyond my immediate neighborhood, and often went to St. Mary's by the Sea, where I would sit for hours watching the sailboats drifting about the sound. Occasionally, I brought along my guitar and wrote songs. But whenever I would see couples walking by hand-in-hand or kids strolling past with their parents, I began to hurt deep inside, longing for the kind of relationships they shared. It was then that I started to think about my two sons whom I hadn't seen since I left my ex-wife because I'd been too busy feeling sorry for myself. I decided to become a real father to my boys again.

Taking control of my life enabled me to get in touch with the person I once was, and this put a lot of things in perspective for me. Once I felt that I was ready to take another step forward, I returned to my old work place. I was welcomed by my old friends who told me they'd be happy to have me work for them again in any capacity that I could manage. Their show of faith gave me strength to turn the next corner.

It no longer mattered to me that I couldn't be department head, a position I had earned after ten years with the company. What mattered was that I could again be productive. I found myself agreeing to work part-time, soliciting customers by phone, a job I used to train others to do. I swallowed my pride and started making calls. I discovered that I could do it, and do it well. I no longer felt unable. Physically challenged, yes. Unable, no.

Epilogue — From Dark to Light

Here I am, a safe harbor at last. It's been a long journey. It's been a treacherous journey to say the least, and I know that it's not over. There is danger around every corner, but I must be prepared for anything that comes my way. I can't give up or give in to this beast called multiple sclerosis, and I know I never will. It's hard when your own mortality rears its head.

It's hard not to be afraid at times, but I must strengthen my resolve in order for it not to consume me. I will not let it happen.

'It'

by: Denni Evans

'It' comes to haunt me periodically.

'It' makes its presence felt whenever I forget and begin to lead a "normal" life.

"Oh, no you don't," 'It' says. Don't go getting above yourself and try to enjoy life. You're an invalid — disabled — a cripple. You've got a travel pass and mobility allowance to prove it. The Government says you're not an able-bodied person, so don't imagine you can go gallivanting around having *fun!* You're supposed to take things easy — so what's with all this rushing around attending committee meetings, playing with your baby daughter, gardening, being creative?

If the Creator had intended you to do these things He wouldn't have given you an incurable disease.

Well, here's a lesson in humility for you. The power from your limbs will be removed for a period of not less than two months, thereby forcing you to relinquish all control over your life and placing you at the mercy and good will of others — who *know* what's best for you. Concentration will vanish from your mind, rendering you incapable of reading or of coherent speech. And just when you thought you were getting it right! *Ha!* That will teach you — 'It' mocks.

But hold on a moment. I do not have to succumb to this.

'It' took root in my body nearly 20 years ago, and 'It' hasn't won yet. Granted, 'It' takes hold of me and forces me to become another person temporarily, and I don't really know that person even now. I don't recognise the shambling, stumbling, stuttering, weak-limbed creature I am forced to be for the duration of the relapse. How can I? 'It' strikes at random and without warning — an unseen, but not unknown enemy, and each time I am taken by surprise initially. The surprise is quickly replaced by anger, which in turn is speedily removed by fear. I am angry that despite all my efforts, 'It' still has the capacity to take my legs out from under me, metaphorically as well as literally. I have long since ceased to ask "Why?" "How?" is useless too. 'It' is a fact of my life.

'It' is not, however, a major fact as it once was. When I was much younger (21) it was a big deal. Then, I was scared beyond all reason and not very good at dealing with 'It'. Then, I was more than happy, relieved even, to hand over the care and welfare of myself to others in whom I placed all my trust. They knew what they were doing, or so they told me.

They didn't really know. They still don't. But then, as now, they handed me their drugs, and I, in the belief that the drugs would make me better — make 'It' go away — took what they prescribed for me.

I stopped taking their drugs in 1977. I looked for other treatments: potions, lotions, meditations, sedations, rationalisations. I found none of them and all of them. I didn't keep a catalogue; I was too busy trying to run from 'It'.

Now, I no longer run away. I confront 'It' in the only way I know. To ignore 'It' is useless, and so I acknowledge 'It's' existence, and treat 'It' accordingly. I am wary of over–fatiguing my body, because then 'It' can gain control over me. But that doesn't prevent me from walking in the Lake District, and climbing great hills that leave some fit people gasping. I just take care to rest my body fully afterwards in order to replenish my stocks of energy. I do this in hundreds, if not thousands of ways all the time. It is second nature to me now. I have ambitions still. They have altered in some ways, but I can hold onto them. I am kinder to myself now because I have learned that my anger is the weapon that 'It' uses most effectively against me. I don't live easily with 'It'. But I manage. Very well.

My Hands

by: *Mary Martin Farrell*

It was on December 17, 1988, while I was walking the dogs, when I slipped and fell on the ice. I was a bit jolted, but it did not appear that I was seriously injured. I had long forgotten the incident ten days later when I began experiencing distorted sensation on my left side. Within a few days I was having difficulty writing, and then lost sensation and coordination in both hands. It felt as though I was wearing a baseball glove on each hand. What was happening to me didn't really sink in until I tried to make a phone call, and realized that not only couldn't I hang onto the receiver, but operating the rotary dial was clearly out of the question. I had lost the use of my hands. My first MS symptoms manifested themselves in 1973 as "misty vision," literally seeing the world through a fog. I had to make a few adjustments, such as wearing sunglasses more often, but did nothing else to significantly alter my lifestyle. The neurologist was uncertain to make a diagnosis, even though I had been through a series of "torture tests," such as a visual evoked response test, where a bright black and white checkerboard was flashed in front of my eyes; another test was where water was flushed into my ears to make me dizzy and consequently vomit. Next, there was an electrical response test in which electrodes were attached to my scalp with airplane glue, a spinal tap which didn't seal off, resulting in a severe headache plus another procedure to seal off the puncture site. "Possibly multiple sclerosis," the neurologist said. "Keep track of your symptoms for five years, and we'll discuss it again at that time." Five Years? I didn't want to know in five years, I wanted to know now!

So, for the next five years I continued to have vision problems, including rapid eye movements which blurred my vision momentarily without notice. Five years later, almost to the day, I called the neurologist's office to make an appointment to revisit the situation. After reviewing the neurological activity of the last five years and a long conversation, MS was diagnosed. The disease was not new to me.

I have two cousins with MS. I lived the next ten years basically symptom free, hardly thinking about MS. After all, there really wasn't much there to remind me.

After Christmas vacation 1988 I returned to work still in this "baseball glove" condition, convinced that I could perform my job. I thought that if I worked at a slow pace I would be able to carry out my responsibilities as a receptionist at the local Health Maintenance Organization Mental Health Clinic. The phone kept ringing with messages for the staff, and after one hour and a few missed messages I realized I was not able to do my job. With tears in my eyes and fear in my heart I notified my supervisor, explaining that I would have to leave, and did not know when I could return. Leaving the office with the five staff members waving good-bye and wishing me luck, I walked out. They looked as confused as I felt.

The neurologist with his cold metal tools and safety pin confirmed that I was having an MS exacerbation. He started me on ACTH injections, twice a day for ten days, then once a day for four days. The next fourteen days would prove to be painful both emotionally and physically. I drove myself to the clinic, a forty mile round trip, twice a day. The fact that I was behind the wheel of a car frightens me to this day, but it was my freedom. It meant I could still carry out a fraction of my life, and a fraction seemed as big as the world. I was willing to go through this routine if it meant I would get my hands back; I really missed them. I needed them for the very basics of life, but right now they just weren't receiving messages from my brain. Brushing my teeth took intense concentration. Buttons were defiant. Liquid soap was a must. Eating was laborious, and velcro closures and elastic waistbands were essential.

My life had gone from enjoying a new home, new property and a new job to anger, bewilderment, feelings of abandonment, and general confusion. I was prone to outbursts of anger and crying, which occurred frequently. After seven days of ACTH injections I began to have side effects. Colors were brighter. Nights were basically sleepless, and a metallic taste took over my mouth. I felt as though I had enough energy to split rails, and fence our five acres. In reality I didn't have enough energy to get up off the couch. When I went to bed at night my heart would pound for what seemed like hours. By the time my heart would settle down, I would be ready to shift positions or have to use the bathroom, and the heart pounding would start all over again. Clearly my system was out of balance. I explained all of this to the injection nurse and she suggested I eat foods having potassium in them. I didn't want to eat more potassium. I didn't want any of this.

During the next two weeks I watched more talk shows than I care to count, read books and magazines, and slept when I could. My favorite hobbies, sewing and quilting, weren't even an option. This troubled me greatly, as the creative juices were flowing, but I had no way to channel them. My husband and I tried to continue with as much normalcy in our lives as possible. He was great, knowing when to back off and let me try, and knowing when to step in and take over. His anger surfaced primarily around finances, because we still did not know if I would be able to return to work. At this point in our lives we needed two incomes. What we didn't need was the fear. One day a friend stopped by while I was attempting to make apple sauce. There I stood barely hanging onto a butcher knife with one hand and trying to steady an apple with the other... what a sight. I guess this friend expected to see me bedridden because her eyes got big as she drew in a deep breath and asked, "Doesn't your husband cook?"

"Yes," I replied," and so do I."

At the end of two weeks I took a bouquet of irises to the injection nurse who had daily searched my backside for a spot that hadn't been punctured. She gave me a hug, and joked that the flowers were the same color as my backside — purple and yellow. I was crushed. I cried all the way home, and when I got there I made my way into the house and looked at the bruises for the first and last time.

After these three weeks I gradually regained enough use of my hands to return to work. It was wonderful. My co-workers had been very supportive, and it was great to see them again. I was slow in functioning, but I was functioning! At the same time it was strange performing my job again. The first week I made many mistakes. Some co-workers were understanding, and others weren't. I guess they wondered just what had happened during the past three weeks. I hadn't been in bed with the flu. I had been debilitated, confused, and scared. I forgave them for not understanding. Maybe they were scared too.

Before long, I could tie my shoes again. This accomplishment was more exciting at age thirty-five than it had been at age five. Gradually my life regained some normalcy. I read several updated books on MS, and continued with Evening of Primrose Oil ("Essence of Nightlife," as a well-meaning co-worker once called it!).

On and off for the next six months I experienced stiffness and pain in my fingers, and a severe burning sensation in my left hand. The skin was so hypersensitive that it often meant wearing cotton socks on my hands at night. The air current across my skin felt like a bad sunburn being massaged with sandpaper, and at other times I experienced a feeling of extreme cold. During the day I was often seen with long sleeves pulled over my hands. The warmth did help. I began to realize these sensations were just my body talking to me. It let me know when I needed to rest, to stop, to pay attention. When I learned to listen, I could control the pain to an extent, but not totally.

From July, 1989 to November, 1989 I did very well. Even though I knew this was the nature of the disease, I found myself hoping this had been a one-time experience.

However, by mid-November, new symptoms started all over again. This time it wasn't just my hands and distorted sensations, but weakness in both legs, and a feeling of a tight band around my midsection. The neurologist prescribed Prednisone which proved to be a better choice than ACTH, but it was not without side effects either. I looked so funny being "moon-faced." The mirror didn't reflect my normal vivacious self. So here I was at home again with the TV and the books, and since I didn't have to go into the clinic for injections, I began to feel very isolated without human contact during the day. I dreaded each morning when my husband left for work. When the door shut behind him it was like a cell door closing. I didn't want to be alone, and cried until the feeling passed. However, by that time, between crying and the "moon face," my eyes would be nearly swollen shut. I allowed myself this release, and then got on with the planned activity of the day. It was very important to have a planned activity, even if that meant saying, "I'll rest from noon until one." Structure kept me from becoming too anxious; it kept my mind occupied. The time passed quickly. After all I had been through this before, and had recovered somewhat. And so, I found myself patiently waiting to get better.

Again, after three weeks I returned to work, and did somewhat better than the first time around. Due to a lack of total coordination, misdialing phone numbers was my biggest problem. I didn't always push the button for which I was aiming, but wrong numbers turned out to be friendly voices letting me know I had misdialed. No one hung up on me or became angry. It was as though they somehow understood.

I have not experienced debilitation since 1989, but symptoms still persist. I experience varying degrees of burning in my left hand, numbness in my left arm, back, and neck. When I get too tired my right leg tends to become heavy and drags. I still lack total coordination in both hands as well. I can live with all of this, but the episodes of debilitation are much more difficult for me to face, as I never know if or when I will recover. So far I consider myself lucky.

How has MS changed my life? Three inch heels are a thing of the past, and the toes of my shoes take a beating. I trip over nothing, which usually generates a comment like, "Did you have a nice trip?"

Once a co-worker tripped over nothing and stated, "I must be catching Mary's MS." I try to handle these comments with humor, but there is a certain amount of emotional pain as well. The checkbook register is a challenge, as sometimes I am unable to hone in on those little squares. Sometimes when I use the word processor, any given finger will not lift off of a key, and I'll end up with a whole row of a specific letter. Cleaning the bathroom isn't as important as it used to be. I use a walking stick when trekking around our five acres, and when walking the dogs. I do not test water temperature with my left hand, as it gives a false reading, and I rest when I feel the need. I sometimes become anxious when climbing stairs in public places, as I am not able to move as fast as everyone else, and if I am having problems with my hands, I will often sign and date several checks before leaving home when running errands. Spirituality has played a big part in my recovery. I practice it daily and relish the comfort it provides. I also practice creative visualization, where I picture my spinal column, and massage the areas affected by plaque to increase blood flow, while visualizing new myelin sheath being produced. I feel renewed each time I practice visualization, and feel it has played a large part in my recovery as well. I continue to work at the Mental Health Clinic thirty-two hours a week, have been promoted to office supervisor, and feel fortunate and proud that I am able to continue with my job.

Following my second debilitating episode I started a tradition of creating Christmas tree skirts to give to friends and family. These are done completely by hand, and I spend six to eight months out of the year creating them. I have entered two in the county fair, and have won a blue ribbon each year for art and craftsmanship, but for me the ribbons have come to mean healing and hope in celebration of my hands.

MS (Multiple Sclerosis: Many Scars)
− or −
"Things Went Down We Don't Understand,
but I Think in Time We Will..."
— Grateful Dead (of *course*)

by: Lisa Frank

MS is a *trip*: it is *very* important to understand that! That's what I mean about my ancient drug-use days "helping" me through the physical/mental/physical/MENTAL/PHYSICAL changes that MY MS *introduced* me to, albeit I was neither a willing/compliant, nor *especially* a *quick* learner; essentially, I "freaked." I was NOT the wondrous patient that most neurologists and books about MS would have me be — the smart, intelligent (by WHOSE criteria?), well informed, *again* . COMPLIANT docile little MS patient. Oh, NO, I was (and AM) NOT someone who "should" get a disease — especially a disease like MS. In MS it is nearly all speculative; how bad you will be, how long it will take to become bad, what IS "bad?" Dear sir, I would have you read McAlpine's text on MS if you want to learn about all the SHIT that can happen to a body with MS (In the genes? Perhaps MS is from measles? What the hell kicks it in, anyway?) THEY don't know; sorry. No, we can't answer *that* either, but research is always being done, don't WORRY about it; just go live your life — (yeah, RIGHT).

My eyes crossed; rather, I lost lateral control of my right eye the day after I'd gone home early from work because I felt weird. The medical term is — spontaneous lateral optic nystagmus — or some such thing (I learned the term after my most recent MS attack). Anyway, my eyes crossed 4 years ago. I went to the emergency room, they kept me sitting in an examining room for an hour and a half, gave me an eye patch, TOLD ME NOTHING (standard procedure) and sent me home after calling the traveling neurologist and setting me up to see him the next week. In about 4 days, my eyes were tracking correctly again, before I even got to see the TN (traveling neurologist), yay Fortune/God/Little Repair Guys. Not fast enough though — I called my Mom/Dad/The New England Home For Little Wanderers (I had been adopted from that agency) and Massachusetts Eye and Ear. None of the above told me ANYTHING (though Massachusetts Eye & Ear said "Wow, interesting, we'd like to see her!"), and Mom said "I'll call your father, dear. Oh WHY do you have to live up there (NH) with NO GOOD hospitals?" I forget what Dear Old Dad said, but he came up to NH and went with me to see the TN who scheduled me for a CAT scan the next week — At long last, after the CAT scan, before the MRI, I was told that THEY? (the PROFESSIONALS?) suspected multiple sclerosis. I said, "Huh? What is it?" and received from my TN a brief and (now obscenely) positive synopsis which left me just as bewildered, and added another element of FEAR to the already insane things I was being told by acquaintances/family/anyone I talked to. Let's remember, I'm talking about my brain, here, that thing that RUNS my body, and controls everything from my thoughts to my bladder! One thing I have learned is that my ENTIRE brain and spinal cord are at risk. Anything I can possibly have the potential to do — the MS and I share ALL I HAVE as a resource to draw on. At any rate, I'd been living with the Ed of my life for 10 years before we married after my diagnosis in 1987. We did it for insurance, of all things, but those scans cost $$$$$ and I was NOT insured. So, OK, I'd made A COMMITMENT and I LIVED!) — wow.

Looking through my computer files, I found that in 1987 I must have been STRESSED; I had A LOT of strange MS attacks, and a bout with a new one for me — shingles, for God's sakes! STRESS and MS react together, and I still haven't found my way around that one yet! The TN told me not to worry; people told me not to worry, but, well, I'm a worrier. Especially when THEY can't/won't give me a prognosis. I assumed when you got a disease, THEY tell you about your chances of survival, give you SOME percentage of OUTCOME. Well, 2/3 of MS patients do well (WHAT'S WELL??!), 1/3 end up in a wheelchair. Or, do I have the stats reversed?

OK, from Grateful Dead lyrics: "Gone are the broken eyes we saw through in dreams; Gone both dream and lie..." In 1987, being of not perfect mind nor body, the following occurred, in order: Eyes; tingles in left hand; left side of face tingles; left side of tongue, too; the tingles turned to numbness — (half of my face and my tongue, my chin, my TEETH and gums, my NOSE >>>½ of my nose!!!!!! was numb. I had fatigue at times, bladder retention, (you DON'T want to know about that, believe me!) and tingles in the upper part of ?my lungs? — that's all for sensation. Motor control of my right leg, and right arm was affected in January, 1988. I'll explain it a little better; it has happened often enough so that I have some kind of grip on it, nebulous though it be! I cannot explain what it is to have half of your face numb (there was a line near the middle of my nose where sensation returned to normal). Think dentist and novocain, but remember, only *half* of your face, for a week or so. The tingles you'll be familiar with if you've ever sanded wood with a Makita or other oscillating sander. I forgot to mention the trigeminal nerve pain I had for a week or so. Sharp searing pain from above the left eyebrow, through the left eye, and down to the chin. Imagine a splatter of ??? burning napalm in a thin line, hitting your face. It was over very quickly, in seconds, but it struck when it struck. OK, you've drunk 2 quarts of beer quickly and you JUST HAVE TO PEE. !Urgency you !dance! and finally get to a bathroom and...... you...... can't...... GO! The TN gave me a cute pink pill which put a stop to my spastic bladder spasticizing. (How do YOU spell relief?) Fatigue is — you've been awake for 24 hours, and you need to be awake, alert, attentive for the next 8 hours. Bone weary and more, brain weary. I feel like a harpy, anti-social to the extreme, I feel MEAN, and I know I *need* REST when I feel so mean. I think I have a good idea of what REST/rest is — FINALLY! My understanding is you rest, I REST. Longer, much longer than anyone (especially myself wants to) to recharge and to revitalize back into being a human sans harpyism. It can take me days to recover from a weekend camping trip. I had to learn REST. It means: pretend you're in the hospital.

I'm learning not to expect or even hope) for my family to understand, or to *want* to accept what MS means to me/my life, HELL,

I still fight against it. MS is all pervasive, affecting my LIFE *&* THOUGHTS: (I'm on 300 mg of Imipramine and STILL not in control of my emotions) OR my body, as I'm having *another* attack as I write — it seems to be an upper body spasticity type of attack. My neck rigidifies my head and I try to breathe like I'm giving birth so I can get through it. Again, it is fleeting, but DAMN scary, and neither my neurologist nor my MD is available. This *does suck*, believe me. I am working on the bitterness and anger I feel against my family, Mom, Dad, and brother. It is a process; I'm not there yet. As for physical/ mental STRESS and MS — Stress can lead to an attack. In March after doing a lot of travelling and visiting all month, we ended up at my mother's on Easter. I had an attack the day we left of spontaneous vertical optic nystagmus. Which means, essentially, my vertical hold was NOT holding. Most people have met that with their TVs. I AM very bitter and very upset (stressed?!) NAW — Anyway, physical and/ or mental stress can bring on an attack. Women have had their first MS attacks while giving birth, planning weddings — S T R E S S. SIGH. Is there life without stress? Not mine, so far!

In short, THEY can tell you NOTHING in the way of prognosis for the first 5 years. They want to spend that time observing you, scanning you (MRI *&* CAT scans). One thing I HATE in our psychology book is their definition of intelligence. I do NOT "...readily adapt to a changing environment," nor do I have "...the ability to solve problems..." when fatigued. I believe I used to be better in readily adapting as well as problem solving than I am now. I *do* think I am intelligent (not Einstein, of course), but I *am* a mammal of a higher order; I think, I read, et cetera. I AM learning that definitions made by other people are not necessarily for me, and Huffman's definition of intelligence is one of those definitions that do *not* fit me. Can you imagine the Donahue show as a tonic? Soap operas as tonics? If not, if you are saying something to the effect of, "MY, what a small, sad, *pitiful* little life she has!" you are beginning to understand what my multiple sclerosis (many scars) has done to *me*. But then, you don't know me, what I was, how I lived, and took what joy I could from life. I'd love to say that I had a perfect, happy, well-adjusted existence before

Many Scars showed up, but I think there is a limit to your credibility. There certainly is to mine.

* Psychology in Action*
** Mastering Multiple Sclerosis*

—·— ▓◆▓ —·—

    Last week, I drove to town for a meeting with my VocRehab officer just as the heat of a summer day was settling in. I then managed to cash a check, drop off a sheet of some kind of paper in the "Office of the Registrar," talk to the business office, and hoof it to the P.O. to mail some shoes back to L.L. Bean. *Whew*!!! After all that in the very humid heat, Ed and I went A C R O S S town — through the never-ending construction project on RTE 2, in the vehicle, *in the heat* — and of course it took way too long — in order to get to the pharmacy to get my all important anti-depressants. Here's the telling part — I've been on antidepressants just over a year now — the same drugstore all that time, *the same pharmacy*. I finally got them to put the easy open caps on the bottle for me! YAY *team*!!! But, I have been asking them for 6 months to NOT GLUE THE LITTLE TAG TO THE BAG — (Once in a while they've remembered, I admit, which is nice. I appreciate not having to F* around with the bag to obtain the damn sticker to send to the insurance company) — BUT, I'd called in the prescription and did NOT remind them about the GD sticker.

    It was — YET AGAIN stuck to the bag, and I lost ALL composure, told my wonderful (but placating at the time) husband to SHUT UP! In public!!! Upon which he sort of slunk away (smart dude that he is) while I proceeded to corner a pharmacist and ask him WHY >>>*after all this time*<<<, they (somehow, (((they don't have MS after all, so I'm not forgiving with them a bit, AT ALL, anymore)), seem to stick the

@%$&&)*! sticker on the @#%^&^) bag!!! Ed tells me later of course, that I had quite an audience for this little — shall I say, "faux pas." I KNOW what pharmacy software is like, Ed used to work for a company that sold it, so you'd think I'd be reasonable about this, right? Uh uh. I had hit the end of my endurance and had become myself, a harpy, A HARPY for God's sake!!!

Multiple Sclerosis — My Way

by: Heather Lewton

The booklet says I'm disabled with an auto-immune disease,
Which together with public opinion means I no longer do as I please.

Agreed, I do have some problems, I visit the ground quite a bit,
And if at the time it's too hard to get up, I'll enjoy the view and just sit!

My nerves all now live a life of their own, their reactions change
hour by hour.
A neurologist's test of knees, ankles and feet prove my reflexes
have their own power.
Eyes, arms and legs, internal organs, will function fine — off and on —
Walk into the doctor's surgery and the whole lot have got up and gone!

It's the same with hospital visits when the nurse requests "Just one
wee drop."
I'd as soon she required a pint of my blood for demands on this
bladder will flop!
Go shopping and the problem reverses, I know every loo in the town.
I stumble from one to another whilst praying the deluge slows down!

My eyes and their vision are quite literally a pain,
(As too my back, shoulders and neck)
The Telegraph crossword gets harder to read, my eyes hurt —
But I think — What the heck!
I can't sit around doing nothing, simply watching the world go by;
So I'm gardener, decorator, cook, mother and wife,
All perfected with just one good eye!

The doctor said "Think positive. Keep fit. Try swimming. It's good
exercise."
So I bravely jumped...sank...then learnt how to swim!
Will tenacity gain me a prize?

The moral of my words is quite plain to see.
It's "You others" who suffer the neurosis!
So do please take note — I've not changed — I'm still ME —
As I tolerate — multiple sclerosis.

Reflections on a Hospital Stay

"Come into hospital, we'll help you improve,
With the best that medicine can offer to date"
A Paras' Assault Course would now be no hassle
As this stay "Inside" is nearing "of late."

The nurses say calmly "Welcome. Relax."
While the doctors they seriously add,
"Put up the drip. Yes relax, do please rest —
With X-rays, some physio and just this small test."
(They then check to see what else they can find,
But really they're only doing their best.)
And with all the tests equally "pleasant"
They have the choice of a host,
But bank on this alone my friend —
The one they repeat — you hated the most!

Now physiotherapy is such a great aid
To regain your strength and mobility,
The only requisite here is —
That you start with perfect agility!
You wobble off wobble boards, walk imperfect lines,

Roll silicon "pastry" to "perfection!"
But peeping at others failing the same,
Gives you cause for quiet reflection,

Your hospital stay has been useful
For you truly have been assisted.
Drugs, drips and tests served their purpose,
Results were carefully listed.
Frustrations now are surely worthwhile,
For knowledge gained may yet help another.
"No man" — sick or well — "is an island"
And each person here — "my brother."

MS: Through the Looking Glass

by: *Alison D. Kovaleski*

We walked into the doctor's office, a place I'd seen many times before. We chatted a moment, all of us, and then she said it. "You have multiple sclerosis." The verdict hung in the air as I tried to grasp the concept. I didn't know what it was, except a name given to the reason why I couldn't walk straight, why my feet were numb. She explained to us — my mother, my boyfriend, and me — that my body was like an electrical wiring system with a short, or series of shorts. Something had bitten my wires and the colored rubber coating was gone, so the remote for the TV wasn't going to work right any more. She was not a repairman, and there was no repairman listed in the Yellow Pages for me. If I was to be like 70% of MS patients, I would have episodes of problems, called exacerbations, on and off all my life. I nodded, signaling that I understood the explanation. I asked questions about causes and treatments, only to receive vague answers. I got up and said, "Well, if there's nothing else, then I have to be getting back to my office now." I'd been given the reason for symptoms I'd been experiencing for the past two months, and now I had to get back to the other, more important facets of my life. I was relieved to find out it wasn't all in my head, that I wasn't crazy. I paid the bill and we walked outside, but suddenly I was alone. It was raining, but there weren't any clouds in the sky. There was just a cloud inside. MS had been explained medically in simple terms; the personal definition was much harder to realize.

At first, I ignored the diagnosis. I tried to lead my life as if nothing was wrong, as if that visit never happened. MS was a disease that other people had. It was something I raised money for in grade school, by reading books or jumping rope. It was not in my plan for life. I pretended it wasn't there.

Several weeks later, I was leaving the wedding ceremony of a friend. I had seen an old flame there, and was feeling on top of the world, remembering the great times we had spent together. I was reflecting upon the happiness I had found with Andy, my current boyfriend, when the MS again reminded me that life was not as perfect as I was dreaming it to be. I was headed out of the church when I was stopped by three simple steps. I looked for a railing to grab onto; there wasn't one, and I was lost. I stood there for a few moments, panic-stricken because I was all alone. For the first time, I had to reach out for a stranger's hand to help me down the stairs. When I got back to my car, I slumped over the wheel and cried for twenty minutes. I finally realized I could ignore it no longer. As uninvited as it was, I had to accept it in order to go on living my life.

Over the next few weeks, I read everything I could about the disease. A few of my sisters hunted down all the information they could find, to help me understand what was happening. I read about other people who had MS, about the latest research in laboratory animals, about possible nutritional avenues for treatment. I poured through books and magazines and pamphlets, reading about all the crazy symptoms and the genetic factors involved. Yet through all that reading, nothing reached out to touch me. The words were cold and black on the page. I couldn't feel them, hold them in my hands, let them dance in my stomach until I understood. The words were not real.

Against everyone's wishes and better judgement, I enrolled in a college program the following month. Here I was, a handicapped person, whose main prescription was rest, and I was giving another ten hours away every week. But I soon loved the classes, the work, the teachers, and my fellow students. I was happy to be learning again, to be reading about other people and other places far from my own troubles. During one class, my English professor made an eye-opening analogy. "Life," she said, "is a kaleidoscope. With each turn, your outlook is shaken and reflected in a whole new way." That was it! That was my real definition for MS — a kaleidoscope! While mine was different from everyone else's, it was still something that people everywhere had to deal with.

As I drove home that night, I thought more about what she had said. When I couldn't walk without stumbling, I was afraid my legs would never work right again; but amazingly enough, after a few weeks of such panic, they got better. The kaleidoscope had turned, and the new pattern would take away some old problems and present me with new ones. In this case, my legs were better, but my vision became fogged and I had trouble using my right hand. Yet, I could take comfort in knowing that this would pass, that maybe next week I could paint or write again. I would just have to wait for the next spin of the crystals.

When all of this began, I thought of MS as my own private prison. My English professor had unknowingly made me see this was wrong. MS is not something I can break out of, not some place in which I can do my time and leave. It *is* a kaleidoscope, and through it I can see the patience and understanding I possess and continue to pursue. And the reflection of the courage and love given to me by my family and friends is evident in each pattern I hold up to the light.

When All Else Fails — Hang on to Hope

by: Barbara B. McInturf

I've had multiple sclerosis for nearly twenty years now. The progression of the disease was fairly slow until the birth of my daughter six years ago. Since then I've lost all movement in my body with the exception of my head. Some would say that I had nothing to live for, but I have a different story to tell you!

I've never been one to give up on life. Even after being diagnosed with MS, I entered college and became a teacher. I went on to further my education by getting my Masters degree. When I became too weak to walk, I used an Amigo to get around at school, home, and to take me shopping. My husband, Eric, has always been the president of my support system. He gladly took me wherever I needed or wanted to go. My pregnancy was a blessed surprise for all! Praise God! Despite all odds, Megan was born healthy and naturally on December 19, 1984!

Megan's birth left me weaker than I had anticipated. Because I had lost most of my upper body strength, I could not take care of her physical needs. I could feed her if someone brought her to me; I could hold her, sing to her, and play with her, but I could not dress or change her. I was too weak to walk at all. I couldn't even use my Amigo wheelchair. My husband assumed most of the household responsibilities as well as caring for me and a new baby. Fortunately he was and is a fireman with a flexible schedule, working 24 hours in a row, and then off for 48.

During the time Eric was at work I needed help. We enlisted the assistance of home health aides. Not only were they unreliable and mostly unskilled, but they were very expensive. We tried unsuccessfully to get financial help through many sources, including our local MS Society. Needless to say, I was more depressed than I had ever been in my life. I was so useless to everyone. I hated someone else taking care of my baby. I had been such an immaculate housekeeper, and now no one could take care of my house the way I liked. And I felt so sorry for my husband. He rarely complained and did his best to cope with our new lifestyle.

After Megan was nine months old, my doctor thought I should enter Dodd Hall at Ohio State University, a rehabilitation hospital for people suffering from neurological conditions such as mine. Supposedly they had a program which would help teach me how to care for Megan by myself. I waited a month and a half to enter the hospital, only to find out when I got there that the program no longer existed. You can only imagine how disappointed Eric and I were. However we decided to have me stay for the physical therapy as well as an evaluation for a new wheelchair. I wanted an electric one so I could get around without the help of someone pushing me. The therapists decided on a chair with an elaborate lapboard because of the limited range of my arm movement. It would have to be specially made for me at Dodd Hall. Be patient, they said, because we are short staffed. A year later I got a chair with an electric system I could not use, because during that year I had lost complete use of my arms. Fortunately we could take the electric pack off the chair, and I had a more comfortable one in which to ride.

While in Dodd Hall the doctors decided I needed to be catheterized. This meant I no longer needed home health aides because they can't catheterize patients. I now needed a licensed practical nurse (LPN). My insurance company would pay for a nurse. After many months of working with people at my insurance company, Eric finally got them to agree to pay for my nurses 100% when he's at work. This definitely was an answer to our prayers for us, because our finances were in bad shape.

My spirits began to rise. I still hated others helping raise Megan, but I was doing my best to live with the situation. I was doing a lot to teach her sounds, colors, numbers, as well as reading to her often. I did my best to be at all her preschool and Sunday School functions.

She seemed (and still does seem) to be a remarkably well-adjusted child. I was becoming more assertive with the nurses. I decided that my home would be run more on my schedule than theirs. You could say I was gaining new confidence in myself.

Despite all this, there was the ever-growing need to be independent, to have something to do in my life besides being a victim of multiple sclerosis. My mind raced ahead to the day when Megan would be in school all day long. How would I fill the time?

In March of 1988 we decided to travel from Ohio to Texas to visit a good friend of mine from college. We had recently purchased a van with a wheelchair lift, making traveling easier for our family. My friend Mary is a bubbly person who works with handicapped children in Austin. She called before we left to tell me of a place in San Antonio called the Freedom Center where I could be evaluated to see if I could operate a computer using my voice or my head. I have to admit I was somewhat annoyed with her because I felt she wasn't happy with me as I was. Reluctantly, I let her make an appointment. Deep down I was scared of possibly finding an answer to my questions concerning my future.

The equipment at the Freedom Center was unlike any I had ever seen. There were computers for all types of people with disabilities. I was evaluated on two different types. With one, the therapist placed a band around my head. On the band was a long stick that had a light on the end. On the table in front of me was a large board containing alphabet letters. Whenever I wished to spell a word, I had to beam the light at a letter and it would be transferred to the computer monitor. I did very well with this. The only problem I encountered was fatigue; the head band became very heavy if I wore it for more than a half hour. I was also tested on a voice activated computer. In 1988 these types of computers were relatively new. One had to speak very loudly in order to operate this type of computer. Unfortunately the strength of my voice is unpredictable, so this kind of equipment was not recommended for me. However, the model using the light beam was thought to be one I could use. The therapist wrote a letter of recommendation for me to take to a rehabilitation counselor in hopes of getting a computer for my own use.

When we got home, my husband contacted a counselor at the Ohio Rehabilitation Services Commission. My initial counselor had us fill out many forms and explained how the system worked. He also let us know that he knew little about computers and how they could be used for people with disabilities! Ohio was years behind Texas! He also said that in order to receive any help financially from the state for rehabilitation purposes, I would have to make myself mobile. This meant that I would have to be evaluated for an electric wheelchair. He would contact an occupational therapist to begin working on my case.

I had had few dealings with state government before, so I was unprepared for the frustrations that lay ahead. The occupational therapist did come to my home, and evaluated me for not only a wheelchair, but for other devices that might be useful for me. She scheduled an appointment at a company specializing in chin-controlled wheelchairs for me to try. No one was more surprised than I when I got into that chair and could move myself around the room! My daughter looked at me and said, "It's like magic, Mommy!" The salesman made many helpful suggestions, and both he and my therapist felt I would have no trouble operating this kind of wheel-chair. This therapist also knew little about computers, and requested that I find out from the Freedom Center a place in Ohio that evaluated people like they did in Texas. In the meantime, a report was sent to my counselor concerning the type of wheelchair best suited for my condition. When my counselor finally received the report (and it seemed to take forever!), he had to write three identical purchase orders to get bids from three different vendors. Again we waited until the counselor received the lowest bid from one of the companies selected. While waiting, I became restless about the computer. By now I'd found a hospital in Dayton near my home town of Columbus that would test me as I had been tested in Texas. I don't know exactly why, but both the counselor and the therapist never followed through on this testing. Instead it was decided that I should go for a week of testing at a rehabilitation center in Columbus to discover if I had enough intelligence to operate a computer!

This was one week I'll never forget! I knew I was smart enough to use a computer and I believe my counselor did too, but he was trying to buy some time in order to figure out what to do with my case. The clients at this testing site ranged from those who really wanted a new career because of a change in his or her lifestyle, to those persons who were there only to continue getting state benefits. I was the only one there who was in a wheelchair. A nurse had to be with me to write my answers down or to do the manual tasks, because I couldn't use my arms or hands. The teachers gave me every possible intelligence test, college entrance test, and computer-related test they had available. But when it came time to see if I could actually operate a computer, this is where the testing fell short; there were *no* computers at this center! The teachers told me, "You can't expect us to have everything here!"

What was supposed to be three weeks of testing turned out only to last one week. There were no other tests to give me, so the staff decided to release me early. Another letter of recommendation was sent to my counselor, strongly endorsing me for computer usage. I found myself in the holding pattern again, waiting for someone with knowledge of this kind of technology to come through for me.

I did soon receive some good news. A vendor had been picked to build my chin-operated wheelchair! It was not the vendor of my choice, but at least progress was being made! The state decided that my insurance could pay for my chair. At first I was upset about this, because I felt if it was their rule that I must be mobile before they could help me pay for the chair. But, I finally realized that my ultimate goal was to get the computer, and I would do anything necessary to get it.

In December, two months after my testing and a month and a half after learning of the wheelchair decision, I went for my wheelchair fitting. From the beginning, I felt uncomfortable with the salesman. He seemed less than knowledgeable about the chair. I never got to sit in it and try it out. He took lots of measurements, but never adjusted anything on the chair. He promised to have it to me the week after Christmas. I asked him how much the chair would cost. He said I would pay the cost that had been quoted to the state ($12, 000) plus maybe a few hundred more for the adjustments we had decided on that day.

Christmas came and went, but no chair. I didn't call the salesman, because I figured with the holidays there had been a slow–down. In about a week I received a payment notice from my insurance company informing me that they had paid the vendor for my chair, a chair I had never received! And to top it all off, the vendor charged $6,000 more than I had been quoted at the store! My husband and I were furious! We immediately called my insurance company, informing them of the fraud. We also called my counselor at the state rehabilitation office. Was he ever surprised, because he also had been billed by the same company, even though my wheelchair was being paid through private sources. The state was just about to pay for it, and would have if they hadn't received my call. This unscrupulous vendor would have been paid twice for the same chair! I'm happy to say that this company is no longer in business!

Fortunately, the vendor of my choice picked up my case and became the builder of the wheelchair I finally bought and received in May. The two persons who designed the chair were wonderful. They were also helpful and supportive. Even though they lost money by picking up my case, I never heard a complaint, nor did they treat me as a charity case.

You can't believe how wonderful it felt to be free to get around by myself once again! For the first time in over five years I could take myself when and where I wanted to go. One of the first things I did after mastering the chin-control was take my five-year-old daughter for a walk. It was the first time we'd ever been able to go by ourselves without the aid of someone to push my wheelchair. I'll never forget how happy I was that day!

With the wheelchair here, could the computer be far behind? That summer I had a change in counselors, a change that was beneficial for me. The new counselor didn't know much more about computers than the old one, but her boss did. He was pushing for computers for people like me. Lo and behold, a new voice-activated system came on the market called *Dragon Dictate*. It was much more advanced than the one I had tried in Texas. With this model the strength of my voice didn't matter. The user wears a head band with a microphone attached, and simply says the word he wishes to write. The computer recognizes this word and prints it onto the screen. If the word isn't recognized by the computer, then the user spells the word. This system is also much faster than the one I tried in Texas. It also would be less tiresome, therefore saving energy which is less than plentiful for me on many days. The *Dragon Dictate* system sounded ideal for me!

Again I had to be evaluated for this system. The company representatives came to my home and tested me, discovering that I could use this new device. I was ecstatic! The state agreed to buy not only the computer, but also a laser printer for me! Two years after being tested in Texas I would have my computer!

It has now been six months since I've had my computer equipment. It's been a real learning process for me because I had no previous computer experience. I had twenty-six hours of training to begin with, but my teacher comes often to help me learn more as problems arise. Many manuals are written for people who can use their hands. Because I cannot, my training takes longer. My teacher often writes pages of directions for me to remember. It takes a lot of practice, but it is all worth it! Finally I can write my own thoughts to loved ones and friends without having to dictate to another person.

What do I plan to do in the future? I hope to continue to write articles for books and magazines. I hope to be able to do some editing for school book publishers when my skills improve. Because of my new wheelchair, I've been able to volunteer at Megan's school, working with her class once a week. Maybe I'll be able to write helpful suggestions for disabled teachers. I don't know what the Lord has in store for me, but I know that I have a definite future ahead of me now, and I plan to make the best of it!

We Need to Talk —
There's Something I Have to Tell You

by: *Karin Summers*

Among the multitude of problems confronting people with multiple sclerosis is how to handle and form new relationships. Along with that is the problem of when and how to talk about your condition to someone you are becoming involved with romantically. Many articles have been written that give guidelines and suggestions; while these are helpful, when it comes right down to it, we have only our instincts and our consciences to guide us. I hope my story, one version of many being played out daily, will be helpful to anyone struggling with the same dilemma.

My story began in early autumn, 1990. Placing an ad in a singles magazine was part of my grand plan, my New Year's resolution for 1990: to launch an all-out effort to find a man. If this didn't work, I told myself, I must face the dim reality that I might be spending the rest of my life alone. I resorted to placing the ad because I had few other alternatives. I refused to impose on friends or relatives for a fix-up. I don't frequent bars. I was so busy at work that I had little time for new activities in which I might meet available people.

Everything in my world, except my love life, seemed to be going right. I had finished graduate school, found a good job, and my MS was in remission. In fact, I had no visible signs that anything at all was wrong with me. Except for some numbness in my right hand on some days, I almost forgot that I had it.

I had been shaken by the MS — completely undone, as a matter of fact. The memory of the total helplessness and despair I had felt when confined to a wheelchair in the hospital, and later slowly recovering at home, haunted me. I remember thinking my life was over, or at least would never be the same.

So once my strength miraculously returned (I thought it was a miracle, indeed!), I was overjoyed with my slightest accomplishments. Everything was a miracle, but I continued to worry. How normal was I? Was I normal in the sense of being able to participate in an intimate relationship? Would I be able to perform, to keep up?

I wanted to be whole again, and in my mind, a relationship symbolized that wholeness. Healthy, normal people have relationships, and I wanted one. I was a "couples person." You know the type — people who blossom in a relationship and do their best as part of a couple. I'd gotten over thinking my need for connection was a disability; finally able to accept this about myself, I was determined to do something about it.

It wasn't as if I hadn't done just fine alone, because I had. Since my divorce eight years previously, since my last serious relationship four years ago, and since my diagnosis two years ago, I had managed quite well. But, something was missing, and I wanted to have it again. I wanted to feel alive, like a whole woman. I wanted to fall in love just one more time.

What kind of a person would accept me with these limitations, I wondered? But more importantly, who would accept me with the threat of possible future limitations? I knew I'd have to tell this person about my MS sooner or later. Though a myriad of worries and feelings occupied my thoughts, it didn't hold me back. I figured, like Scarlet O'Hara, I would think about it another day.

So, I began my search with an optimistic attitude. Placing a personal ad wasn't easy, but actually phoning the men who responded to my ad was hardest of all. I was calling total strangers, laying myself on the line, so to speak. And I struggled with the realization that there was more to me than met the eye. I had no idea how I would handle that.

Usually, after a lengthy phone call, I and my latest dating game candidate would arrange to meet in a public place. I found that no matter how promising the initial conversation had been, within thirty seconds of our meeting, I knew if this was someone who interested me or not.

Call it chemistry, or whatever; I knew what I was looking for. I wanted that zing that happens when you hit it off with somebody right away. I wanted that attraction, that immediate sense of comfort and familiarity. Remembering how it had happened several times in the past, I was sure it existed, and I wanted it again.

But, after more and more of these "blind dates," I was becoming discouraged. Let me make one thing clear: I did not meet one single creep this way. These men were very nice, respectful, even funny. But I just hadn't made that love connection. Then came Bud. He was the ninth, maybe tenth man I met this way, his letter being one of the most promising I'd singled out from the three dozen responses I'd received.

For some reason, after our first phone conversation, which lasted three hours, I broke the cardinal rule of personal ad dating. Instead of arranging to meet in a safe public place, I told him to pick me up at my apartment, since we planned to do something near where I lived. I felt secure, I told him, adding with a laugh, "If you were a felon or a pervert, I think I would have figured that out by now."

Saturday at noon he rang the bell. I took one last look in the mirror to fluff my hair, buzzed him into the building and went to the open stairway to greet him. As the phrase goes, "Our eyes met..." and I knew immediately this was someone interesting. As I would tell him much later, "I knew I liked you before you were half-way up my stairs." He had a great smile and bright beautiful eyes. We joked a little to relieve the tension and then left for our scheduled walk on the lake front.

Up to now, these personal ad "dates" usually lasted about an hour with the usual scenario of small talk, lunch or a drink, and then saying the usual dishonest, polite things like: "It's been nice meeting you," or "Maybe we should get together soon," etc., etc.

Then I'd sigh as I headed for my car and thought "How often must I go through this?" Or, "I've had it. I'm never doing that again!" But the next week I'd look over those letters just one more time and start dialing.

Well, my first date with Bud lasted ten hours! We walked on the lake front, talking non-stop, laughing and having fun. At one point during the walk he nonchalantly took my hand. It was a little chilly that day, so he put my hand and his into his jacket pocket. Then after a while he switched sides and did the same thing with our other hands.

"Why do I feel like we've been doing this for a long time already?" he asked. And I had to admit I felt that way too. By the time the night ended, we realized we had a great deal in common and had talked about everything, absolutely everything, except for one little thing.

For the next week and a half we sent a torrent of cards back and forth to make up for the fact that, due to previous commitments, we would not be able to see each other. When we finally did get together again, the chemistry was there, stronger than ever. Bud came right to the point. He wanted to be part of a couple. He was looking for a serious relationship.

Both he and I had been looking for some time, so I knew it wasn't desperation that motivated either of us. He was as determined as I was to settle for nothing less than that right and special person. And this was something special. Bud made it clear, he was as smitten as I was, and things began moving very quickly. While I was happy and excited, I was also scared.

I began to have feelings of near panic, thinking maybe I was just kidding myself. Maybe I couldn't really do this. Maybe he would be disappointed. Maybe, once I told him, he would say he couldn't handle it.

After the next date I realized I had to be honest with this man, and I had to do it quickly. He wanted to be involved with me, and was already talking "...for the rest of our lives" involved. I knew for sure that before we became intimate I had to tell him everything.

Some of the articles I had read said that one way to handle the issue was to wait until you know the person well. Maybe by that time they will have seen what you can do instead of your limitations. Good advice in some instances, but not in this one.

Another article said you should plan everything from what you say to how and where you say it. Don't do it haphazardly or jokingly. Be straightforward, honest and calm. I remember it saying if you act upset, the person you are telling will also get upset. If you are saying it's not a big deal, you need to prove it by your behavior; show them by how you talk about it that it really doesn't have to be the focal point of the relationship.

This made more sense to me. I was not limited in any way by the MS, though that guaranteed nothing in the future. I wanted to do this right, giving him accurate and realistic information.

I have always closely guarded this little secret of mine. That was important to me because many people had treated me differently after I was diagnosed, either like a helpless invalid, or as though I had something they didn't want to catch. I knew I did not want to deal with that again. So I never mentioned it to new friends or to employers. And I never discussed it much, even with people who did know. It was a very small part of my life.

My dilemma, in that I had known him for such a short time, meant we did not have a track record of being able to solve problems together. Why did this have to be our first problem? Scared as I was,

I made up my mind that I had to play it straight. How would he feel, I reasoned, if I put off telling him until we were more involved? How could he ever trust me in the future if I withheld this information now? I knew I wouldn't be able to live with myself.

So there really was no choice. The next time we got together I went over to his apartment. This would be perfect, a private place, so there would be no interruptions. Before we did or said anything, I got right to the point.

"Bud, we need to talk. There's something I have to tell you," I began. "It's about my health." I was following directions from the article. It said to tell the story calmly and honestly.

"You know," he said, "I was going to ask about that. We seem to have talked about everything else, and I wanted to talk about our health too. So, it's good you brought that up. Both of my parents died of cancer and it's something I worry about. I just thought you should know about that."

"Well, I'm glad you feel that way. It makes this a little easier, because I have a problem, too. First of all, let me say it's nothing terminal and I'm not contagious, but it is something I will have to deal with for the rest of my life. Do you know what multiple sclerosis is?"

He said he thought it was something like muscular dystrophy or something to do with the muscles, but he wasn't sure. I then told him about MS, and he listened intently, asking questions now and then. When we finished the question and answer session, he sat for a minute in silence. I expected the worst.

"You know," he finally said, "this could actually be a good thing for us. It will make us take things slower and enjoy everything we do. I'm always in a hurry, wanting to do too much. This could make us take our time and sort of force us to have a more sensible and slowed down lifestyle."

The rush I felt at that moment was relief. Bud was understanding and accepting then, and as our relationship has developed, his initial acceptance has been reaffirmed again and again. I am forever thankful that I risked total honesty, because it has paid off unbelievably.

I'm not saying we haven't had some of the usual relationship problems experienced by most people, because we certainly have. We are the same as most divorced people trying to start over with someone new, both bringing a lot of baggage with us from our past. It may sound strange, but what makes me happiest is that neither of us has ever avoided discussing something that's bothering us. He doesn't treat me like I'm less than a whole person, or too frail to handle a disagreement. He has never been afraid to express an opposing opinion or to ask questions, getting to the heart of what is on his mind. And neither have I.

For example, when we were just getting to know each other, we did many active and rather strenuous things that were sometimes tiring for me. When I got tired and wanted to rest, Bud would ask if something was wrong, or was I acting tired because I was losing interest in him. Each time I would patiently remind him that some days, because of the MS, I would simply be tired. It was as uncomplicated as that. Now, when I'm tired he just takes a nap with me.

While the hopeless romantic side of me likes to think we were made for each other and this was meant to be, another side of me believes it's just a matter of pure luck. Had Bud been a different kind of person, not so tolerant, understanding, and open minded, my story would have a different ending. I know, no matter how well I would have told my story, no matter what a good job I did explaining the circumstances, another kind of person would have walked away from the situation. So I can't help but feel lucky.

We have just celebrated one year together. Bud is a kind, considerate, respectful man. We have a lot in common, and a mutual respect for our differences. I think that is rare. We do so many active things together, like photography, which usually means long hikes to get that perfect picture. We love boating and have spent many summer weekends taking the boat to any lake within a reasonable distance. We love to shop, especially antique sales, used book stores, and art galleries.

Just last week, as we discussed our future once again, I reintroduced the topic of my illness. I told him I still worry that my condition might worsen, and some day I might not be able to work or do many of the things I do now. I seem to have this need to remind him, as if I expect him to come to his senses one day and bolt; and if that's going to happen, I want it to happen now. Bud's answer is plain and simple.

"Something could happen to me too, you know. I don't have an especially safe job; I could get hurt someday and not be able to work again. Or I could get sick. There are no guarantees. We'd manage."

And yes, things have changed. The torrent of cards has been reduced to a trickle. But they still arrive. We still talk about whatever is on our minds, though less, since most things have been talked through and are settled. Now whenever something comes up, we make a "talk appointment." All relationships mellow with age, and ours has begun to do that.

Today it feels good, but I remain realistic. I guess we all reach a stage when life has dealt us so many surprises and disappointments we finally abandon our childish wish for total security. That's about where I am. I know things change, and I know life offers no guarantees. If MS has taught me anything, it's that.

It's also taught me to roll with the punches, make the best of things, and appreciate what I have.

So, for the time being, everything is fine. I'm not sure where I would be had I not met Bud. The optimist in me says someone else would have come along. The realist in me says, I'm not so sure. All I know is, right now, today, I would not trade my life for anyone's.

But You "Look" So Good

by: *Kathy Young*

How can I make you understand? Actually,
why would I even try?
I may *"look"* good to the average person,
but really, sometimes, I just want to cry.

You can *look* at me, and what you see is a
person in a chair.
You may think, "What's wrong with her? Why
doesn't she get up and out of there?"

I've learned to become an actress, of sorts,
— on the stage just playing my role.
But, oh what a difference you would see — if
you could look deep into my soul.

There are days I feel so awful — days I just
want to throw in the towel.
I cry, complain, moan, and sulk — in general,
all I do is growl.

The sun comes up on a brand new day — it's
time to put on my mask.
What I have to do now — getting ready for this
day, is, of itself, quite a task.

I take a bath, brush my teeth, put in my contacts
and put on my clothes.
This all sounds simple enough, you say, but
the time it takes *me* — God only knows!

I HATE hearing the phrase — "But you *look* so
good. You really do look well."
But if the truth were known, I'd rather hear
that, than hear "You sure look like hell."

I have had MS for several years now — I'm
still waiting for the cure.
But I'm not going to give up without a fight,
— and of *THAT* you can be sure!!!

What Others Take for Granted —
Taking a Bath and Washing Their Hair

How do I take a bath? *What* is that you say?
All I do is jump in the shower — and then I'm
on my way.

How *long* does it take me? Is that the
question you ask?
Oh, an hour at the *very* most — and that will
finish that task.

Another question you want answered? How long
does it take me to dress?
Well, not long at all, quick as a wink, three
minutes, I would guess.

Now — all these questions I find quite amusing,
but I've really got to jam.
Grab me a shower, wash my hair, and out the
door I'll scram!

A-a-a-ah! The memories of times gone by —
when I could do the same.
But to hurry now — to hurry at all, is only
a pretend game.

Yes, times have changed, and — it's time to
awake from my dream.
It's a brand new day, God loves me — and
things aren't as bad as they seem.

So you can jump in a shower and hurry real
fast — what's the big rush anyway?
When you are *forced* to slow down, you have
time to enjoy — the start of a brand new
day!!!

It's All in Your Head

by: Joan Cottle

My arms feel like lead, my fingers like wood.
"Have you ever tried Yoga? I think that you should."

My voice is so shaky, I sound drunk when I speak.
"You need to relax, stay off work for a week."

My balance has gone, I can't sit up or walk.
"You should see a therapist and have a good talk."

My eyes can't see clearly, my vision is blurred.
"So have your eyes tested, you're being absurd."

But you don't understand, I'm wetting the bed.
"You are just over-anxious, it's all in your head."

Many months later, my life in a mess,
He looks at the floor when he says "It's MS."

Hello Out There

by: Jody H. Wrightson

I was diagnosed with MS in 1976, at the age of 25. I spent several days in the hospital undergoing a series of tests, all of which came back normal, with the exception of the spinal tap. After repeating that test to ensure against lab error, the doctors woke me up from a nap, told me what I had, and sent me home the same day. I had been terrified that I had a cancerous tumor which would rapidly kill me, so the diagnosis of MS was actually a relief. Although I was afraid of cancer, I distinctly remember telling my parents several days before I went to the hospital that I thought I had MS. It's rather eerie the way I seemed to sense what was wrong; I knew nothing about the disease, other than it was one of those nebulous crippling diseases. I was started on a course of prednisone and sent home, where I slowly regained my ability to walk. My mother said at the time that it reminded her of my attempts at walking as a toddler.

The first neurologist I went to after leaving the hospital very bluntly told me at my first appointment that I could expect to live another 30 years, 15 of which I would be up walking around. The doctor who had pronounced the diagnosis told me virtually nothing about the disease. Thus, knowing nothing about MS, this new doctor's words upset me, to say the least. I think more upsetting than the words was the matter-of-fact way in which he just threw them at me. I do not think I fully comprehended what he was telling me; at that point I was feeling fine, and he was telling me it couldn't last. I determined to prove him wrong.

For many years I led a relatively normal life, aside from minor bladder and fatigue problems. If I did have any exacerbations, I would take prednisone or ACTH, and it would bring me back into remission. I was told by two doctors that I would probably always have a mild form of the disease. I became a bit concerned at one point when my neurologist did a myelogram to see why my bladder problems were more severe than my overall level of disability. The spinal fluid revealed that the disease was active, even though I had manifested no other symptoms whatsoever. I underwent a round of prednisone, and things were fine. I did not fully comprehend that the disease could be working on me without my feeling any different.

My method of coping during all those years was probably what would be called denial. I wasn't ready to cope with what might happen in the future, and as I said, I didn't fully comprehend that the disease was silently eating away at more of my myelin sheathing, even when I didn't feel badly. I went on about my life; I had never been a very physically active person, so nothing much ever really changed. I did the usual avoidance of heat, and dealing with bladder problems, but otherwise lived my life basically normally.

I went on working and going to school for many years, and in the summer of 1990, took and passed the general exams for my Ph.D. I wrote for twenty hours, and faced two hours of oral examination by my committee. I had begun having difficulties that spring, but thought they were largely due to the stress of facing the exams, and that once I was finished with them, I would begin healing. Although I took a round of ACTH treatment right before my oral exams, I continued to worsen. I will never forget the day of the orals; I was walking with a cane, but the heat and my nerves combined to make it difficult for me to walk down the hall to the room where they were to be held. My advisor saw that I was having difficulty, so she and another member of my committee came down the hall and helped me walk into the room. Then, when the orals were over, instead of sending me out of the room while they decided if I passed, which is normal procedure, the committee left the room!

Still, I continued to worsen, until in September 1990, I fell. I had fallen many times before and never really hurt myself, but this time was different; I dislocated my shoulder. I reluctantly decided it was time for me to do more sitting than standing. Then, through a series of events too numerous to go into, I ended up where I am today, which is unable to walk, with pressure sores on my feet and ankles, and with a bone infection which almost cost me part of my right leg.

So, as my former coping mechanism of denial has been forced to give way to the stark confrontation that I am seriously ill, there are major ways in which my life has changed. The main factor which overrides all others is fear. Despite knowing intellectually that one has a disease like MS, having had more than thirteen years of relatively normal living does not prepare one for the day when body and health start deteriorating at a relatively rapid pace, especially when your coping mechanism has always been to ignore the disease and go on about living. It seems as though when the disease started to worsen, it gathered steam. For me, it reached a point where my life was no longer recognizable as my own. It feels as though the disease controls me, and I'm just along for the ride, waiting to see where it will take me next. And though I do not feel I will die any time soon, the worsening symptoms (and the fact that I just turned 40) have led me to believe that my age is working against my getting better. My own mortality increasingly stares me in the face, and it frightens me more every day.

Under this umbrella of fear are several major ways in which my life has changed. The first of these is loss of privacy. One loses the sense of autonomy, the ability to care for oneself. Needing to be helped into and out of the shower and bed, having catheters put in and taken out, needing to be cleaned by someone else after bowel and bladder mishaps, being asked the most personal questions repeatedly by medical personnel and the like, take away any sense that one is one's own person. It is hard to maintain any sense of dignity through all this when one is laid bare in front of everyone, both metaphorically and literally.

A second major consequence of the disease's progression, in my case at least, is loss of self-identity and self-confidence. Again, the ability to live a fairly normal life made me feel like a pretty "normal" person. My work and home life defined who I was; I was what I could do. Becoming incapacitated has left me wondering who I am if I can't do what I used to do and want to do. What is living in a body that won't and can't do much make me? Before, I was a wife, a scholar, an employee, etc. What am I now? While it's true that I am still technically all those things (with the possible exception of an employee if I don't improve), my sense of self has been turned upside down. I've had to completely restructure my identity, a process I'm still struggling with. Because of that, my self-confidence has dropped to the bottom because I'm not sure what self to be confident in. And if one didn't have a lot of confidence to begin with, as I didn't, the job is even tougher.

A third major area in which MS affects me is in terms of the scope of my life. It has become very narrow, very "bottom line." Where my days used to be filled with activity, with accomplishing what I considered important things, they now seem to revolve around bodily functions and just maintaining basic life. Everything I can do takes twice as long as it used to, and there are so many things I can no longer do, some because I can't physically do them, and some because all the things I have to do take so much time and energy that there's little time or energy for anything else. There is so much I want to do, personally and professionally, that it frustrates me endlessly since I now seem able to do so little. It sounds like a cliché, but there are so many things we take for granted, that when they're no longer possible, it's amazing the insight we gain into what's important and what isn't. I guess if there's a positive side to all this, that's it. I look at people and their preoccupations now, and marvel that they care so much about what seems so trivial to me. In some ways I resent their wasting time worrying about such unimportant matters, and in some ways I'm jealous of what I consider such carefree existence.

Right now, my days consist of bed rest and taking care of bodily functions, and what little energy and time are left are split between trying to maintain a house and do some sort of meaningful endeavors, such as working on my dissertation. The dissertation is all that stands between me and the goal for which I've worked so long and hard, and the thought of not being able to finish it terrifies me. In terms of maintaining the house, my husband and a home health aide take care of it, but there are so many times I wish I could just get up and do things myself. And I've never liked housework!

The area more important than any other is the fourth facet of living with MS. Changes in relationships are sometimes the result of MS, and sometimes can bring on MS–related problems. In this area, I've been very fortunate because my husband and family have gone above and beyond the norm in standing by me and in taking care of me. I know there is a great deal of fear and frustration they cope with too. I don't know what I would have done without them, especially my husband. He comforts me, cares for my physical needs, and kicks me in the butt when he thinks I need it. In short, he's kept me going when I wasn't sure I could go on. And just as my world has narrowed, so has his. He gets very little time to himself, and even when he's able to get out and away from the house, he still worries about me. I worry a lot about how long a marriage can survive under the weight of what my life has become.

But as I said, I'm *very* lucky; I've heard stories about people whose spouses leave them, even when they are first diagnosed. I don't understand how someone could do something like that to a person they claim to love. I can't imagine how devastating it would be to discover one has a disease like MS, and then have one's world turned upside down again by a spouse walking out on them.

Friendship is another type of relationship that is affected by MS. Someone with any serious disease or injury finds out quickly who his/her friends are. In my case, there seem to be several classes into which friends fall. There are those who are there for you no matter what, who make an effort to stay in touch, to do things for and with you, and who show concern. Then there are those friends who make a token effort; they are there for a real crisis situation, but then you don't hear from them again for months. And finally, there are those who really can't or won't be bothered with it at all.

I discovered this when I was first diagnosed, but again, the years of "normal" life faded the memories, and I have had to relearn the lesson during the last year and a half. I know there are some people who can't deal with illness at all, and I'm sure it gets tiresome to always hear about health problems, but the fact that there are people who hang in there through it all make those who don't blatantly obvious. Again, I do not understand how someone who claims to be a friend can just walk away. Sometimes, all I've wanted or needed is a card or a phone call or a small trip out to get ice cream, and yet it seems too much to expect from some people who used to be your friends. I think one key to it is that a disabled person is an inconvenience; to actually do something with them takes too much time and energy, and I think that it hardly seems worth it to many people.

These are just four major areas in which MS affects my life. I strongly suspect they are issues, along with many others, with which most MS patients deal. Today, although I may still have the bone infection, the wounds on my feet are healing, and I'm actually gaining some strength in my entire body. The consensus among the home care nurse and the physical therapist who see me is that if I can heal the pressure sores on my feet and get into a therapeutic pool, I may have a chance of walking again. Although I intend to give it my best shot, I realize that it may not happen, or if it does, my walking days may still be numbered. In short, it's been a long, slow process, but perhaps I've learned a little about acceptance of the disease; at the very least I hope I now realize how precious little triumphs can be.

MS and Me

by: *Yvonne A. Fischer*

A Moment of Change

When I saw the sadness on Dr. Peterson's face, I realized that he knew what was wrong with me. He motioned for me to sit in the high-backed chair directly across from his desk. I sat, leaning my cane up against the wall and set my purse on the floor. Dr. Peterson sat down across from me.

His hands made quick movements straightening papers on the top of the desk. He cleared his throat as he looked me in the eye.

I looked down. My hands had collapsed together, fingers entwined tightly, like my subconscious mind was desperately praying for me to wake up and realize that this has all been a bad dream. The silence roared.

The left side of my face started twitching. The doctor started speaking. His voice seemed to be echoing from far away, yet he was sitting less that four feet away from me.

"The MRI shows lesions throughout your brain matter which have been diagnosed as multiple sclerosis." That's all I heard.

A daze paralyzed me. I could see his lips moving, but I couldn't hear the words. I wanted to speak, to say no, that can't be so, but my throat had closed up like a new seal on a drafty door.

I gulped, then coughed, and covered my mouth with my good hand. Dr. Peterson stopped talking and looked at me as if studying my face. He asked me if I was okay. My head moved from side to side, but the word "yes" came from my mouth.

"Go home. Do as little as possible. See me in a month." Dr. Peterson rose and came around the desk to the door, his hand resting on the knob. He paused before opening the door, as if he wanted to say he was sorry there was nothing more that he could do to help me.

My body rose and went out the opened door, down the long hallway to where the receptionist would schedule my appointment.

Wordlessly, I walked out of the medical complex to my car. As I pulled my keys from my purse and unlocked the car door, a horn sounded. I looked towards the sound. A woman driving a Cadillac wanted my parking place. I nodded, letting her know I understood.

I placed my body behind the wheel, started the car and backed out of the sought-after parking place. I drove carefully out onto the street, keeping out of the way of all the other people going about their normal lives.

That Explains It

Okay, now I know what's wrong with this body of mine. It had a name. It even had initials. But what was it? And why did I have it? There was no trace of MS in my family.

For the next seventy-two hours, I reviewed my entire thirty-five years. Flashes of memories of me being twelve and falling down for no reason; my problem of walking on uneven ground explained away as clumsiness when I was a child; why my arms and legs would jerk for no known reason.

I went to the local library and read every book on MS they had. I hungered for knowledge. I needed to be able to help myself. I asked the librarian to borrow any books I had heard about from larger libraries in the state.

I devoured all available data. I always left hungry. I wanted to rid my body of this suffering. I hated the days when I couldn't walk, couldn't see, and couldn't speak clearly. I hated having MS.

It's My Problem

The reaction of friends and family surprised me. My mother acted "like it was no big deal." Two siblings couldn't face me. My husband didn't believe I had MS, or that anything was wrong with me. My friends would comment, "But you look so good."

I learned quickly that it was up to me to make others feel comfortable with my illness. I played mind games with myself to buoy myself up — one of my favorite phrases to use when I would slowly maneuver my body through a crowd and everyone "seemed" to be aware of my gait problem was to say — "I can handle gray hair, and I can handle wrinkles, but this MS is for the birds."

When I first had health problems (prior to diagnosis) and could no longer work an 8-hour shift, I was "let go" after twelve years of employment in middle management. The day was March 24, 1986. The economy in my county was at an all-time low.

My world was a cruel place. My doctors told me I should do as little as possible, stay home, and collect full disability. Word spread that I suffered from an inexplicable disease. No one would hire me. I needed a job. My savings were gone. My medical bills alone were more debt than I ever had in my entire life. I applied for all jobs within a 60-mile radius. No one would hire me. Bill collectors started calling. My car's transmission broke, and I didn't have money to get it fixed. A tornado damaged my home. A close friend committed suicide. My husband started staying out late every night. My life was hell.

Why do Bad Things Happen to Good People?

Search me. Somehow I got through it all. I forced myself to think positive thoughts, and to listen to myself and not to others. I continually focused myself on what I was capable of doing and what I did have in my life.

I started up my own business late in 1986, and now have a thriving tax preparation and business consulting business in my home town.

My finances have turned around, as has my marriage.

I am a much more private person than before. I have a fear about being around a lot of moving people, but I can't bring myself to say, "Don't you see the invisible wall protecting me?" Or to wear a sign that says: "Fragile — Please Don't Bump."

My mind works much faster and better than my body. I rise above the physical limitations when I work at my desk and focus in on a new challenge.

So How do I do It?

One of the most recent things that finally soaked into my thick head is regardless of what I eat, or what I do, how emotional I may be, or how much I laugh, or cry — the MS is not going to go away! Nor will I go into remission as a result of changing any of my behaviors or attitudes. The MS just doesn't recognize my efforts.

On bad days — I try to work. Last year (1991) I had to cancel three days out of a possible 200, or thereabouts. Not a bad percentage.

If vision problems occur, I can still work if I cover my left eye (I've been meaning to get an eye patch) — the paralysis has never affected my thumbs and index fingers which enables me to use a phone, and in my own jerky way, write.

My ire rises when the paralysis affects my speech and my face, and I no longer am able to work. On these days, I hate the MS.

I talk to myself a lot on those days.

My intellectual self tells my depressed emotional self that the next day will be better, and if not, then the next day after that. I allow myself to do only what I can do on those days and not to worry about what's not getting done. I've learned to not be a Rock of Gibraltar all of the time.

Communication with my loved ones is so important. I've learned it's okay to ask personal things of my husband and my sisters, a close friend or two, and my secretary (but not the rest of my staff).

⁌ ⚎✦⚎ ⁍

Once upon a time, say half a life ago, when my rebellious attitude peaked, I mocked rules; now I accept the rules as my own. I am no longer the slave, but the master.

We tend to live too far within self-imposed limits. What living with MS has given me is to make me familiar with areas out of the comfort zone I had lived in my first thirty-five years.

My life is full and fulfilling. I make a difference in my community. I'm productive and continue to grow. Places have filled I never knew were empty or even knew existed. I'm stronger than ever — emotionally, spiritually, and intellectually. I pray for a cure — but meanwhile — I've got a life to live.

Reflections

by: Marybeth Bland

I sit on the grass, watching the people travel the path around Green Lake. Most people are walking slowly, chatting with the person who walks beside them. Others ride bicycles, run, or roller-skate. Everyone looks carefree. I long to travel with them, to feel the energy in my legs. It has been almost three years since I have traveled the path around Green Lake. Three years since I last climbed on my bike and pedaled the back roads around Seattle, feeling the wind as it whips through my hair.

I long for the days when I could release my anger and energy with long bike rides, or by running as fast as I could down the streets, my legs pumping and energy surging throughout my body. I used to be so physically active. My weekends were filled with long walks, swimming in the local pool, and endless hours spent on my bike. Now I have MS, and my life has changed completely. Fatigue has been my constant companion. It is a bone-tiring fatigue. A feeling that can send me to bed for the whole day, even after I have slept soundly for 12 hours. It is a fatigue that has forced me to quit work and live on a disability stipend.

Fatigue is not all that makes it difficult for me to exercise. My legs are weak. The 3-mile walk around Green Lake is now impossible. Walking a block is more in my league. Even that can be difficult on a bad day.

I envy all those people traveling around the lake. They seem so happy. My life is so different than theirs. I am constantly reminded of my disease, and the limitations it imposes on me. It would be so nice to have a week to do whatever I wanted, and not have to be reminded of my disease. I would go on a long bike ride and walks with my husband and friends. I'd stay up late, making love in front of the fire.

When morning came I'd awake full of energy, ready to start the day. How I would cherish that week!

A large brown dog suddenly runs by, his tail wagging. A small blond boy runs after him. I smile and lay back on the grass, staring at the clouds as they blow by. I close my eyes and visualize myself as a healthy person with strong legs and no fatigue. It is a peaceful visualization; one that I do often. I had read somewhere that visualizations can help the body to heal itself. I am not sure if it works, but it relaxes me and does no damage to my body.

A slow breeze begins to stir, and I feel chilled. I sit up and decide to head back to my car. The car is parked across the street. I was lucky today to find a spot so near the lake. Some days there are no spots within walking distance for me, and I must go home and forget my day by the lake.

I am content as I head to the car. Contentment is different for me these days. Being free of MS exacerbations, having days with some energy, and time spent with my husband and friends fills me with peace. At times, I am frustrated because I do not have the energy to pursue my career. Instead, I look at it as ways to explore new alternatives. I want to make the most of my life. No one knows how long I will be able to walk, or what the future holds for me. I know I must live in the moment, for the moment is all I have. Each day I do the most I can with that day, and I am thankful for the days to come.

❦

The Diagnosis

I sat in the doctor's office, listening to him speak. The words entered my brain, but I could not process them. I clutched onto the arms of the chair, my fingernails scraping the wood. My husband sat next to me, his face white and devoid of any expression. Could he make sense of the doctor's words?

I thought back to what had brought me to this room today. It had all began the day after Christmas, 1987. I awoke feeling as if I was coming down with another sinus infection. My one eye felt puffy and tender to the touch. As the day progressed, I began to lose partial sight in my eye. It was as if someone had placed a round black circle over the middle of my pupil, erasing all the middle vision. I remember how I thought I must have a brain tumor, and I was going to die. I told no one of this fear, and instead hurried to my doctor's office. After examining me, he could find nothing wrong, and referred me to my eye doctor. I knew, though, something was wrong. Something was dreadfully wrong! After a quick examination, the eye doctor told me that I had optic neuritis.

"What would cause this?" I asked.

"It is a symptom of multiple sclerosis, but don't worry; you are too old for that. If this strikes again, you should be tested for MS." He gave me some medication, and told me to return in a week.

I did worry, though, because I knew something was wrong with my body. It was just little differences, a tingling sensation in my legs, electric-like currents in my spine, sometimes fatigue would set in for no apparent reason.

I decided to see a neurologist. The appointment was set up for the end of January. During that time, my eyesight returned, and I decided nothing was wrong. I *did* keep the appointment.

After the neurologist examined me, he told me that he wanted to have an MRI test done to rule out MS. The day the test result came in his office called, stating he wanted to see me the next day. I knew then that something was wrong. Since he wanted to see me right away, I decided I must have a brain tumor, and not MS. If it was MS, I felt he would have waited to tell me at our scheduled visit two weeks hence. So here I sat, listening to the doctor explain why he had ordered more tests. My fingernails scraped deeper into the wood.

"Please hurry," I thought." Just tell me what is wrong." And then I heard the words: "You have multiple sclerosis."

I uttered a sigh of relief. It was not a brain tumor. I could handle MS. My disease would be mild. It would not interfere with anything. I needed to tell myself that. I had to have some control.

I looked over at my husband. He seemed a little calmer now that the diagnosis had been given. "It is OK," I thought. "Mine would be an easy disease."

The doctor gave me a book to read about living with MS, and set up an appointment for me to return in a month's time. My husband and I went home, speaking not a word of the disease. "It could be worse," we said to each other.

While my husband made dinner, I called my parents. "It is not a brain tumor," I said. "It is just MS." I made it sound as insignificant as possible. It was important to hold onto that thought.

Two days later, I broke down and cried. My thoughts became obsessed with the disease. I could think of nothing else. My dreams were filled with people in wheelchairs. Suddenly I realized I was no longer in control of my body. Maybe I never was.

Disclosure

by: Bridget Shaw

I left the examining room where the diagnosis of multiple sclerosis had just been given to me. In the waiting room, those whom I loved with an intensity strong enough to sustain me through the changes and compromises which were to come both to me and to them, awaited my return. My husband, Jim, held Emily, who at the age of one had an innate joy about her that was to remain as a constant source of happiness to us. Beside them, playing on the toy-strewn floor, was my lovely, soft Annie, three, my Annie with the golden hair. The knowledge of the impact this uncertain disease might have on all our lives struck me with a force that was physical. When I murmured the words describing the disease I had long suspected, when I established that after ten years of botched diagnoses and periods of physical illness, my symptoms did indeed have a name, Jim's response took me aback." Well, there goes your career in championship tennis."

Say — he had a point. A good, actually a damn good point. I had always been totally inept at things athletic, and had been disinterested in them as well. My personal and professional interests were independent of excellent coordination. In Jim's reasonable, humorous answer, I found both hope and determination enough to believe that, together, we could transcend this shared pain. Although I didn't fully realize it at the time, telling Jim that I had MS was the beginning of a very long process: the process of informing others of my disease, and the many facets in my years of deciding when, and if, to do so. This is the story of the process which I chose.

Initially, the problem of how to tell people of my condition was simple. Because my MS was "invisible" except for a barely perceptible limp, I decided to tell no one for the time being. I reasoned that because I had had the disease for ten years prior to the diagnosis, and was classified as a mild case, there was a good chance that I would not be badly disabled. My life was full: I was blessed with a brilliant, funny, and devoted husband, I had two beautiful children, I enjoyed my part-time work on the counseling staff of a community college, and I found time for volunteer work with the American Cancer Society. I was unwilling to surrender any of it to multiple sclerosis. I wanted my children to learn of it from Jim and me when they were old enough to understand it. My greatest fear was that they would learn of it from someone else, perhaps from a playmate who had overheard their parents' talking. No. Definitely better to wait. I realized from the start the ramifications of divulging that I had acquired MS.

The dynamics of admitting my illness were not simple. I did not want to worry my elderly father, who had been ill for several years. He had always been easily worried, and was apt to see only the darkest aspect of any scenario. My mother, a refined and stoic woman, was devoted to him and solely responsible for his care. To add to the burden of his worsening emphysema and depression was out of the question. The next logical conclusion was that nobody in my hometown where my parents still lived could be told, lest news of my MS get back to them. For the next few years, in retrospect, my solution was both workable and appropriate.

In 1984, Jim accepted a job with Bell Laboratories in New Jersey. My gait had worsened noticeably, and in our last few months in Maryland I used arthritis to explain my difficulty walking. Making excuses to others became increasingly uncomfortable for me. I left without telling anyone that I had multiple sclerosis. To this day, no one knows, and I must admit that my reasons for not telling anyone were not entirely altruistic. In order to confide the details of my health, I would have been required to have the emotional stamina to deal with others' reactions to the facts. Even now, when my friends from so many years ago come to mind, it is somehow a comfort to be thought of as whole, as the way I used to be. It is my only concession to vanity, I think. I hope so.

Our first few years in our new home were busy with the activity and happy confusion that only children can bring. I volunteered to teach conversational French to my daughter's nursery school class as I had done in Maryland, and was the class mother for my daughter Ann's first grade class. Knowing that the time might come when I would be unable to do so, I volunteered for every activity with my children I could, hoping that the memories of our happiness then would remain fresh.

After an exacerbation in 1985 left me with foot-drop, I began using a simple leg orthosis. I also confided my diagnosis to my younger sister, Leslie, who lives in Washington. Her response was the unqualified love which I had always counted on and received. I trusted her implicitly not to tell the family and, true to form, she did not. I also informed my darling sister-in-law and her husband, and their response was touching: "I just want you to be all right!"

When a cane was recommended by my physical therapist, my attempts to conceal my growing disability became increasingly wearing. I was beginning to dread meeting new people for fear they would guess and badger poor Jim with questions after each social engagement. "Did anyone say anything? Do you think they suspect?" I asked.

I confided the truth to my close friend, Linda, afraid she might start to think of me largely in terms of MS and disability. Two days later she called with an interesting and funny anecdote about a recent PTA meeting. We both laughed a great deal; no mention was made of multiple sclerosis. I will always be grateful for that phone call, always aware of how lucky I have been to have such outstanding men and women care for me.

Ann and Emily were now in the second and fifth grades, respectively, and becoming increasingly curious and concerned. I sat with them and told them the facts as succinctly as I was able." I have a disease called multiple sclerosis, which makes it hard for me to walk.

The important thing is that I am not going to die. Dad and I are very happy and we will always take care of you. If you ever have any questions, or ever, ever want to talk about it, just tell me."Next, I called their school and talked to both of their teachers and the school nurse. "Don't worry, Bridget, we'll take care of things on this end," came the reply.

A few months later, I told my niece. She is a lovely young woman and an R.N., and she was exemplary in her acceptance and help. Later, I was to realize that not being able to be frank with everyone in the family was a burden to her, and I am sorry for that.

My father died on Christmas Eve, 1989. He died without knowing. It was my gift to him. He was very sick for a long time, and deserved any respite from unhappiness we could offer. At his funeral, I was unable to stand to greet visitors because I had contracted the flu. My condition caused a great deal of speculation and concern. Clearly, it was time for candor.

The final stage of this long process of disclosure came before our next visit to our hometown, which was happily to attend our nephew's wedding. Several weeks before, I called my mother and broke the news. Her reaction? "I'm so sorry, Bridget, but I'm so glad to finally know the truth. I've never bought that arthritis story!"

She called the next day to say that she had been devastated by the news and had been unable to sleep. About 2 A.M. she had picked up a magazine given her by a friend. In it was an article written by an MS patient entitled *Every Day a Victory*, and it told of the full life the author led in spite of the disease. Mother was moved by her courage, and by the fact that she was, indeed, happy. That article was the decisive point in Mother's acceptance. My sister Kathé echoed the support of the others; her response was of particular importance to me.

My nephew Steve's wedding was my first venture into public in my hometown since my disclosure, and I was very apprehensive. The night before the trip home, my new electric scooter was delivered. After a few trial runs and an unfortunate run-in with our bedroom door jamb, I was ready. The wedding was perfect. I transferred to a pew in the church, and at the reception to a chair, while I used my scooter as needed. It was clear from the first time I interacted with the other guests, that word of my MS had spread quickly. There were no problems at all and I had a thoroughly enjoyable time. At no time was there any hint of discomfort about my disability, or the pity that I so feared. My process of disclosure had ended.

Did I handle my disclosure correctly? At this time I think so. There were, as with any decision of importance, options from which I had to choose, and compromises which had to be made at each stage of my ten-year process. There were the needs and strengths of others to be considered, as well as my own, and a myriad of emotions and fears that had to be dealt with.

Perhaps time will erode my certainty in the choices I made. But in the end, at least I will be secure in the knowledge that the process of telling others that I have multiple sclerosis was mine to decide and structure. This journey of sharing such an immense part of my life required, like so many facets of the disease, belief in myself.

Something Snapped

by: J. D. Huxtable

Last night my husband made me a chocolate "instant breakfast" for supper, as I did not feel up to eating anything solid. It was in a very heavy tall glass. I was sitting in my big easy chair watching TV while I drank it. My hand seemed to become suddenly nerveless and the three–quarters–full glass fell from my fingers to the floor. The chocolate drink spilled all over the light grey wall–to–wall carpet. My husband leaped out of his chair, yelling "How can you be so clumsy?" as he rushed to get a towel to sop up the mess. He kept yelling "You can't tell *me* that dropping that glass has anything to do with MS; you're just being lazy and not paying attention to what you're doing!" as he frantically tried to clean the carpet before the chocolate stained the carpet.

Of course, I was mortified at what I had done. I could not defend myself except to yell back that, of course, it was MS; and that he'd have known that, if he would have ever brought himself to read the book written for MSers and their families. I then promptly burst into tears and found myself howling like a banshee and sobbing uncontrollably. That mortified me even more. My poor husband didn't know what to do. He asked me what was wrong, and all I could do was to howl even louder. He asked me if he could do anything. I shook my head. My darling husband was by now thoroughly rattled. He hovered over me anxiously and asked me again if there was anything he could do. I desperately wanted to be left alone to regain my composure, so I jerked my thumb over my shoulder, indicating that he should go downstairs. By this time the poor man was so shaken by my howling that he crept down the stairs without saying another word.

I really didn't know what possessed me. I think now that the reality of MS, which I had been trying to keep at bay, hit me. I realized with complete and pitiless clarity that this disease that I am encumbered with is not going to go away. All of a sudden, with that silly little accident, grief overtook me, shaking my whole being to its roots. I think for the first time I allowed myself to understand that I would never again be able to paint, dance, play racquet ball, or, worst of all, walk in the woods. I felt that I was looking upon a devastated, crumbling wasteland. Horrible.

My poor darling husband, who has so many other worries besides myself, really didn't deserve the emotional beating that I gave him. I think that his yelling at me because of the spilled chocolate milk was a symptom of the stress that he was under.

Something just snapped in both of us, that's all. Something snapped.

February 2, 1991

I've just re-read the above piece and realize that it is 3 years later. I'd just been diagnosed a few months earlier and was still coming to terms with MS as well as being still stiff with shock at the turn my life had taken. How different things are today.

My friend Ginny (a fellow MSer) and I go to the New Canaan "Y" three times a week for aquacise classes, and I now walk almost as well as I did 3 years ago. I work for my physician husband every third Saturday morning, and do all the Medicare forms by electronic transmission on the computer at home. Since I get very tired in the afternoon, I do a great deal of needlepoint now which fulfills my need for color (I was a textile designer). Ginny and I have travelled with our husbands to several places (we're going to Alaska on a cruise in the fall!). We are now involved with getting the foodshare program going

in Norwalk and Bridgeport, as we think that those towns are among
the hardest hit in Fairfield County. I think the key to my change in
attitude is having a friend to do things with, and doing things for other
people and not thinking of our aches and pains all the time.

Life

by: *Anne Dixon*

Life is like water
It's fluent and strong
It has many courses
And changes its actions, when things go wrong.
Life can be peaceful like a tranquil stream,
Or full of excitement as a babbling brook,
Which sparkles and bubbles on the journey it takes,
Quiet and still when it becomes a lake.

As it meanders on it can take a fall,
Crashing and tumbling far below,
Sending steam high in the air,
Horrendous noise of roaring is heard,
Then sudden quiet as it becomes a stream,
As in life it's gathering strength,
Flowing onwards joining other sources,
Uniting together gaining strength
Ready to meet a bigger strength,
Its final outfall into the sea,
Fighting and merging losing strength,
Being sucked down by a mighty force.

Fighting for life to remain as before,
Being drawn gently into the air,
Drawing great breaths feeling release again,
Falling to Earth as gentle rain,
Starting the cycle of life again,
To live is to die, and to die is to live,
This is the continuing cycle of life,
Existing forever in the eternities.

Born Not Good Enough

This life of mine is all I have,
A moment of time in this universe,
Full of hopes and dreams and new beginnings,
What could I do where could I start,
To put right the wrongs of imperfect birth.

Knowing your faults and learning to grow,
Making the best use of what you know,
Learning to laugh at the wrong turns in life,
And learning to cope with its stresses and strife,
Giving love when no love is given,
Cherishing the children you have been given,
Filling the void left of other past loves,
Keeping the memory of past happiness,
Not regretting what might have been if life's journey
      had taken a different course.

Keeping faith with one's inner man
Knowing that inside this imperfect shell
Is still the same person when life began.
Not allowing the pain too much to show,
Of the sharp barbs that pierce the heart,
But try to give love and help to those,
Whose life is filled with so much pain,
The pain of rejection from those we love dear,
And teach how to rise above that fear,
And then you feel life's not a waste,
And that in this world you have a place,
That to the world you look incomplete,
The inner man is now at peace.

I am Still Me

I'm sorry for the way I am
But it's really not my fault
I'm sorry that I cannot do
The things I used to do
And if you shout and yell at me
You only make me worse.

I realise I'm not the same
As when you first knew me
But all that changed was the outer me
The inner me's still me.
You don't have to point out my failings
I am only too aware of what I cannot do
Don't raise my spirits by expecting to
Enjoy a little of a job I used to do
Spoiling all the pleasure by shouting
After asking how it should be done
You take away the pleasure
And a little of my fun.

I have now lost all my confidence
And all my self esteem
For all the things I try and do
To make up for what I am
I feel I am not capable to now even try and do
Because in order to achieve them
I have to ask some help from you.

I have now come to realise
How much worse I have become
The belief of getting better
Has been taken away from me
But shouting will not help us to achieve.
Just try and remember it is just as difficult for us

Especially always to be cheerful
When inside we feel so sad
Don't crush what little spirit's left
Sometimes that's all we have
To get through each new day
And cope with all it brings
And try and lift our spirits with
Enjoyment of little things
The things you take for granted
So be thankful for what you have
And if you truly love
Be grateful we're still here
At least sharing all you do.

Dreams: One Day at a Time

by: *Sheila V. Crabtree*

It was the winter of 1989, and I'd returned home. I rekindled the fire, and as I sat down, I began to remember another winter seven years previously —

I was finishing my college English course in night school at the university. It was a demanding course, and I was grateful for my tutor. I was tired beyond my wildest concepts: I remember falling while going to the library to check out *The Elizabethan World* for my exam reading.

I thought, "If only I can get through this course, I'll be home free." Well, that was just the beginning.

I felt like I was catching a flu bug. I rode home with my brother-in-law and sister-in-law. I waited while they ran an errand in the store. As I watched them approach the car, I couldn't focus my eyes on them. They both had a fuzzy outline. Yeah, I was catching the flu! But, I was tired with school, working full time, and all that.

Christmas came, and I felt nauseated. I made an appointment to see my doctor, who was also a good friend. After examining me, he sent me to the Ear, Nose, and Throat Clinic to have my inner ear checked. It was all right, but the nausea didn't subside, so I took Dramamine for two weeks.

My vision became worse, and I called my doctor again. I still couldn't focus my eyes — the world was spinning around all the time — the images tried to come together, but never quite made it.

I was scared, and physically felt like my life was draining out of me. I became more depressed, couldn't eat, and felt certain I had a brain tumor.

I was a medical secretary working in a hospital. I knew the fuzzy vision, nausea, and tiredness were symptoms. I was overwhelmed, and didn't understand how my world could so quickly turn upside down. *Why me?*

My doctor made arrangements for me to be admitted to the hospital on January 5, 1982. I was so sick, I wanted to confirm what was wrong with me. I called my mother, who came to be close by while I was in the hospital.

She was a wonderful lady who always smiled, and I knew with her close by I'd be OK. I cried, and asked my friends to say a prayer for me. I didn't want to die and leave my husband and family, and the sun and grass and trees. I was only 34. That year, though, I began to deal with death.

I entered the hospital, still unable to focus my eyes. I was poked and tested; blood was drawn. I underwent a computerized tomography scan and a spinal tap. After the test results came back, the neurologist came into my room, and told me I had multiple sclerosis.

"Well," I thought, "It wasn't a brain tumor or cancer, so it couldn't be all that bad!"

That day was only the beginning of the most uncertain years I've ever faced. I didn't know then how weak — and how strong — I would become.

I was discharged from the hospital, and rolled in a wheelchair to the front door, where my husband picked me up. I went home, still not able to see well. But now I had double vision, and things were at least still — even if there were two of them. I was given an eye patch.

I began feeling stronger, so I began to walk around my house every day. This wasn't easy, but the fight to conquer this obscure enemy in my body had begun.

I slowly and carefully walked onto the porch, held onto the rail, and because my balance was also in question, slowly chose a distance from which I could get back.

I was outside in the sunshine. I felt like I was taking my first steps. That's what counted. I was not going to die.

Three weeks later I was back at work part-time. I was blessed to be working for those caring and supportive people at the hospital. They were behind me 100 percent, and were willing to learn what "MS" was. These folks are due applause for not treating me differently, but watching when I went left instead of right, and being aware of how tired I became. They gave me strength to face those days patiently, and to look to a well future. That *did* happen.

Spring has a healing component built in. By April I was working full-time. My fatigue level was still awful, but remission had begun. I began to start my garden, plant my flowers, wash windows, and go for long walks up the road with my dog.

Life was so precious; and it wasn't the big things. It was the new leaves, green grass, new beginnings of the most minute form, ant hills, and Stars of Bethlehem blooming. It was children laughing, my mother's smiling brown eyes, her crocheting, and me learning to make a broom from straw.

For two years I was able to compensate for any neurological damage I had experienced. Meanwhile, I learned all I could about the disease.

I was in remission. I took a new job in June, 1985, and refocused my career goals. I wanted to move up the career ladder, and learn new skills.

I was cleaning my house, and one day while washing the mirrors behind my couch on which I was freely standing, I fell backwards. I was stunned. I had jarred my back. I went to the doctor, but noticed I wasn't popping back. My stumbling became more noticeable. Stress in my new job was high, and I was so tired. However, I ignored it.

Finally, I went back to my orthopedist. This was the year I was to learn about the ins and outs of "toe drop." My right toes were curling down. He ordered a special brace to support my ankle and to hold my foot in a straight lateral position.

Those wonderful people in the brace shop built me one to my specific orders. They had patience to be admired. I was becoming an aggressive, assertive patient.

My friends helped me to accept the first prosthetic in my battle with this unpredictable disease. I was so vain. I loved my 3-inch heels, but there was no way I could continue to wear them.

I wore my ankle brace at home, and when I went shopping on my "off" days. These bad days seemed to come closer together. My neurologist explained that as the disease became active, new MS lesions forming in my brain and spinal cord caused me to have poorer balance, and were also responsible for causing my vertigo. I could not turn my head quickly or swing my body in the opposite direction rapidly. I knew, though, this was only temporary. My denial was fine-tuned. I felt I would go into total remission one of these days. I knew I would. I dreamed and hoped; I had to. I had to get on with my life. After all, I was only 37.

These last four years have been tough, and that's a mild statement. I've had to deal with more medical symptoms of restless legs, limping, numb hands, numb feet, and fatigue. The summer days are spent inside, because the heat zaps my coordination and stamina.

I applied for a handicapped parking space at work, and a handicapped license plate for the car. These don't sound like much, but emotionally, each one has been a mountain to climb, as with my first brace.

My anger at having to accept my own deterioration, and lose another piece of my physical independence has brought some of the blackest depression I've ever worked through. I felt like a burden. I was fearful that I could not take care of myself, and pride wouldn't let me ask for help.

My husband was suffering, too. We'd only been married for five years. The hope of having children was gone. My mother died in 1983, and I felt alone to face a dark and bleak future ahead of me. After my mother's death, I would come home after work, sit by the fireplace, and cry every day. This went on for months.

Then, a friend I had known for years began to talk to me. My slowness didn't bother him. He was willing to wait for me and hold me steady while I traversed stairs and hills. He escorted me places, and called often to see if I was OK. I talked to him about my feelings of having cheated my husband out of a better future. I was so sad for my husband and myself. My friend listened, and told me how special I was, and that I was worth knowing.

He said my husband was lucky to have me. This friend is now, and always will be my friend; my MS doesn't matter to him.

In 1989, I still was working full time, but with more difficulty than before. My physical limitations were now more pronounced. However, I've developed a beautiful limp because of my hyperextended right knee. I wear good flat shoes all the time, but daydream about high heels often.

I needed a new direction. Events in my life directed me to contact someone to help me deal with stress. For six years I had fought an uphill battle creating a stressful lifestyle for myself and my husband. My bullheadedness is strong. I am now going to a counselor who works with clients to help them deal with stress. It has been a true learning experience, but it takes a lot of honest work. However, the rewards cannot be measured. My hopes and dreams that I'd put on hold waiting for total remission are back intact.

I want to live to be 90, at least. I've thrown the alleged 30 year survival rate after diagnosis out the window. I am writing now, too, something that I have always wanted to do. I plan to get my BS degree, sail more, and love more. After all, I am only 41.

I am learning to conquer my disease. Through creative visualization, I see my MS disappearing. I see myself running a mile every day. My dream is to one day be in total remission; I dream of a cure being found in my lifetime.

My right leg is no stronger, but emotionally I have gained tremendous ground. The mechanical function of my leg is not all of my focus. My mind is in great shape. I'm happier, and life is ironically funnier.

I'm in control, not my disease. I will win. I've only just begun. The past experiences and wisdom gained are my allies.

One day, mind you, I will walk gracefully. For now, through my meditation and creative imagination, I already do. My mother encouraged me as a child to hold on to my hope and dreams. I'm still holding tight.

It Can't Happen to Me

by: Lisa Daly

Wouldn't Happen to Me

In a trance I walked out of the doctor's surgery and drove home, too bewildered to cry and too confused to think straight. I'd gone in with a trapped nerve, and walked out with no future. It's true, the pessimist in me had considered multiple sclerosis, but I knew that wouldn't happen to me.

The doctor had talked all around the subject without actually saying it, until I suggested, "Could it be MS?" She seemed relieved that I'd already considered it.

"Could anything else produce these symptoms?" I asked, grasping at straws. Her answer was so unconvincing that I knew the truth was *no*.

In the Beginning

I was 29 years old and had a nine-month-old daughter, Jennifer. About three months after the birth, I suffered a mild blurring of vision in one eye. After I had seen the eye specialist and had a visual evoked-response test, it was suggested that I'd had a virus, and that was that. Five months later numbness developed in my big toe, which gradually spread up my legs and body, then to my arms and hands.

It was this attack which took me to that never-to-be forgotten day at the doctor's office. She was marvellous; she neither held anything back, nor did she imply that there was no hope.

I rang my husband, Steve, as soon as I got home, and told him it was possible I had MS. It was only then that I began to cry, fighting to hold back the tears for his sake. Steve was so upset he was sent home from work.

Contemplation

I sat alone contemplating the future. I looked at my daughter and thought how I'd ruined her life, how she would have to grow up too quickly, how she would have to suffer taunts at school about my wheelchair. My poor husband, his life would be ruined too. He thought he'd married a young healthy woman, when in reality he'd tied himself to someone imperfect, a living time-bomb. Suddenly he was forced to face the prospect of caring for an incapable invalid.

When Steve arrived home that afternoon I fell into his arms and wept.

That evening we discussed all the consequences of having multiple sclerosis, completely accepting that it was what I had even before we'd seen the neurologist. I told Steve I wouldn't blame him if he decided he wanted a divorce; of course he told me not to be so ridiculous.

It is frightening to think that my body is defective in some way, that it is gradually deteriorating, and I can't even see it.

New Regime

Convinced I had MS, I bought Judy Graham's book *Multiple Sclerosis*, and read it from cover to cover. This book changed my attitude totally. I was no longer despondent, but hopeful and determined. I resolved that I would follow all its advice. I wrote to everybody recommended in the book, I started a low-fat diet, started taking Evening Primrose oil capsules plus a multi-vitamin, began to exercise regularly, and rested when I felt tired.

Diagnosis

Eventually the day I'd been waiting for arrived. Steve and I were ushered into the neurologist's office, and after the introductions the doctor proceeded to tell me why I was there.

"Now there is something that would explain your symptoms," he said.

"Well I think I have MS," I interrupted calmly.

"Yes, so do I," he said. I was so relieved; at least he was able to make an immediate diagnosis, and it was not a brain tumour.

I cannot praise the neurologist enough. He answered every one of my long list of questions fully and (I think) honestly. He said my prognosis was good, and as far as he could tell I had a mild form of MS, and my main problem would be with fatigue. He said he wouldn't need to see me again unless I wanted to for some reason.

Friends and Relatives

The next problem was to tell our parents. I let Steve tell his mum and dad by telephone, since he preferred to do it that way.

I'd warned my mum and sister that I had something upsetting to tell them. Preparing for the worst, they assumed that I was emigrating or getting a divorce. The actual news came as an even harder blow. They were extremely sympathetic, and tactfully only shed a few tears while I was there. I know it seems ungrateful, but I hate receiving sympathy; I feel it is misplaced at the moment, and it should be saved for later on when I will really need it. I told my family I just wanted to be treated normally. I would say when I could or couldn't do something. However, I didn't make it easy for them, because I'm very stubborn and independent, and try to do more than I can really manage.

I'm also fortunate to have so many good friends who often get taken for granted by me. They all spoil me, not letting me do anything when I visit them.

My best friend is marvellous; she cheers me up by joking about my condition, saying we'll be able to go out together in our wheelchairs when we're older (she has arthritis quite badly).

Equally, she can be serious, saying that she would like to buy a large house for our two families to share so that she could look after me, and so that Jennifer would have her two children as adoptive sisters to play with.

Death Sentence

It was my friend who made me realise that many people will not live a full life span, and that many of them will have painful or uncomfortable older years, not just MS sufferers. This helped me to put my life into perspective, to think about the many other illnesses that people have, such as diabetes, or blindness, and that they still manage to live normal lives. The difference between me and a normal person is that I know my fate in advance, like a death sentence, whereas "normal" people do not.

I always feel sorry for the effect my condition has on others. For instance, I regret not being able to eat out easily, and having to rest frequently. Nevertheless, none of my family or friends ever complain.

My health visitor once gave me some good advice, which was not to push the MS out of my mind or try to ignore it, but equally not to let it rule my life. Accept it, but live a balanced life, avoiding too many large ups and downs. This is what I try to do.

Steve has had to revise his plans for an active retirement, and we don't choose holidays in hot countries.

Sometimes I feel that planning my days in such detail so as not to expend too much energy can be quite a burden, especially trying to fit everything in around resting, although in some ways I'm more relaxed than before. I've changed my priorities and housework is now at the bottom of my list.

Acceptance

Deep down I don't believe Steve has accepted my illness. He never discusses it any more, and doesn't even like to say the words. He is ashamed of and tries to suppress his anger over the MS, instead of talking about it.

Sometimes I feel I would like to use a wheelchair when visiting a stately home or gardens, but haven't as yet, partly because I wonder if I will have to change mentally in some way before I become a wheelchair user. However, it is also because it would upset Steve, bringing it home to him that I really am deteriorating.

Despite this, he is very understanding about my need to rest, and tries hard not to let me overdo things.

I surprise myself on how well I've accepted the illness. I never feel sorry for myself or am depressed, but of course that is easy at the moment, as most of my symptoms have been fairly mild. I know I was a hypochondriac before I was diagnosed, and now I almost feel satisfied with my life; now I have a purpose, something to fight for.

This peace of mind was achieved by allowing myself a period of grief, and treating my loss of health as a bereavement. Actually thinking and talking about all my feelings has also been beneficial. I have had feelings of anger, guilt, and of being cheated; for me this involved lots of tears, while Steve listened and comforted patiently.

Black Moments

In the odd black moments, usually lying in bed at night, I come over in a cold sweat thinking about the possible future. My own particular fears are that Jennifer will develop MS, or that I will have early dementia, blindness, loss of feeling in my hands, and the consequential loss of dignity. These thoughts last for a few seconds, and then I put them to the back of my mind.

Today I'm 31 years old, have a daughter of four years, and still have the energy for a job two days a week.

Now and again parts of my body go numb or tingle with pins and needles. Very occasionally one eye develops a slight blur, and during one attack I felt extremely unsteady on my feet.

As yet I've not had a single day off work sick due to the MS. I don't tell employers immediately that I have the illness, unless they specifically ask about health. I want my work to be judged on its own merits before I tell them. My present employers are wonderful, and will do anything they can to make things easier for me.

Well, I've done my crying, and now I just try to stay positive and cheerful. After all, every "normal" day is a bonus to me.

Letters from Miss Stacey Thompson

Paisley, Scotland

19th Feb. '91

I was very young when I was diagnosed with having MS – 16 years old, having had first symptoms at 15 years of age.

Due to my doctor initially thinking I was neurotic, I began to believe I was imagining it all. But, due to worsening eyesight, I was sent to the neurological department where tests were carried out and a definite diagnosis was made.

Attacks over my first two years were very bad, ranging from losing my sight, to being hardly able to walk.

Things weren't made easy by the fact that I was diagnosed in August, '89, and I started a B.Sc. in biology in September of the same year. This was my worst year physically. I lost complete use of my hands, and was unable to sit my Christmas exams. Extreme difficulty in walking resulted in me having to use lifts, and then bad double vision occurred – along with the usual fatigue.

Of course, I have been depressed, but I've decided that this thing is <u>not</u> going to beat me. I have become vegetarian and take Evening Primrose and fish oil capsules daily – which I feel have made a remarkable difference. Along with the overwhelming love and support of my family and friends, e.g., fund raising (I now have a first-class word processor due to the disability in my hands). I am beating it!

I am now 18 years old with my whole future ahead of me. I realise I will have to approach life differently, and there will be certain things I won't be able to do, but life will not be any less exciting or eventful. After all, I am a full-time student! And the world is waiting to be conquered.

Yours sincerely,

Stacey Thompson

Paisley, Scotland
3rd February '92

Just a small note to let you know I am feeling great, and in my final year of a B.Sc. in biology. A friend and I "back-packed" 'round France last year, and a bigger group of us are hoping to go 'round Europe this summer.

I hope this letter finds you in better health. Good luck for 1992, and with the book.

Yours sincerely,

Stacey Thompson

MS and a Free Spirit

by: Barbara Gurman

When I first found out about it, I was relieved. For years I had known something was wrong. Now I had to face what had always been so frightening to me, and learn to live with it.

It began many years ago, when I was twenty-two, on a warm summer day with the sun shining through my bedroom window, making playful shadows on the wall. I put my favorite record on the stereo, and as I listened to the music my body began to sway. Faster and faster I moved until I could no longer feel anything but the pulse of the music and my own heart pounding. Suddenly I felt a quick, sharp pain on my left side. A few days later the left side of my body from my waist down was numb and tingly.

I went to several doctors during the next few months. The internist said that it might be a slipped disc; however, after I was hospitalized and X-rayed, that theory was eliminated. It seemed silly when the neurologist asked me to walk with one foot in front of the other, but I was astonished to realize I could not do it. After he pricked me with pins, some of which I could not feel, he said that if my symptoms did not go away in a couple of weeks, I should have a myelogram. I improved and never had the myelogram; nonetheless, the neurologist told me that I might have a growth on my spine, but since that was unlikely, I should not worry about it.

During the next twelve years, I did not go near another neurologist. The only doctor I mentioned my occasional numbness and tingliness to was an osteopath who told me that I should see a neurologist. I did not even talk to my husband about my symptoms. Throughout my life, beginning with the time I started to walk, I had been treated as if I was made of porcelain, and I grew up believing that I was. I was much too afraid to find out what I had; instead I chose to live with the fear of not knowing, rather than handle the reality of knowing.

It was not until I lost most of the vision in my right eye, due to optic neuritis, that I learned what I had, and was then able to see myself and my life more clearly. The ophthalmologist I saw asked me if I had a neurological history; I said "Yes." He made an appointment for me to see a neurologist, the first doctor in twelve years to whom I gave my complete medical history, including my neurological symptoms. I had finally realized that although I was petrified to find out what I had, I could no longer hide from it. I waited ten days for the results of the neurological tests, the longest ten days of my life. I drove my husband Ben crazy with my questions. My favorite one was "Ben, what if I have a brain tumor?" It never occurred to me that it might be something that was not serious.

On May 28, 1979, Ben and I walked nervously into the neurologist's office. The doctor closed the door, while we stiffly sat down in the chairs facing his desk. The sandy-haired doctor, with horn-rimmed glasses and a pleasant, kind face, told me that the results of all my blood tests were good, and then he said in a calm, steady voice without raising or lowering his tone, that my lumbar puncture revealed I had multiple sclerosis. For what seemed like an eternity, Ben and I just sat there trying to absorb the information. Finally I swallowed hard and asked the doctor the question that was most on my mind. "Will I be paralyzed?"

The doctor must have been asked this question many times before, because without the slightest hesitation, he said that it did not have to happen. He told us about one of his patients with MS who travels throughout South America, whose only symptom has been an occasional loss of vision which has always returned. Ben and I were relieved. The revelation that I had MS, however, was not a total shock to me. I had read about the disease a few years before, and the symptoms were so similar to mine that I had wondered if this is what I had, although I had not seen a doctor about it.

My vision returned to normal in a couple of months, but I was having difficulty walking straight, and any turn or sudden movement could throw me off balance. I decided that rather than look inebriated, which was almost impossible since I rarely drank more than a glass of wine, I would get a cane. So one bright Saturday afternoon Ben and I went to Uncle Sam's Umbrella Shop to buy me one.

Buying my first cane was as difficult as my buying a pair of shoes —shoe salesmen disappear in droves when they see me. Fortunately, I had a very patient salesman who must have shown me every cane in the store; he even showed me how to hold it. There are two kinds of canes, one with a round handle, and another one which I preferred that had a fairly flat handle. As the salesman explained, each of these canes would enable me to use a different kind of pressure on the cane while walking; my choice depended on the kind of support I needed. However, it was not easy determining which cane was comfortable, especially since canes, like most everything else I buy, are made for people much taller than my five feet. After I finally made my selection, and the salesman sawed the cane down to my size, but until I decided which one to buy, I walked up and down the store with canes that I felt were meant for giraffes.

Using a cane forced me to accept the reality of my having MS, and encouraged Ben and me to take out several books from the library about the disease. This was particularly frightening to me, but we felt the unknown, which I had lived with for over twelve years, would be more frightening than if we knew the real symptoms that could develop from my MS, and we wanted to be prepared in case any new symptoms did develop. Initially, the books we looked at confirmed our worst fears.

It was still not clear which type of MS I had — so far, my attacks and symptoms had been mild. Most likely I was either slow chronic-progressive or relapsing-remitting. I was frightened and angry with my body for being so vulnerable. I had always assumed my body would be well; now I was not sure I could depend upon it. I said to myself over and over again, "Why me? It's not fair!"

On an especially cool fall day Ben and I took the subway to the Bronx Zoo to attend a bird watching course at the Aquatic Bird House. After the walk from the station, I sank to the curb outside the entrance to the zoo. Exhausted, I said, "I can't go on, Ben." Ben looked at me incredulously. "How can you be so tired? We've only walked six blocks! Come on, Barbara, we're late!"

Slowly I got up and started walking again, but I had to sit down on the first bench we came to. I began to cry. I could not believe what had happened to me. Ben stood there helplessly. Although I used a cane, I walked normally; several people had even thought my cane was a fashionable walking stick, so Ben had never realized, until then, how much I needed my cane, and I had never realized, until then, how tired I could get after such a short walk. This was the first time we knew that my MS had changed our lives. It was a frightening revelation, but we decided to continue on our way to the bird watching course, and greatly enjoyed learning how to spot and identify the beautiful creatures of the sky.

I began to notice that my legs felt weak when I walked. I panicked, and was convinced I was getting worse by the minute — a wheelchair loomed in the not too distant future. When there was something I could not do, I would say, "The leg doesn't want to do that." I did not feel that the leg was my leg, because I no longer had complete control over my legs. I dwelled on the things I could no longer do and had never found the time for, or had been too afraid to try taking the tennis lessons I had been meaning to take and the jogging I never really started. I was disappointed and angry with my body. It was an anger I was to feel many times, until I was able to say to myself, "The hell with it! It's not going to get the best of me and mess up my life." For a long time I forced myself to fight it, knowing the worst thing I could do was to feel sorry for myself.

I learned that when my legs felt tired, I should stop walking and rest until my legs felt stronger. I would find a place to sit and depending on what was surrounding me, I would either watch people (a never-ending fascination of mine), or look at beautiful trees and flowers, or interesting architecture. It had become evident to me that my cane was more than just an aid; I relied on it to walk. I compared my walk before I used my cane and I felt I had gone from a light, bouncy walk to a heavy, clumsy gait. I believed my difficulty in walking detracted enormously from my appearance, and I was convinced that people stared at my cane and never looked at me. I finally realized that most people were just curious about my cane.

One beautiful, warm spring day, a young woman came over to me. "Where did you buy your cane?" she said.

I was a little surprised, but I quickly answered, "Uncle Sam's Umbrella Shop on 57th Street."

"It's pretty. Is it made of wood?"

"Oh no," I said. "It's plastic; that's why it's so light."

"I have arthritis," she blurted out," and sometimes I use a cane."

I nodded my head understandingly. She was a small, thin, dark haired woman, who did not look more than thirty. I wondered how many people had said to her, "You're too young to have arthritis."

Then she asked me why I used a cane — a question that was hard for me to answer. I usually told people that I had a problem with my coordination, but there were times when I said, "I have multiple sclerosis."

After a few awkward moments, she looked at me and said, with genuine concern, "Are you in remission?"

This is another question that was hard for me to answer. I have always said "Yes," but there were times I wondered if I actually was in remission.

Quite a few people have stopped me to ask the same questions, and to tell me about their illness or injury. It hurts me to see the pained looks on their faces when I tell them I have MS, but I appreciate knowing they care.

For some time after I found out I had MS, I thought I should treat myself with extra care. One cold Sunday morning, Ben and I were going to have brunch at our favorite place. We huddled together, trying to brace ourselves against the biting wind, when suddenly I tripped. Looking down at the sidewalk Ben shook his head in disbelief. "What did you trip over?" he said. The sidewalk appeared perfectly even to him until I showed him the slight rise between one block of cement and the next. When I did fall, however, the startling revelation that I was no longer upright, but on the ground, was extremely unnerving. But I was always able to pick myself up without so much as a scratch, and continue on my way; I did not break in two. I have since discovered that I instinctively know how to fall. I just relax, and when I land, I do not hurt myself, but each time I fall I feel like a human flying saucer, landing quite unexpectedly on its underside. However, I gradually learned not to let my mind wander, and to look down as I walk.

When we first found out I had MS, we stopped trying to have a baby, because of the medication I was on, and because we were not sure if we still wanted to have children. However, since I was thirty-six, we thought we should start to think about it again. The thought of delivering a baby had always frightened me. I had been taken care of all my life as if I was extremely fragile, and I was anxious about not being strong enough to carry a baby and give birth. However, learning to live with MS, as well as talking to Ben and my doctors about our having a child helped me overcome my fear of pregnancy.

How simple it would have been if one of my doctors had said that pregnancy was not advisable because of my age or my MS, but that was not the case. My neurologist and my urologist told Ben and I that there was no reason why I could not have a baby. My gynecologist said that his patients with MS had given birth without any problems for them or their babies. None of the doctors thought my age was anything to be concerned about.

That left Ben and I to struggle with how we would handle a child, considering my MS.

"What will happen if I become paralyzed? How will I be able to take care of a baby?" I asked.

"I don't know," said Ben," but if you can't, who will? I don't know if I want that kind of responsibility."

"I don't want to be a burden," I said, hurt and angry at Ben, myself, and my MS.

Frustrated, Ben looked at me and with a deep sigh, he said, "I guess we could hire someone to take care of you and the baby — but can we afford it?"

"I don't know if we can," I said, "but what kind of mother will I be if I use a wheelchair?"

"I suppose you'll do the best you can — that's the most anybody can do."

For several minutes neither of us spoke. In so many ways it would be easier not to have children, but we did want them.

As time passed, we became less frightened about our future and the uncertainties of MS, and we began to feel more confident about living with it. During our vacation that summer we went on a hike through the woods, and as we neared the ocean, Ben helped me climb several rocks to reach the top of a cliff overlooking the ocean that had a magnificent view of the surrounding mountains. After lunch I took a picture of a fishing weir and its reflection in the water, a reminder of my climb up the cliff, and what I could still do.

The last time I saw my neurologist, I told him that I felt my legs had gotten weaker, and he said that it was not evident from his examination of me. "I don't think I'm imagining it," I said, and the doctor agreed. Maybe I thought, since my doctor did not notice this, it was not as bad as I thought. I learned to divide my head into two parts; one part that notices everything that is happening to my body and makes a mental note of it, and the other part that says, "The hell with it; just do what you can." I learned to be more patient with myself, while trying not to make unreasonable demands on myself to go faster or to do more that I could.

I had my hair re-styled and my ears pierced. I bought new glasses, and I started wearing eye make-up, something I had not done in years. I no longer felt ashamed of my appearance because I used a cane, and I found that people, including men, did look at me and not just at my cane.

That spring we went to the Brooklyn Botanical Gardens. Holding hands, we stood between two rows of apple trees in full bloom, their branches bursting with radiant pink flowers outlined against the deep blue sky, the fresh grass beneath them scattered with their soft pink petals. Suddenly, a flock of Canada geese soared overhead. We watched them move together, as if they were one. "Such free spirits," Ben said. I smiled and thought, "Just like me."

Ten long years have passed since Ben and I stood and watched those magnificent birds fly in formation. During this time we learned that after being in remission for eleven years my MS had become chronic progressive. I was then diagnosed with an infertility problem, and found I was unable to conceive. After seriously considering adoption we decided not to have children, because we felt having a child would be too physically, emotionally, and financially difficult for Ben and me.

For the past nine years I have been working 3 days a week as a secretary. I use a wheelchair and a battery operated scooter. I also drive a van adapted with a lift and hand controls. For a number of years I was a peer counselor for the MS Society where I made several long-lasting friendships. We recently bought a vacation home in northeast Pennsylvania where Ben goes skiing and biking, and I use my scooter. With the help of several bird feeders, a bird bath, binoculars, and bird watching books we both enjoy bird watching, and I have become a serious amateur bird watcher. At home we enjoy our life in the city and indulge our two beautiful cats.

I discovered that MS or not, wheelchair or not, children or not, life goes on, and yes, it can still be wonderful!

Is There Life After Diagnosis?

by: Eric Smirnow

Chapter I — Iowa
Setting the Stage — July, 1976

After being married in December, 1975 my wife "J" and I decided to forsake the security of my tenured federal job with the U.S. Geological Survey at the Denver Federal Center, and make a break for a more agriculturally oriented life in the rich farmland of Iowa. Not that we weren't already living out in the country, mind you, on our rented Evergreen, Colorado ranch of 23 acres with our horses, chickens, geese, ducks, Guinea hens, and all. Being 30 and 27 respectively, and in perfect health, we just felt that we were not being adequately rewarded in a number of ways for the hard work we felt we could put out in a true-to-life farming environment. And besides, we shared common aspirations (so we thought) for the rewards, both personal as well as financial, we felt we could reap from such a major change in the direction, purpose, and efforts of our day-to-day lives.

As I now reflect back on my own miniscule chapter in the history of human events some 16 years later, little did I know at the time that by following through on our decision, I would be setting in motion a series of events and circumstances that would have far-reaching — no, unfathomed lifetime changes for myself, not to mention others. Some, perhaps most, of these alterations in my life would be for the better, although some have come slowly, indeed. One consequence in particular, however, would in due course become a personal calamity — a loss of major, and ineffable proportions.

So, we left Colorado in a typical March Rocky Mountain snowstorm, which soon turned into a Midwest ice storm as we headed eastwards across the prairies of Kansas.

In those days, the words stress and fatigue were not in my vocabulary. With the typical bravado and myopic notions of invulnerability conveyed by youth and good health, "J" and I launched into 10-hour days and 7-day weeks upon our arrival in Iowa. We had advertised for work in a Midwest farming magazine some months previously, and when we were offered a job with a turkey breeding operation, we had scouted out the situation with a personal visit to Iowa earlier that winter.

In just a couple of months, the job from our erstwhile magazine advertisement disintegrated into a morass of personality differences with some of the other farm hands and real or imagined falsehoods with promises the non-resident owner down in town had made to us when we had come to Iowa for our "look-see" visit earlier in the winter. I wound up losing my cool one evening, and made the perhaps injudicious decision to quit the turkey farm. I told the owner to shove it. Just like that, and so there we were, without work and without income.

Things didn't seem too bad at first. We were actually living on a dairy farm (we had commuted to the job at the turkey breeder farm, which was a few miles away) in a great house with surprisingly low rent, and had talked Barney, the owner, into letting us help with field work preparatory to planting corn, as well as helping his resident young hired hand milk his Holsteins. It was May; the days were long, and the hours which had now jumped to 12–14 hour days, 7 days a week, didn't seem that difficult to cope with.

I had never worked so hard in all my life. The milking and feeding of the dairy herd, not to mention dealing with the milking equipment and the bulk tank, cleaning up the barn, hauling manure, and whatever else needed to be done twice a day was just "chores." After these morning chores beginning at 4:30 or 5:00 A.M. until about 8:00 (and a real breakfast rather than the first thing get-started coffee and roll or doughnut) came field work until noon. Then, after an hour for lunch, more field work. It was, of course, chores again in the evening from about 5, until 7 or 8. Although tired all the time, I felt great. We had a huge garden that didn't know the word stop. I was eating like a horse, but didn't have a spare pound anywhere, and we were making just enough money to get by. Life was good. Or so it seemed.

In July, the bottom fell out of our little world when good old Bernard informed us one fine day that our services would no longer be required on his group of three farms. Now that the spring field work had been taken care of, his son-in-law's family and the one other hired hand could handle things by themselves, thank you very much, and we could stick around or leave as we pleased. Just pay the rent. We started looking for a new place to work, and began worrying about if and/or when we would have to begin the arduous task of moving again.

To further complicate matters were our horses. We had trans- ported the two horses I owned in Colorado to Iowa when we moved. They were never a liability out west; we soon found out how much of one they could be in a place where people feel that dairy cows are the only large animals worthy of consuming forage. At first when we were making pretty good money at the turkey farm, we boarded the horses at a stable. When we started working for Barney (for a good deal less money), we moved them to a nearby "farmette" where a tornado had skipped in one summer day, demolishing the entire spread a few years earlier. A young couple had built a new home on the few acres of the old farm compound amidst the rubble of the old barn, other outbuildings, and the twisted rebar sticking out of the concrete shell of the old silo. Here, we laboriously cleared saplings and erected a barbed wire fence around a pasture of several acres.

One night, something spooked Zia the younger horse, and he ran full-tilt into the fence, actually hitting it hard enough to break a strand of the wire right in the middle. In doing so he cut himself deeply on his front left shoulder. Not only was it a terrible sight to see, but then came the vet bills and the extra worry/duties of doctoring the horse several times a day in addition to everything else.

Money rapidly became a problem — a big problem.

I called a friend back in Colorado and told him that if he would come get the horses, I would give them to him for nothing if he would just transport them back out west, and get them out of Iowa once and for all. So a few days later, my saddle horse Rusty and just-broke three year old Zia (whom I had raised from birth) departed westwards on a journey to points unknown, never to be seen again. I cried silently in my heart and in my dreams. Real tears would come later. And not just once.

Meanwhile, "J" had found a dairy/beef operation in Dorchester, Iowa (check *that* one out in your atlas) that was looking for a new farm couple to work there on the dairy farm. We were to start the first of August. Plans to pack up and move from Sumner to Dorchester slowly got underway as hot July days drifted on under a Midwest sky with towering cumulonimbus clouds.

One morning in mid-July I awakened with an opaque "hole" in the vision of my right eye. Little did I know at the time that my personal odyssey with multiple sclerosis had just begun.

—•—〓◆〓—•—

15 years later — July, 1991

It has been more than 15 years since MS first made its presence known in my body. I certainly wasn't aware of it at any level or what was happening then or in the next 13 years to come. Although rather innocuous at first in my case, the increasingly firm grasp this disease has had (and continues to have) as time passes on virtually every aspect of my existence is a source of some considerable, even detached scientifically curious interest to me, if no one else. Like most people, I used to think that this kind of dreadful thing happened to other people, and definitely not myself.

By now you may be wondering what in the world the first part of this story has to do with multiple sclerosis. What it has to do with it, friend, is *stress*. Plain old-fashioned short on sleep, too much hard physical work, no time off for vacation/recreation, short on money, worried about today, tomorrow, next week, next month, wake up in the middle of the night and can't get back to sleep stress.

Personally, I am convinced that extreme stress often sets the *susceptible* individual up for diseases such as MS. Predisposing circumstances that are statistically significant, but not well understood at the present time such as ethnic background, familial relationships and genetics, viral and/or environmental agents, geography, etc. are only part of the whole picture, at least as far as I am concerned. There is *zero* doubt in my own mind that stress was the primary initiator of my own MS process, just like the primer in a cartridge initiates the event of discharging a bullet from the barrel of a firearm. I am also *firmly* convinced that the two major exacerbations of this disease I have now had were *fully* preventable, and that had they not occurred I would have developed a far less significant case of MS, as well as being a whole lot better off than I am today in terms of my own condition and prognosis.

Not having learned my lesson with stress well enough in 1976, I was to get a far more significant crash course in physiological reality thirteen years later when MS returned into my life with a vengeance.

Chapter II — Iowa

The Presenting Complaint — July, 1976

What was to become a landmark day, my first day with what would eventually become a full blown case of multiple sclerosis, started out innocently enough. Of course, I didn't even know that I had MS that day, or even for the next 13 years, as I was not "officially" diagnosed until June, 1989. I don't even remember what the exact date was, that summer day in 1976, since I didn't keep a diary in those days. Why should I have jotted down how I felt or what I did? Life was easy, or so it seemed. I certainly didn't have to worry about not being well. I felt great, and was trim, tanned, and hard. It was some time in mid-July, the days were long, there had been plenty of rain, and the corn was looking good in the fields.

Although we had found a new dairy/beef farm to move to in the beautiful hilly hardwood farm country just west of the Mississippi River, we were still milking Barney's Holsteins so we could get a break on our last month's rent. "J" and I were going to start moving in a couple of weeks, a task we estimated would take only a few days if we really buckled down and got after it when the time to move actually arrived.

One morning when we awoke at 4:30, hustling to get ready to head out to the barn by 5 for milking and chores, it seemed that something wasn't "quite right" with my vision while I was in the bathroom. The lighting in the bathroom wasn't the greatest, it was still dark outside, and I didn't have time to investigate more thoroughly —right then anyway. We went about our business, and returned to the house around 8 for breakfast.

It is strange how some memories remain crystal clear in one's mind over the years, while others become hazy or are forgotten entirely, or almost so. I do not really remember the setup of the fixtures or color of the paint in the bathroom of Barney's farm house.

But I remember quite clearly what the kitchen looked like, and even what I was eating, as I began to explore the strange "hole" in the vision of my right eye that morning.

Putting one hand over one eye and then the other it was obvious that something was going on. Or perhaps I should say that something wasn't there any more. The vision in each eye was different! There was a centrally located area of opacity, or loss of color/contrast which appeared somehow "brighter" in my right eye. I "played" this little game of the hands over the eyes for a while, wondering what in the hell was going on, anyway. I said something to "J" about it, and picked up a magazine to try to read it, first normally with both eyes, then with each one separately. I could no longer read the text when I used only my right eye. I was beginning to become concerned, as clearly this was not a trifling discovery. Otherwise I felt fine, and since it was now time to get on with the day's work in the fields, I went on about my business. As the day wore on, I began to check my vision more and more often. It did not improve, and I went to bed with concern building in my mind.

The next morning was a different story entirely. I woke up with a start when the alarm clock went off at 4:30. When "J" turned on the light on the night table by the side of the bed, I gasped, and my hand involuntarily flew to my right eye in an effort to ward off the instantaneous pain that burned back into my head from the light passing through the dilated pupil. I slowly, cautiously, began to allow some light to enter, and the sharpness of the pain began to subside. Chores were not easy to deal with that morning, and I struggled to maintain my composure as the pain continued to build with the coming of full daylight. I managed to get through the rest of the morning and afternoon by putting on my sunglasses while I was outside, and by taking some aspirin. I was becoming quite alarmed. We decided to seek medical attention the next day if the problem had not resolved itself by the following morning.

Day three. I still felt fine physically, but the tiny corridor of pain extending a couple of inches back into my brain from my eye had become a virtually preemptive presence which occupied my every moment. I had taken to wearing the sunglasses indoors in an effort to find some relief from the pain. I made an appointment to be seen at the local doctor's office. I explained my situation, and they told me to come right on in that afternoon.

In rural areas where there frequently are few physicians and lots of relatively sparsely populated country, physician's assistants often routinely cover non-emergency office visits for the regular doctor when he/she is at the hospital, making house calls, etc. These people have some amount of medical education and expertise, but they are not doctors per se.

After filling out the usual papers, I was ushered into an examining room. After introducing himself, and asking me a few questions, the P.A. wanted to examine my eye with his ophthalmoscope. Although I had cautioned him about my hypersensitivity to light in that eye, I gasped and jerked backwards involuntarily in an attempt to get away from the searing needle of white hot light of the ophthalmoscope when he shined it in my eye. We were both surprised at my reaction, and by mutual agreement, we decided not to pursue that part of the examination. He decided to arrange an appointment with an ophthalmologist in a neighboring large city to attempt to ascertain what my problem was, since something of an acute and serious nature was clearly underway. Vital signs and temperature were checked, and samples of blood and urine were taken to be sent to the local hospital for analysis. My vital signs appeared to be absolutely normal, and the rest of the cursory general physical examination also revealed nothing obviously out of the ordinary.

An appointment was made through the doctor's office with an ophthalmologist in Waterloo for late that afternoon after normal business hours, as an emergency situation. "J" had to chauffeur me around in the car as I was no longer able to deal with driving. Scared, worried, and hurting, I hunkered down and waited out the rest of the day as best I could.

The ophthalmologist's examining room was cool from air conditioning, and was mercifully dimly lighted (thank goodness for small favors!). He said that it would be necessary to dilate both my eyes, so he could have a good "look/see" inside both. I of course had told him about the experience at the P.A.'s office, and he said that he would not have to use a bright light during the examination of the interior of my eyes when my pupils were dilated, but that he wanted to see the reaction of both eyes to light from a distance prior to administering the drops that would induce dilation. With some considerable care, Dr. X watched my reaction to light as he shined a small penlight here and there, to and fro. Acuity, color vision, and several other functions which I no longer recall were also checked. Then, the dreaded drops were placed in my eyes, and I was left alone for a while so the drug could take effect.

The doctor returned, and the examination continued as he peered into each eye with various colors of light, filtered light of one kind or another, and what-have-you through some unknown named multi-lensed machine suspended on an articulated frame. The different colored lights were uncomfortable, but not especially painful in my now fully dilated right eye. In a particularly weird way, I could actually *feel* the light moving around on the fundus of the retina of my right eye as the examination proceeded.

The examination finished, and unable to see anything but fuzzy indistinct colors from the dilation, I was led into the doctor's office with "J," and we both took a seat. The long and short of it was that he, too, was unsure as to what in fact my problem was, except that the fundus of each retina clearly looked different, the right one being somewhat paler than the other. He said he would call the Ophthalmology Department at the State University of Iowa Medical Center in Iowa City first thing the following morning to make an appointment for me to be seen there; we were to call his office after 9 A.M. to find out when to arrive. I was given an eye patch, and "J" led me to the car. I was indeed thankful that the sun was low in the sky as we returned home, even with the sunglasses and patch.

The next morning when we called Dr. "X," we were told to arrive at the Medical Center in Iowa City as soon as we could make the drive, a journey of about 100 miles. And so off we went to the south on secondary country highways through the Amish country and corn fields. Several times a bearded farmer holding the traces of his team as he rode on a spoke wheeled cultivator would look up as we went on by, and we would exchange waves.

Arriving at the hospital complex about noon, there were seemingly endless papers to be filled out, and what seemed to be an interminable wait to be seen while sitting in a large public waiting area. People with various problems of obvious or not so obvious ocular nature were seated here and there about the room. By this time, the whole business of the last four days was wearing on me heavily, and I was becoming exhausted and scattered, not to mention still being just plain scared and nervous. Fantasies of brain tumors and other dreadful maladies drifted in and out of my thoughts. Finally my name was called, and I was escorted into another semi–dark examining area. Numerous tests of one kind or another ensued, along with another dilation. Several other doctors also examined me, photographs were taken of the interior of my right eye, and apparently I made quite a stir with the medical staff that day. I do not remember much of the details of what transpired during that afternoon–long examination, except that the primary physician, Dr. "T," had a thick Australian accent of all things, and that he was quite personable, a very likeable fellow.

Dr. "T" had someone go find "J" in the waiting area, and we both took seats in his office. I was straining to make out the doctor's indistinct features with my unfocusable, dilated eyes as I listened to his diagnosis. Dr. "T" told us that I had optic neuritis. I might fully recover my vision in my eye, or that I might not, or I could recover any amount of my former vision. He was going to have me begin a course of treatment with prednisone. And, last, but certainly not least, that there was a 25–40% chance I would go on to get multiple sclerosis as I got older, since the disease often presented itself this way. One thing I *do* remember quite clearly about those few minutes in Dr. "T"'s office all these years later is thinking "Bullshit. Other people get things like MS. Not me. It can't/won't happen to me."

Thirteen years later I found out I was wrong about that little string of thoughts I fleetingly had that afternoon as I listened to my diagnosis/prognosis. Wrong, indeed.

＊＊＊

Epilogue to Chapter II

I started taking the prednisone that afternoon, and continued doing so for several weeks afterward. Each time I took a dose, there was at least at first, a noticeable "pulse" of improvement in the vision of my eye. The strange "hole" in the center of my field of vision seemed to be slowly closing, and a more normal sense of color and contrast were returning. Although I do not recall the exact dosage, I remember that it was at first rather substantial, and tapered off for some time afterwards. Physically, I still felt fine, and although I was still wearing my sunglasses both in and out of doors, the sensitivity to light was ever-so-slowly diminishing, as was the pain.

During the period of taking the steroids, we moved out of Barney's place and into our new home in Dorchester. I remember that quite clearly, because I had developed a hair-trigger temper, insomnia, and some other nasty side effects from the prednisone. It was tough on "J" and tough on me. I tried to keep as even a keel as I could, but I was definitely not easy to get along with. Even though I explained my medical situation at some length to our new farm owner/boss, his wife, and the other hired hands, every one of them must have thought I was one strange and creepy character for wearing my shades indoors and out for the next few weeks. The improvement in my vision eventually ceased to continue to improve, and I was left with what I estimated was about a 20% loss in color/contrast vision in that eye. To this day, that loss has remained constant.

Slowly, I was able to dispense with the sunglasses, but the damage had been done with the farm owner and other workers. It all too soon became clear that we (especially myself) were viewed with some considerable suspicion/distrust for whatever reason(s), and that we were going to be asked to find other work somewhere else in the very near future. Both "J" and I were at our saturation points with moving, being short on money, and our very tenuous situation in the Midwest. I called a friend who was in the personnel department of the U.S. Geological Survey back in Denver, and asked if I could be reinstated to my old job back at the Federal Center in Lakewood. Not possible, she said, but there *was* an opening available in a Water Resources Division Subdistrict office in Meeker. A date was set for me to start, and I made a hurried journey to Meeker to find housing and meet my new supervisor and co-workers. I drove about 2,000 miles, found a place for us to live, introduced myself at the office, and returned to Iowa in just three days. Once again, we began the process of packing and moving. It was September, 1976.

Chapter III — Lone Pine, California

The Western States 100 Mile Cross–Country Race and Other Atrophied Dreams

—••— ▄◆▄ —••—

Meeker, Colorado — September, 1976

"J" and I had settled into our new home near Meeker in September. Ten miles south of town on State Highway 13, it was as much as a rural loving person could reasonably hope for. There were no one else's lights to see at night, rather, a celestial backdrop of blackness and twinkling stars, frequently heard nocturnal wailing of coyotes, bugling elk, and deer in the yard virtually every day. We loved it.

Unfortunately, for whatever reason(s), the office supervisor and I did not hit it off, and animosity between he and I began to build rapidly. By next spring things had come to a head in the office. I was foolishly insubordinate on more than one occasion, and soon found myself up against the proverbial wall, in this case a bureaucratic one. It was not a nice scene for all concerned, but I prevailed vocationally by a variety of civil service regulation flukes. To make a long story short, I began reading the vacancy announcement listings on the bulletin board in earnest every time they were updated. Tension at the office, as well as at home, had become the name of the game virtually daily.

To make things even more tense, "J" had begun corresponding with and telephoning an old boyfriend of hers regularly. One day in the dead of winter a letter addressed to her had arrived from back east from this person. Apparently, he had just gotten divorced from his new wife of a year or so, and although he had dumped all over "J" previously in favor of his now newly divorced wife, he was now interested in re-establishing contact with "J." So it went, and an old fire was rekindled, although at the time I didn't pay much attention to it because of my own worries. One evening, a critical juncture came to pass when "J" asked me whether or not I trusted her. In all honesty, I replied "Are you *sure* you want to know the answer?" She said "Yes," and so I told her that I did not. In retrospect all these years later, that was in effect the end of our marriage, although we continued to go through the motions for some time to come.

Late in the summer of 1977, while the office supervisor was away on vacation, I saw a vacancy announcement for which I was qualified, and which was in Grand Junction of all places! Straightaway, I sent off my application with the blessings and positive references of previous supervisors and co-workers. I was immediately called for an interview, and was hired, all before my USGS boss returned. He was livid when he found out that I had successfully pulled off such a preemptive stunt, but there was nothing whatsoever he could do about it. Amazingly, not only did I get a promotion to go along with my new job, but the move and "house hunting" expenses were going to be covered by my new employer!

Elated with this turn of events, I took up residence for the next month at a rather scroungy kitchenette-equipped motel on North Avenue in Grand Junction, while "J" (one more time) began to pack up our belongings during the week. On weekends she traveled to Junction, and we would go house shopping.

Having little to do after work on those still long and mild late summer days, I began to take lengthy evening walks here and there around town. Before many days passed, I noticed a bearded fellow who appeared to be about my age effortlessly running around the perimeter of the Lincoln Park golf course for more than an hour at a time. I was incredulous how someone could do this. Thinking I was in good shape since I felt great (even though I had been going through 20–30 Camels or Lucky Strikes daily since my college days), I decided to see how I would fare at this jogging/running business. And, I had heard from a variety of sources that running was unsurpassed for helping one to relax. I decided that I could definitely use some relaxation, all right, so I soon gave the running a try.

How I fared that first time out one evening was not so good. Mr. X, the unknown/unnamed bearded guy just happened to be coming past me from the opposite direction as I started out that very first time. About 100 yards later I was gasping for air, my chest heaving, and I could feel every single major blood vessel in my entire body. Holy moly, was I in poor condition! I couldn't believe it!!! I kept on walking, tried to jog a bit more, but couldn't. My legs, especially my quadriceps on the front of my thighs, hurt as they had never hurt before with charley horses for almost a week, a physiological reminder of years of physical and pulmonary self abuse with tobacco. But, a different kind of seed had been sown in myself than I had ever known before — a seed of physical goal setting, of determination and dedication, of denial at times, a growing tolerance for non–injury discomfort and pain, and a strange kind of slowly building self confidence. These traits were to stand me in good stead in years to come, and in ways I never could have imagined then. They would help me deal with MS.

"J" and I finally found an old stone house with 5 acres of land, as well as irrigation water in Fruita that we could afford, and we soon moved into our new little farm on the outskirts of town. I settled down to my new job; "J" settled down to taking care of the house, our animals, and her crafts. But the business of her corresponding and telephoning her old boyfriend continued. Slowly, but very surely, we were drifting apart in our marriage. At Christmastime, 1977, she flew back to Virginia, ostensibly to visit her family and friends over the holidays. She never returned.

Emotionally devastated, I turned to ever–increasing athletic activities of one kind or another in a numbed attempt to restore some sense of self-worth to my damaged psyche. Amazingly, after numerous failed attempts over the years, I finally managed to stop smoking once and for all. Next summer I started divorce proceedings.

Distraught, I begin a bizarre multi-faceted journey of sorts that would soon take me from Fruita to the backcountry hollows of West Virginia, and thence to Durango, Colorado all in the space of less than a year. All the while, I kept running longer and longer distances, adding hills, more hills, and steeper hills to my training runs. Soon those hills would become mountains.

———— ❑◆❑ ————

July 4th Holiday, 1991

For a number of years I've been making an annual vehicular pilgrimage to southern California around the time of the summer solstice to indulge myself in sun, surf, sand, semi-exotic restaurant meals, and any unpredictable adventures that might come my way in the process. Since the journeys as well as arriving at my final destination are in fact my vacation, I often deliberately choose routes of travel less than direct and expeditious so I can see some new turf coming and/or going. Sometimes, I just point myself generally to the west or east as the case may be, and just start driving.

It was on such an aimless return journey homewards this past summer, after having spent the better part of a week at the coast that I abruptly found myself passing through Lone Pine, California, home of the highest peak in the lower 48 states, Mt. Whitney. 10-12 years ago when I faithfully followed such events in running magazines, I recalled that the Western States 100 Mile Cross-Country Endurance Race was held in this small and relatively out-of-the-way mountain town. At one point in my life (my pre-MS life, that is) I had entertained the outrageous notion that I might — *just might* — be able to compete in this prestigious event for the athletically hard-core elite. The goal was to complete the arduous 100 mile course in under 24 hours, thereby garnering one of a number of impressive belt buckles — a prize of prizes. Many finishers of much less than world-class ability had an overall pace of only about 10 minutes/mile, something I felt I just might be able to handle for a day, given enough training, bullheadedness, and raw gumption. If a person could maintain a pace of a little better than 4 miles/hour (actually just a fast walk) for an entire day, they could theoretically complete the race within the allotted time period. It was a dream within a dream, and I began to fixate on it when I trained on the hills around Durango, Colorado.

I pulled off the highway outside of Lone Pine, and as I stood on my now weakened, wobbly, and cramped legs from too much driving and sitting that day, I unlimbered my camcorder and pointed it at what I assumed was Mt. Whitney. Zooming in and out with the camera, I found myself zooming backwards in my mind to another time in my life — a time of 10 mile training runs every other day, no-nonsense weight lifting sessions, endless sit-ups on an incline board, hard bike rides, walking anywhere and everywhere rather than driving, and running in competition up and down thirteeners and fourteeners in Colorado.

Why did I invest all this energy in such a strange goal? I did it as an attempt to recover some sense of my shattered self esteem after my divorce. And I did it simply for "grins"; because not many other people could or even had any kind of notion to do things like that. Running was something special, and it made me feel special, too. And — it was one thing I *had* to do myself; no one else could do it for me. No one could run to the summits of mountains as my proxy. Memories of a decade past poured back in a flash flood of thought, and I was on the verge of tears as I stood there staring at Mt. Whitney that hot July afternoon in 1991, remembering the person I once had been and hoped to be, the person I had become, and the person I *might* become as my MS worked on me while future, unknown years drifted by.

Let's pause for a moment in my story while I change verbal and temporal gears — Let me tell you right up front that disabilities, disease, death, and a few other aspects of the "human condition" scare the wits out of me. They have ever since I was a small child. Here's how it happened —

—◦—≡◦≡—◦—

Swain's Lock, the Chesapeake & Ohio Canal Suburban Maryland — circa 1951

Several people are gathered around an individual in a wheelchair who is being slowly pushed along the canal towpath towards the lock keeper's house. The man in the wheelchair (I can tell from looking at him that he is not a child or adolescent) is misshapen, small framed and physically grotesque, and his facial features are contorted as if he was in pain. He is also distressingly spastic in his movements. He appears to be trying to talk to his companions, and I'm close enough to them that I can hear his virtually unintelligible speech. I have never seen anyone like this before, and I am shocked beyond belief and words as I stare transfixed at this scene with my five-year-old child's uncomprehending eyes and ears. I know it is wrong to stare so brazenly, but I cannot take my eyes off this person.

My father sees me gawking at this scene as it passes us, and a little while later he tries to explain to me that the person in the wheelchair is a relative of the Swain family, and that he has cerebral palsy. My child's mind and base of knowledge/experience are unable to understand my father's technical-type (although accurate) explanation.

Thus within my young self is planted a seed of fear. A fear of disabilities, disease, injury, being unable to communicate, of being deformed or grotesque, different and somehow strangely less than human. What would I do if I ever became a prisoner within my body or mind? What would I do if I were no longer in control of myself or my own life??? This fear becomes something nameless, silently terrifying, and gut-shrinking in its grip on me as I grow older. And so begins a lifetime of behind-the-scenes dread that someday, some-how (some way?!?) I might become one of "them." Forty years later that is exactly what happens.

— ⵜⵜ◆ⵜⵜ —

Swain's Lock — November 1, 1981

I have returned to Maryland from Durango to visit my family. Once again, I'm on the C & O Canal at Swain's Lock, this time with "P," the husband of a cousin. We have planned a leisurely run of just less than 16 miles down to Georgetown in Washington, D.C., having made arrangements with my father to pick us up at the canal's terminus at M Street a couple of hours later. "P" is a marathoner, logs many more weekly miles than I do, and is considerably faster than I am. Although by this time I have competed in a number of mountain races in Colorado, I am not particularly fleet-footed, but "P" has no problem with that and agrees to just "loaf along" with me. It's a beautiful clear and colorful fall day in the Nation's Capital.

"P" and I take off at about an 8½ minute-per-mile pace. This is slow for him, but just about right for me for a long training run. It's easy for both of us to talk, laugh, and carry on at this pace. After a few miles we both fall silent, lost in our own thoughts as the scenery and mile markers pass, one by one. About two hours later, and somewhat upriver from Fletcher's Boathouse which is perhaps two miles from the end of the canal, "P" says that he wants to run at his own pace. I say "OK," and off he goes. His stride lengthens, his pace quickens. He's just cruising along, his long legs carrying him seemingly without effort, as he pulls away from me. It is everything I can do to try to stay close to him, but I can't even do that. Any notion of challenging him is absolutely out of the question, and I am running at close to 100% of my personal capacity. Steadily, at his less than six minute-a-mile pace, he pulls away from me until we arrive in Georgetown, myself hundreds of anoxic yards behind him.

I had been wearing a brand new pair of running shoes for this run. They had much wider heels than the shoes I had been using for the past three years. Although very supple and well-cushioned, I noticed that my right knee hurt a little bit after the run. By the following morning the knee hurt like hell, and it was clear that some kind of fairly serious damage had occurred — an "overuse" injury as we say in the trade. Later, I would discover that it had been the beginning of the end of my running career.

A few years later (as the story my father told me has it) "P" discovered a strange sore on one of his toes. The sore refused to heal, and it wasn't long until he was diagnosed with a particularly aggressive form of leukemia. Within a few months he was terminal, and in the intensive care unit of a local hospital. Shortly thereafter he died. He was still in his thirties.

The long and short of this unpleasant portion of my story is that "P" died a dreadful death at the hands of well-intentioned, but apparently insensitive, probably over-zealous hospital staff who were possibly more concerned about litigation than they were about allowing a terminal patient to die with dignity. Attached to a ventilator and unable to speak, "P" finally went into cardiac arrest. He was resuscitated by being shocked, but again his heart failed. This scene was repeated perhaps half a dozen times, until my cousin as well as my father jointly demanded that the ICU staff stop doing this to him.

After hearing my father recount this bizarre story, and seeing "P" go silently screaming off into eternity like that in my own mind's eye, I was brought straight to the brink of confronting my own fears about disabilities, disease, and death. I tried to confront these personal bugbears which started to form in my own mind so many years ago when I saw the person with cerebral palsy in his wheelchair at Swain's

Lock. Although I made a vow never, **ever**, to allow myself to get into a situation such as befell "P," I was not successful in purging my own specters from my mind. Just a few years later, but under very different circumstances, it would be *my* turn to learn about, and try to deal with, a body out of control with itself.

Chapter IV — Left Hand Canyon

Boulder, Colorado — May, 1989

I will begin my fourth year as a "bona fide" MS person this May, just two months from now. I do not count the period from July, 1976 to April, 1989 as part of my MS life, as my optic neuritis was more of an inconvenience than anything else (for example, making it hard for me to aim a rifle quickly). In retrospect, I now know that some of the little health "weird-outs" I had during those years were in fact tiny MS exacerbations, short periods when I thought I had some kind of inconsequential, unknown "flu bug," or when the fingers on my right hand were a little tingly, which I attributed to operating a chainsaw, lawn mower, driving too much with the ball of my thumb on a vibration-filled truck steering wheel, and so on. But — now I know better.

It felt good to be in Boulder again that spring, the place where I had finished my college education so many years earlier. Although much had changed over the years, I was glad to be back in this familiar and active place, and I felt healthy and strong, too.

However, these good feelings were not destined to last long. Not many have a figurative opportunity to attend their own funeral, yet live to tell about it. In ways that are beyond words, parts of myself literally, as well as symbolically, died the summer of 1989. The body that had served me well for well over 40 years would soon become a prison and a mystery. The "rules" I had lived my life by were going to change; they would be altered in ways hitherto unforeseen, unimaginable, profound, and point-blank frightening. Soon I would have to chart a new course in life, and it would be without any kind of compass to guide me. Here's what happened —

I had been out of work for about a year and a half, and was scrounging to make ends meet. For the last four years what had been a full-time, but seasonal job without tenure as a watershed technician with a government agency had been terminated, ostensibly for "lack of funds." When I heard through the proverbial grapevine about an intensive sedimentation research project on the Front Range that would involve field as well as laboratory work for at least six months, I jumped at the chance to apply. The long and short of it is that I was hired, and at the salary I had been earning previously. There would be time–and–a–half overtime available for months to come — virtually as much as I wanted and could handle — perhaps 30–40 hours per week extra, plus per diem in the form of lodging, meals, and vehicle expense. I would be staying at a motel in Boulder, and could travel back to the Western Slope every other weekend to take care of my property. I estimated that by working my tail off and by watching what I spent on food, I could earn the better part of a full year's wages in those six months, and I was ecstatic over my good fortune. The furthest thing from my mind was something like multiple sclerosis.

So, in April I made my way to Boulder, got myself set up in an attractive kitchenette–equipped motel as had the others who would be working on this project, and began logging what would often be 12–14 hour days, 7 days a week. All too quickly any kind of spare time, even for such things as grocery shopping, preparing food, laundry, or any kind of recreational activities after work on those long spring evenings would command a premium. Fatigue soon set in, and there was little extra time for anything other than working and sleeping.

However, although it was springtime in Boulder, we were traveling to Nederland daily to measure streamflow and collect sediment samples in two streams, and it was a long way from being springtime in the high country. It seemed to either rain or snow on us daily, regardless of where we were, and we were wet and cold more often than not. Standing in fast moving, thigh–deep, ice–cold water for hours at a time while I did one thing or another drew the heat out of my body like a sponge. On the plus side, we had been provided with the very latest (and brand new) field gear. Rather than have to count the revolutions of my current meter while measuring streamflow, I used a device that could either count revolutions of my current meter, or give a reading of the actual velocity of the water on an LCD display on a small "black box" that I wore around my neck. Each time I had to determine the velocity at a particular spot in a cross section going across a stream channel, I would have to press a rather stiff button on the counter of this device to reset it. Each day I would have to press this switch several hundred times in the course of my work, and it wasn't long before the flesh of my thumb became tender and sore doing so.

One thing I hadn't really anticipated were the various noises of one kind or another that would abound at my motel after dark when I was trying to sleep. Apparently the facility had been remodeled in the not distant past, but the renovations had failed to lower the overall noise coefficient of the place. The floors on the second story rooms creaked. Doors slammed. Phones rang. Vehicle engines started and were revved up, while all kinds of less than considerate characters came and went at all hours of the day and night. I was getting only perhaps 5 hours of rather fitful sleep each night, and soon I was exhausted and somewhat spaced out during the day.

One morning in mid-May, it happened. Hauling myself up out of bed at about 5:00 A.M. to get ready for the day's work, I felt an odd tingliness in the ball of the thumb of my right hand as well as my index finger. Also, there was a weird, but very convincing sensation of cold water evaporating on the skin of my upper right arm and shoulder. I didn't think much of it at the time, and went about my business. As the day wore on it became quite uncomfortable, if not actually painful, to press the switch on the velocity meter with my thumb.

The next morning, the slight tingling in my thumb and finger had been replaced with what I can only call a strange numb and tingly stiffness in most of my hand. The phantasm of the evaporating water on my skin was now more intense and covered more area. It also seemed that my entire hand and arm were becoming strangely weakened, and it was becoming difficult to close my hand tightly and hold it clenched. Since I felt fine and there were no other symptoms,

I wrote it off as just some kind of weird, but unknown, harmless malaise of one kind or another.

With each passing day these strange symptoms became more and more pronounced, until I could no longer bear to press the switch on the Swoffer unit with my right thumb it was so painful. I was now having trouble even holding a pencil in my hand, it had become so weakened and strangely clumsy. Writing at all, let alone legibly, had become particularly difficult, and took a great deal of concentration. After more than a week of this, I got it through my thick head that clearly, something of a serious medical nature was underway, and that come what may, I would have to seek help. Moreover, frankly, at this point I was becoming frightened.

I made an appointment to see Dr. "R," an internist in Denver whom I had known for 20 years, and whose judgement in medical matters I felt I could trust explicitly.

Unlike many others who go through one kind of hell or another, sometimes for years prior to being formally diagnosed with MS, after a rather brief examination and discussion of my present symptoms, Dr. "R" said right up front that he felt I had multiple sclerosis, especially considering the fact of my previous presenting complaint of optic neuritis in 1976.

I quite clearly recall sitting on the examining room table listening to this personable and confidence inspiring white-haired physician with the kind voice tell me that I had MS. I was inwardly surprised at how calmly I took this pronouncement of my present and possibly future ill-fortune and ill-health, and all the various consequences that might present themselves in my life's time yet to come, however long that might wind up being. Although I certainly didn't like what Dr. "R"'s diagnosis could mean for me, I couldn't help but agree with him, like it or not.

My vital signs were, as one might expect, normal, so Dr. "R" ordered a battery of blood tests, a couple of X-rays, and had a urine specimen taken, all to rule out other possible problems and help confirm his diagnosis of MS. He told me that if I wished, he would make arrangements for me to have a MRI done, but I (as well as he) felt that there was no real point in doing so; the situation seemed to be pretty clear-cut, and I concurred with his evaluation that yes, it certainly appeared to be pretty obvious what was going on. We discussed the possibility of my taking prednisone as I had done way back when for my optic neuritis, but mutually decided against doing so for the time being. He told me to get in touch with him the following week for the results of the lab work-ups. He also felt that I should be evaluated by a neurologist to confirm his diagnosis, and arrangements were made to do so in a week or so. As it would turn out, I would be getting the results of my tests via the telephone (they were all normal), and my appointment with the neurologist would be postponed for more than a month.

As I was trying to absorb all the ramifications of what was happening, a detached part of my mind recalled my conversation with Dr. "T," the Australian ophthalmologist at the University of Iowa Hospital almost 15 years before, and his pronouncement that I had a 25–40% chance of going on to develop full-blown MS as time went on. I thought of my "This can't/won't happen to me." attitude since that humid July afternoon in the farm country of the Midwest. I thought of my utter stupidity in allowing myself to get physiologically strung out again, and to suffer the consequences for doing so, all in the name of earning a few thousand crummy dollars. But, outside of the weakness and sensory hallucinations in my hand and arm, I still felt fine and had no other symptoms. How could I possibly know that I had only just begun my *real* MS journey, the one I had been waiting for 15 years to take. How could I have any idea at all what would lie ahead for me? Soon enough, I would find out. Welcome aboard, sir; have a pleasant trip.

I went back to work the next day, trying to make the best of what was rapidly becoming an increasingly difficult situation. My hand and arm continued to bother me constantly, my hand being so weak, clumsy, and tactilely oversensitive as to make writing a real effort, let alone doing much of anything else requiring any kind of strength or dexterity. It also seemed that just getting through each day was becoming more and more difficult, and I was feeling strangely weak and over-tired at the end of each day. A few days later I started to have trouble standing up in the increasingly swift current the snowmelt runoff was contributing to the streams while making discharge measurements or obtaining sediment samples. Looking down at the thigh–deep water rushing past me as I struggled to stay upright in the streams in Left Hand Canyon or Middle Boulder Creek was making me feel somewhat vertiginous, something that had never happened before.

At the end of work on the Friday that would begin the long Memorial Day weekend, I somehow strangely sensed that the physiological bottom was falling out of my ability to cope with whatever was happening to me. In the same kind of instinctive way a pet might wander off to die alone somewhere, I felt that I *had* to get myself back home before I became unable to do so. I left my co-workers at the end of the day, telling them that I was going to start taking sick leave, and would call the Regional Office the following Monday. I drove the 300 or so miles back home that evening on autopilot in a semi–daze that would herald the beginning of what would become more than a month of transcendentally profound unwellness and partial amnesia.

— ·· ≖◆≖ ·· —

I have only scattered recollections of what transpired in my life for the entire month of June, and into the first part of July. Each day was spent in a virtually indescribable and bizarre veiled world of torpor and lassitude that was beyond anything I had ever experienced before, sick or otherwise. The weakness, fatigue, and clouded thinking I was experiencing went far beyond prior experience — I felt rotten beyond belief. I felt so unbelievably unwell and dazed that it occurred to me that perhaps Dr. "R" had been wrong in his diagnosis. Maybe I might actually have Lou Gehrig's Disease, or some other dreadful and terminal malady rather than MS, and that I might in fact be dying. I just didn't know; I couldn't tell for sure.

I called the people at work, told them I was having a rough go of it, and that I didn't know when I would be able to return to work. I added that I would call them every week to give them a progress report. I also called Dr. "R" and told him I wanted some prednisone, and that I was up against the proverbial wall.

So *this* was multiple sclerosis — my own personal version of it, anyway. Day after day after dreadful day was spent in a foggy stupor of unbelievable weakness and semi–catatonia, either sitting at my kitchen table watching the sun pass from east to west, trying to read or do something constructive, but being unable to. Other days were spent sitting propped up against the log that I split my firewood on out by the creek that flows though my property, watching and listening to the water go by. More than once, how I felt reminded me of a science fiction story I had read as a teenager, H. P. Lovecraft's *The Color Out of Space*. In this story, a mysterious meteorite had fallen to Earth which was later found to contain an oddly colored bubble of sorts. The bubble was inadvertently broken by those examining it, and before long, bizarre things began to happen in the surrounding area. To make a long story short, an "evil vapor" had been released with the bursting of the bubble, and soon all living things — it mattered not whether they were human, animal or vegetable — had the very essence of life drawn out of them. In the end, all were reduced to powdery ashes, fine and deep as last night's fire in the old woodstove, gray as a sullen winter's day.

Soon after starting on the prednisone, I became physiologically and psychologically betwixt and between, drifting from complete lethargy during the day to insomnia all night long, with fitful sleep interrupted by weird dreams and nightmares. I thought specutively that had this happened in the winter rather than during the time of the long days, I would probably have to have been hospitalized; I didn't see how I could have taken care of myself during the winter. I thought that if this was going to be the way I was going to feel for the balance of my life, suicide would soon become a very attractive option indeed, and I would have to give some serious thought as to how I should do myself in. I have to tell you that more than once I wondered if I should unlimber my shotgun or my .45, chamber a round, and take a one-way, no-exit ride on the gunpowder express to oblivion. Wryly, crazily, I bantered with myself that if I decided to "pull it," one thing was certain: I wouldn't have to worry about going to hell. I was already there.

Through my haze of unwellness, it occurred to me at one point that being *sick* was when one had a contagious disease of some kind or the other, and that given good health and/or medical care you could usually expect to recover from whatever was ailing you. *Unwell*, on the other hand, meant you were in dire physiological straits, and that you might, or might not ever be restored to the whatever measure of health you had previously enjoyed. Knowing a few things about MS, I had to face the possibility that my present situation could improve completely or partially, get worse, or anything else in between, and could do so at any time for the remainder of my life.

I tried to lay out in the sun one day, but found out in short order that sunbathing was out of the question. For whatever reason(s), the steroids were making me photosensitive, especially on the areas of my arm and shoulder that had "the water evaporating on them." My skin started to blister within minutes, something that had never happened before. I have no recollection whatsoever of doing household chores, watering and mowing the lawn around the house, irrigating the rest of my property, or of all the other routine things one does from day to day. But I *must* have done these things; no one else was there to do them for me. I do recall a trip to the City Market in Montrose, where I was hard pressed just to push in the clutch on my pickup truck when I needed to, let alone remain on my feet to do my shopping. Holding the steering wheel in my super–sensitive right hand just wasn't possible, so I was forced to use my left hand exclusively to drive, something new for a right handed person such as myself. Just standing up for more than a few minutes seemed to now border on the impossible. Me, Mr. Mountain Marathon Man, runner to the summits of fourteeners and back down again, now unable to stand up long enough to wash the dishes in the sink at one crack! I couldn't believe it!!!

The fingers on my hand had become so hypersensitive that it was torture to turn the small serrated knob of the switch on a lamp. Trying to find a water temperature that was comfortable or even tolerable for bathing or dishwashing proved to be variable and elusive. Putting picks on my fingers to attempt to play my guitar was totally out of the question. Daily, I tried to "explore" my hand (especially my hand!) and arm. The hand's stiffness, semi–paralysis, weird almost novocaine-like numbness, and hypersensitivity to temperature and touch waxed and waned, as did other aspects of this acute MS episode. Sometimes the symptoms in my hand would do unpredictable flip-flops from one fifteen minute period of time to the next, going from almost feeling like normal, to being virtually unmovable. I wondered if it was going to be possible to ever learn to live with it. Would it change, or stay like this forever?

I felt disconnected from my body. I was scared and bewildered by what was happening to me. No one could answer my questions; I didn't even know what questions to ask! The "rules" of life, living, and experience learned from 40–plus years of healthy existence were now worthless. I had become a stranger to my own self, within myself, a prisoner inside my own body. I focused on getting through one day, sometimes an hour, or just a few minutes at a time. Sometimes I thought of a 14 mile training run one afternoon in West Virginia when my calves started aching with brutal cramps after 10 miles out, and I breathed a kind of mantra through my teeth to myself over and over again with each stride, each breath, to try to escape the pain in my legs that day: "I'm not a quitter." "I'm not a quitter." "I'm not a quitter."

Ever so slowly, and after more than a month, the veil began to lift.

Chapter V — Beyond the Mirror

If you'll recall from the previous chapter of my story, I spent over a month in a foggy half-dream of an acute MS exacerbation during the early summer of 1989. I literally hid out on my place out in the country, venturing out only when I absolutely had to, in order to buy food or other necessities. I stayed holed up in my home, waiting out the unknown things that had happened, and were continuing to happen to me, while I did my best to physiologically retreat and regroup. It was not a fun summer.

By and by, I recovered sufficiently so that I made plans to return to the Front Range, and return to work. However, I had become so weakened, so enervated by doing the simplest things, that there was no possible way I could resume doing the arduous field work I had done previously. Fortunately, my supervisor was able to accommodate me in my new condition by allowing me to work in the sedimentation laboratory that was processing the samples collected by the field personnel in the Boulder area. This time Fort Collins was my duty station, and I would be working 8 hour days — 10 days on, 4 days off. As I had done before, I would return to the Western Slope on those long weekends to care for my property, and now, also to rest.

Things were different for me now. I couldn't stand in place for more than a few minutes at a time, and I found that walking any distance at all was out of the question. I sat on a bar stool at home when I was in the kitchen preparing a meal, or even when I washed the dishes. I packed this same stool with me each time I returned to the lab in Fort Collins to sit on as I worked. I spent so much time with my tail parked on it, I wound up adding an extra layer of high density foam to the seat, lest I get too tender from so much sitting. I got sore anyway.

Late in June, I finally saw the neurologist in Denver whom Dr. "R" had wanted me to see to confirm his diagnosis of MS. Dr. "D" asked me a variety of questions, poked and prodded me here and there, looked into my eyes with his ophthalmoscope, watched me walk up and down the hall, scratched various parts of my body with one thing or the other, and had me test the strength in my hands with a recording "squeeze meter," among other things. At the end of a the better part of an hour of this, the examination concluded, I sat in Dr. "D"'s office while he pronounced his concurrence with Dr. "R"'s prior diagnosis. Great. What else was new?

I had an endless array of questions I would have liked to ask this pleasant, slightly corpulent man of what I estimated to be about 60 years of age, not to mention answers I would have liked to receive. But, I did not know what questions *to* ask; after all, I was a newcomer to the MS game. He mentioned things I already knew, mostly of a physiological nature. I told him I already knew those things. I asked several questions that he must have heard hundreds of times already, things that must have made me appear to be the proper fool. Was it possible to have a "relapse?" Food? Alcohol? Paralysis? Exercise? Prescription medication? Prognosis? He answered my questions, such as they were. Then again, the questions I really wanted answered, *really needed* an answer to were left dangling, floating will-o-the-wisp-like in my mind. Only the passage of time could and would answer these questions, as I would soon start to find out.

The office visit approaching its conclusion, the doctor left me with: "When you get tired, rest for a while, and let the batteries recharge. Meanwhile, just get on with the 'show'." Huh? Do *what???* All I knew at that point was that I felt as if I had aged 30 years in a month, and that I now felt like my own grandfather most of the time. I was doing my best to absorb what this man was telling me, but I didn't have the faintest idea what he was talking about. I had been doing whatever I damn well pleased, all day long — thank you, for more than 40 years. Now I was supposed to do *What?* Let the "batteries recharge?" I couldn't grasp the concept.

$250.00 poorer, and totally preoccupied with saturation–point incredulity, I left the doctor's air conditioned office, and began making my way down the corridor of the hospital annex to the elevators. It occurred to me that perhaps a black robe with matching cone shaped hat, sporting pentagrams and crescent moons on it might be more appropriate garb than a white lab coat and tie for some folks in the medical profession. With that thought in mind, out the hospital annex's double doors I went, into the blazing mid–summer Denver sun, and back into my own life, such as it was. And such as it would be, now that I was officially "diagnosed."

⚜

Even though I had a mostly sit–down type job now, just getting through each day was tough. Merely sitting on my stool, let alone standing for extended periods of time was getting to me, and soon the muscles in my back started cramping along with my legs. It seemed like I was always uncomfortable, no matter what I did, or didn't do. Every evening I would try to go for a short walk, or better yet, ride my mountain bike which I had brought with me to Fort Collins. At first, I was aghast at how little I could walk or ride without becoming exhausted and trembly in my legs. Slowly, carefully, gingerly — I began to walk a little farther, ride a little longer each time out. What would happen? Would I grow stronger? Get weaker? Remain the same? Would I have another major MS "episode?" Was I courting disaster? I decided to risk it, and became determined to find out, come what may.

Occasionally it felt as if a switch was flipped to the "off" position in my legs for an instant while I was walking, and I thought I might fall down. I never did, and "bounced" back up each time this happened. Every time I would bend my head forwards, it felt as if I was plugged into a light socket, and a jolt of electricity would surge through my entire body for an instant. I could no longer tell the denominations of the coins in my pocket with my right hand; they all seemed to be the same size. Moreover, I couldn't tell if they were still *in* my hand or *not* after I had touched them! Being right-handed, many times I would reach for something with this hand as I had done countless thousands of times over the course of my life, and miss what I was reaching for, such as the slot on a newspaper vending machine, or the keyhole on my truck's door. Now and then I would drop things involuntarily. Unconsciously, I began to compensate by using my left hand; sometimes, I used both hands. Slowly, I began to extend myself a little more each evening. Nothing happened. Or perhaps I should say that *something* happened, and what that "something" turned out to be was an excruciatingly slow return of strength and increase in endurance, if I can call it that.

As the summer wore on, it became apparent that even an 8-hour tour of duty for 10 days straight, with the drive back to the other side of the divide on alternating weekends, was too much for me to handle at this point. As no further accommodations were forthcoming from my supervisor (I had the distinct impression that they all tacitly thought I was some kind of malingerer, anyway), I resigned from my job, stating MS as the reason for doing so. And so back I went to my place out in the hills, for what would be the last time I hoped.

⊷ ⥥✦✠ ⊶

I was amazed, (impressed, too, in a weird way) at the high-handed presence of MS. The beyond adequate description, soul-deep, bone-tired weakness and fatigue I now had from day-to-day were beyond anything I had ever experienced previously, either from illness, physical labor, or any kind of exercise or competition. This presence was commanding, inescapable, overriding, and supremely control-ling; it was something that could not be ignored or denied, and certainly not overridden or countermanded. This malaise was pal-pable in its depth, and it forced acknowledgment of its existence. It was something that *had* to be kowtowed to; it was now the master of my life, and was in command of my life. I no longer was the captain of my own ship; MS was. There were many times when I felt it would perhaps have been easier to just give up and give in to it, and I felt I could at least empathize with others who had seemed to have done so.

However, I instinctively knew that to bow to this nearly over-whelming desire to give up would literally be my personal, physical coup de grâce. To give in, to give up now, would have permanent, probably irrevocable and irreparable physical consequences for the balance of my life. I was not about to let this disease destroy my life and the plans I had worked so hard to attain so far. I'd be damned if I was going to abandon all the things I enjoyed doing outdoors, just because I felt rotten all the time. I made a vow, with an intensity equal to, or exceeding that of any resolve I had ever made previously, that I would fight this outrageous disease to the best of my ability till the day I died, and then some. If I was going to go down in flames, at least I would do so knowing I had given it my best shot.

⊷⊷⊷✦⊶⊷

Some days my legs were weak and trembly, and hurt constantly with cramps. Far, far more, for instance than when I ran up and back down Kendall Mountain in Silverton in my combat boots on my first-time introduction to mountain endurance races (it didn't occur to me to wear my running shoes for my very first race — I had thought: "Running shoes to climb a thirteener? No way." It was the wrong choice, and I paid dearly for it, with brutal charley horses in my legs for the entire next week. The MS had made it tough for me to just stand in place for more than a few minutes to do everyday household chores, but I doggedly forced myself to stand for as long as I could tolerate the discomfort, and often beyond, until my legs were trembling, and I thought I might fall down, although I never did.

Almost imperceptibly as the weeks wore on, I found that I was able to stand for longer and longer periods of time before I had to sit on my bar stool, which I kept handy in the kitchen.

Carefully, tentatively, I kept to a plan of walking up and down the roads near my home several times each week. I walked as far as I felt I could each time, gradually increasing the distance. The weird shocks in my body when I flexed my neck forwards continued, and I thought I still might fall sometime, but I didn't, and in due time I would learn that these strange shocks was *l'Hermitte's sign*, a typical symptom in people whose brain stem and upper spinal cord has been affected with MS lesions. The shocks became less intense as time went on, although to this day they are still there to a lesser degree. By next spring I could walk, sometimes with great effort and considerable discomfort, 2 or 3 miles. I stayed with it, sometimes resting enroute for a few minutes, sometimes "going the distance" if I felt up to it.

I started riding my road bike here and there that summer, slowly adding upgrades as fall approached. At first, it was discouragingly difficult and tiring, particularly on hills, but soon I was riding farther and farther each time. Before long, I confined most of my rides to uphill/downhill only. Although I couldn't stand up in the stirrups and crank away endlessly as I had in my pre–MS days, I marvelled in the fact that the rhythmic contraction of the muscles in my legs when riding my bicycle was nowhere near as tiring as walking, let alone standing. It felt wonderful to get some oxygen into my lungs, and to feel the return of cardio–pulmonary adequacy and fitness.

Winter, short days, and less overall activity posed other problems. Activities that I had previously enjoyed now presented a whole new set of variables that had to be taken into consideration. However, if you don't know what the variables *are*, because your life experience has been something quite different, how can you enter these new factors into your own personal equation? Tentatively, and in some instances with considerable trepidation, I continued to explore my body with its altered sensory input, its diminished strength and endurance.

Some activities were clearly out of the question that first winter. Not knowing anyone who would go with me for a trial cross–country ski trek, I was unwilling (also known as scared) to test myself *by* myself. The thought of my legs failing me and falling, or running out of energy and becoming stranded were too much for me to deal with that first winter. I was forced to admit to myself that indeed, I had lost my previous physical self–confidence.

There were now a plethora of psychological and emotional problems to cope with, too. I spent most of that first year in denial of what had happened. There also was an incredible rage and anger that seethed and festered within me. In all honesty, I must tell you that more than once, I got lit up like a Roman candle on enough Budweiser to launch a battleship in an attempt to numb and drown out the loss of my body — and the death of my dreams. And I cursed God (or the lack thereof), all of His/Her/Its relatives, my parents, my bad luck, my own stupidity, and any other thing that was handy at the time. I would get clear off in a towering rage, and shout myself hoarse until I could almost no longer speak, or I would cry myself dry. But the next morning, the MS was still there, and now there was a plain old–fashioned hangover on top of it.

For most of the first year, I went to bed with the delusional hope that I might wake the next morning with my symptoms gone, and with myself whole once more. More than just a few times I woke in the middle of the night in a panic when either arm went "to sleep" as a result of diminished circulation from being crimped while I slept, thinking that I was now going to be faced with more permanent MS damage. Although I had read about going through different periods or phases of adjustment to injury and/or loss — and people having to deal with denial, anger, bargaining, and finally acceptance, I thought that was just a bunch of hooey — BS fed to folks who didn't know any better, or who were somehow "weak." I learned I was wrong about that too, and that I was in full denial of my present circumstances. It was part of the healing process, if I may call it that; something that had to be learned first-hand, and in person.

Some of these experiences in learning acceptance were, in retrospect, amusing. Some were not so funny.

For example: It's the dead of winter, a cold January night with no moon, and the starlight on the snow doesn't amount to much. As you already know, I live out in the country, and we don't have such things as street lamps out here. Moreover, I have not left a light on inside the house, nor is the porch light on. I've arrived at my place well after dark from a grocery shopping foray, and make my way from my truck to my front door in the darkness. Being a little peculiar in my own way, I always lock my house when I'm away, although there's certainly no need to do so, given where I live. With bag of groceries cradled in my left arm, I fumble with the key ring in my right pants pocket with my numb right hand (the keys are there out of many years of habit), trying to discern which key is the key to my front door. It's square, but I can't tell the difference between it and the other round-headed keys by feel alone anymore. Finally, I get the keys out of my pocket, dropping some coins on the ground in the process, and try to *see* which key is the one I want. But I can't see it in the blackness. Finally, the extent of my thick-headed denial dawns on me as I stand there in the dark, a raw wind coming down off the mountain from the north, shivering outside my warm home on a winter night that's colder than the shady side of a polar bear's patootie as I attempt to figure out which key is which by feel with a hand that *cannot* feel such things anymore. Putting the bag of food down, I transfer the keys to my left hand, pick out the key I want straightaway, and let myself into the house.

The next summer —

I never made it out to the West Coast that first year because of the acute MS episode in May. This year, however, I'm back. Standing at the top of the cliffs and the several hundred vertical feet I must negotiate to actually get to the ocean itself on my uncertain legs, legs that haven't climbed up *or* down anything particularly steep since May of last year, I contemplate the possible consequences of a mishap. I'm somewhat encouraged in that I've been up and down these cliffs previously, and I know from experience that except for right at the bottom where there's a steep ladder I'll have to negotiate for the last few feet, if I stumble and/or fall on the way down the narrow, somewhat skiddy trail, I can't really get hurt until I get to the bottom. But what if I *do* fall? Or what, worse yet, how about if I can't get back *up* after spending the day down there on the beach? Will I have enough nerve to ask for help if I find I really need it? Will I have to get hauled back up to the top by rescue people or the police???

I screw up my courage, and with backpack on back and boogie board in hand, I cautiously start down the sandy switchback path. By the time I reach the bottom a few minutes later, my legs are noticeably weak and starting to tremble almost uncontrollably, but I'm still on my feet, and — I made it!

After finding a spot to set my things, I rest for a while, and to my considerable relief find that my legs (as well as the rest of me) return to a state of equilibrium in only a few minutes. I soon find that if I get too warm from lying in the sun, a swim in the cool water in the surf makes me feel better immediately each time I do it.

After spending the rest of the day alternating between catching waves as well as rays, I pack up my gear in the late afternoon, and prepare for the ascent back up the cliffs from the beach, once again with apprehension. To my complete amazement I find that I'm able to walk right up the steep path without stopping, actually passing a number of other people also leaving the beach who are quite clearly not up to the task, at least from a cardiovascular and pulmonary perspective. On the way up, I savor the thick, moist, oxygen-rich air of sea level that I'm pulling into my lungs as I climb upwards and away from the sound of the ocean. It's always been a treat to come from the high country of Colorado to a lower altitude, and in doing so feel "supercharged" for a few days. I can't help but think of some of the races I ran in the mountains only a few years before as I push myself up the hill. I also remember my runs along the canal, all of them also supercharged when I was back in Maryland, and that long run from Swain's Lock down to Georgetown with "P" on a fall afternoon that now seems to have happened a lifetime ago. Although my legs are burning from the effort by the time I reach the parking area above, I'm immensely buoyed by my physical accomplishments of the day.

The next day, a tiny portion of my physical self-confidence having been restored, I am even more active in my day of surfing and fooling around on the beach. Too active, I would find out that evening when I return to my motel room. Feeling pretty much played out from my unusually active day, I lie down on the bed when I abruptly feel rather strange. I can feel what seems to be every nerve and blood vessel in my entire body pulsing with every beat of my heart, as if I'm incredibly hypertensive. This bizarre feeling is at first frightening and disconcerting, but after about 15 minutes it passes, not to return, and without any apparent consequences.

The Mirror

I am having a bad dream — Or am I?

I have been awakened in the middle of the night with a distressingly full bladder. It's nearly pitch black outside, and the silence is ringing with the slight tinnitus I now have as a side effect from one of the medications I'm taking. Not wanting to turn on the light on the night stand by the side of my bed, lest I blind myself with the light, I tentatively make my way to the bathroom, feeling along the familiar walls of my house as I have done so many times before, treading carefully lest I stub my toes on some floor-bound obstacle on the way there, having done so on several previous, and still very memorable occasions.

With the dull salmon glow of the night light above the sink and the mirror of the medicine cabinet as my guide, I notice something strange in the darkened reflection from the mirror — something that suddenly grabs my attention.

It is a grotesque human face, certainly not my own. It couldn't *possibly* be me. Obscenely bloated, edematous, and almost spherical in appearance, the eyes almost swollen shut from fluid retention in the eyelids, I stare transfixed at this monstrosity, the urgency of my need to urinate forgotten for the moment. Somehow, I intuitively know that this apparition appears as it does as a result of too much prednisone, as well as not watching one's intake of sodium. This person obviously has a severe case of Cushing's syndrome.

I look more closely at the face in the mirror. In startled amazement, I realize that this is *my own self*. The eyes, particularly the right eye (the MS eye), is incredibly swollen, reminiscent of the time when as a child I got downwind of a brush fire that had a good compliment of poison ivy in it, winding up with insanely itching lesions all over my body for the next ten days from the smoke. I got it on my face, in my nostrils and in my mouth, in my ears, my eyes — even on my genitals.

In near panic, and instinctively thinking I might be having a nightmare, I try to find a thread of unreality in the scene before me, something to break the dream, and which will force me to wake up. I reach up and touch my face; yes, it is my own face, with my own hand touching it in the mirror. Everything else is also just as it should be in the bathroom: color and placement of towels, the design on the shower curtain, the cobwebs behind the water heater and the light coating of dust on top of it. Every single detail is perfect, right down to randomly placed tiny white flecks of dried spittle on the mirror here and there, a result of too vigorous tooth-brushings on occasion.

Completely unnerved and in total dismay, I turn on my heels, exit the bathroom, and go back to bed. But, before long, I'm back in the bathroom again, the entire scene the same, the bladder still painfully full and urgent, the face (*my face!*) still leering back at me in the mirror.

This crazy scene repeats itself again and again, perhaps half a dozen times, until on the final repetition, sunlight is streaming in through the east bedroom window. I can tell from the angle of the sunbeam playing on the bed that it's close to noon. The horror of seeing my turgid face in the mirror still fresh in my mind, my bladder still tight and full, I touch my face; it feels as it should. Once again, I make my way to the bathroom, fully expecting to see myself as I had all night long. But no, this time I appear as I should. It was just a dream.

Profoundly distressed by the clarity as well as the implications of my dream, I try to purge the nightmare from my mind, but cannot. Although I have slept for almost 13 hours, I'm exhausted, more tired than when I went to bed the night before. I put some water on the stove for coffee, and in a fog, I begin to try to make something out of what's left of the day, the dream continuing to haunt me relentlessly.

In the summer of 1992 I will be beginning my fourth year as an "official" MS person. Or should I begin my reckoning of my "MS time" beginning in July, 1976, that being the year when the disease first presented itself with my bout of optic neuritis? I guess it depends on your perspective.

At this point (presently) most of the questions I would have liked to ask Dr. "D," as well as some of his colleagues, had I known *what* it was I wanted to ask, have been answered. These queries have for the most part not been answered by physicians, or by reading a scientifically or clinically oriented book on the subject of multiple sclerosis, even though both have tried in their own way(s) to help me. Certain questions, by their very nature, do not and/or cannot have an answer, such as how the disease will affect me as time goes on. My prognosis, as it were. Talking at length with other MS people when I've been able to do so, and reading about the experiences of others in stories they've written has been more helpful than anything but my own personal experience.

A few things, however, have become quite clear (at least to me) in the past three years:

Only people who actually have the disease can truly understand what it is like to have it. Others, including physicians, can only guess at what it's like to have some of the almost impossible-to-describe symptoms, such as fatigue and weakness. Words do not — *cannot* — even begin to do justice to this common, and particularly devastating ancillary effect of the disease. It must be experienced to be truly understood.

I had to work through my denial of what had happened to me before I could get beyond it. It was a wall that had to first be dismantled piece by piece, instead of trying to bull my way through it as I so often did when I was younger. I eventually also learned to stop feeling sorry for myself, and when I did I began to live a meaningful existence again. I had to learn that there is no dishonor, shame, or guilt in being unable to do some of the things I used to do previously, or in only being able to do less, or taking longer to do them.

I've learned that except for certain constants (i.e., the loss of some of the sight in my eye and the partial paralysis in my hand and arm), my disease is a "living" thing, and it waxes and wanes from day-to-day, or even from hour to hour for no discernible rhyme or reason. I've discovered that some days are "good" days, and some are "bad" days; that's just the way it is now. I've learned to live in the present as much as possible, and not to worry about what "might" happen, the future indeed being an unknown.

I have been forced to learn, like it or not (believe me, I don't!), to structure my activities around my disease, and not the other way around as I used to do. When I am having a "good" day, I've found that I can accomplish a great deal (more than I ever dreamed would be possible when MS first laid me low) if I just pace myself, rest for a minute or two or five or ten (or *whatever*), and then go on about my business again. This pacing has come almost naturally, as it did when I was competing athletically, and no longer seems strange for me as I go about my daily business.

A bad night's sleep (part of the "invisible" nature of my own personal version of MS) and/or inadequate rest in general will *invariably* back me up against the MS "wall" the next day, or for the next several days. I rest *when* I feel a need to do so, and for as *long* as I feel a need to. Conversely, if I'm feeling fairly well, I "go for it" as long as I can; doing so isn't going to cause a "relapse" or hurt me, although at times I may be uncomfortable for a while afterwards. I am certain that putting up with this discomfort has paid big dividends in keeping me from further physical deterioration, and as fit as possible given my present circumstances.

I have not found that dietary changes of any kind affect my MS one way or another, nor have things like coffee, alcohol, etc. (nor has anything else in moderation). Furthermore, if you have read in the media, as I have, that among other things, marijuana can help control muscle spasms and associated fatigue and weakness in MS, I will venture to state that as far as I am concerned, those who have thus stated are correct in that assertion. The fact that research into the potential medicinal uses of what millions of people consider to be a relatively harmless herb is stymied by unenlightened bureaucrats and law enforcement officials is unconscionable, and a travesty of the always-present need to remedy disease and human suffering.

I've found that certain drugs help to substantially alleviate some of my symptoms, especially a great deal of the hallmark fatigue and weakness. The first 18 months after my acute flare-up were spent in an almost non-stop string of pain-filled days from severely cramping muscles in my legs. Sometimes, this pain was enough to almost immobilize me for days at a time. Not one single person in the medical profession offered to help me find medication that might help me, although there were certainly enough prescription medications available that might have eased my discomfort. One individual even told me during that time frame that he wasn't sure I actually had the disease! Right.

There is no doubt in my mind that the major factor in my own weakness/fatigue was due simply to the major muscles in my body being in a state of partial clonus all the time; my energy was being "wasted" or "squandered," if you will, by this constant, "inappropri-ate" muscular tension. Mitigating this symptom with prescription drugs has been the key to restoring a fair amount of residual function for me, as it has substantially increased my energy level, which in turn also increases my endurance. And so on, and so on. You might say that it is a pyramid-type effect.

However, I will not soon forget this entire experience with physicians in regard to my MS, and the contempt for the medical profession I have developed as a consequence of hurting for so long without any of them offering to try to help me while I puzzled this enigma out myself. Just being asked to come back for an office visit in six months or a year would have helped, I'm sure.

I learned about drugs that might offer help to me from reading, as well as from other people who had tried them. On occasion (inadvisably and illegally), people would give me a "sample" to try. Much to my amazement, sometimes these trials produced dramatic, positive results. I had to ask for, at times even *demand* to be given a script for this, that, and the other from the doctors. Certain drugs obviously helped, and did so within a day. Others did nothing. And yet, others made me feel worse, again doing so within a day's time. It has been worth the trouble, and perhaps slight danger, to experiment and find suitable chemical help for my problems, although I do not care for some of the side effects that go along with this help. In my own particular case, it comes down to a simple choice: feel halfway decent most of the time, put up with a few side effects and lead a relatively normal life that has almost no ups and downs; or, opt for the wild swings of energy, and feel weak, rotten, and played-out most of the time, and deteriorate as a result of it. Presently, I have chosen the former, and have no regrets about this particular decision.

Exercise (such as riding my bicycle) *always* helps me to feel better immediately afterwards (believe it or not), as well as in the long run, although there may be a small price to pay in the way of a bit of weakness or muscle cramping for a day or two afterwards if I overdo it. I am convinced (repeat — *absolutely certain*) that keeping as active as possible is a key to retaining as much residual function as possible for as long as possible for anyone who has MS. There will be times when it is unpleasant or even painful to keep going, but one *must* stay as active as possible! It is like money in the bank; there will be days when you will have to draw on your own personal account of strength when you are not feeling well.

Attitude — I can tell you right up front that I don't like having MS, and I resent more than I can express in words the "bottom line" for what will be and might come to be the way I have to live for the balance of my life. To say that "it's not fair" or that "it sucks" or whatever — isn't going to change things one bit; that's the way it is. And so it makes sense, just as Dr. "D" said, to "Just get on with the 'show'."

You know, he was right. And, I am doing just that.

━·━ ☷◆☷ ·━

Chapter VI — Pool of Tears

A Story in Two Parts — by Two People
Part I — Sin of Omission

by: Sarah

All right, so you want to know why I broke up with Eric. You've seen the way I talk about him, and smile about him, and look at his picture when I think no one sees. You ask, if I have feelings like that, why on earth I ended the romance — and, having ended it, why I continued a relationship which is now part friendship, partly much more. I wish there was a simple answer, but as there isn't, let me begin by taking you back to a particular day in my life that I could never forget — even if I wanted to.

The morning was cast in the kind of glowing, urgent light that Indian summer brings to the Southwest in October. We had been dating almost a month, and as we drove along in his 4 x 4, we sat bathed in a glow that was a mixture of sunshine and a unique chemistry that was beginning to spring up between us. I had the day off, we were going canyon trekking, and I was filled with a sense of adventure. The dark doubts I had had about moving out west to a more tranquil life-style after half a lifetime spent in Washington, D.C. had vanished for the day. In short, l was happy — happier than I had been for a long time — and I sensed, in the quiet and intense man beside me, that he was happy too.

We had planned a bike ride and a picnic. We chatted about the possibilities of a future together, although my mind was really on what he had said over the phone the night before, and what my reply had been: "Yes, I'll think about spending the night with you." Now I looked more closely at him — at the broad shoulders and strong hands gripping the wheel of the big machine; at his handsome blue eyes surveying the road; at the competence with which he handled himself. The fact that we'd met through a small-town newspaper ad seemed to matter little now, because all the parts seemed to fit into a person almost tailor-made for me. He seemed a master of this rugged, arid country in a way that a citified person like myself could never be, in that he could get almost any machine to bend to his will, not to mention a number of other things as well. At the same time, he was also very well-read and verbally adept, with a vocabulary that tickled the English teacher soul in me. We saw eye to eye on almost everything, it seemed. And, although I was a well-seasoned warrior in the field of love, burned by woman-haters, alcoholics, playboys and worse, I could find no warning signals of any potential problems. Best of all, though, I had been misled by men far too often, and here was a man who constantly spoke of the need for truth, and insisted on it from those around him.

And so it was that I looked, and I listened, and felt myself lifted at the ripe old age of 42 into a thrilling and buoyant optimism. It looked like it could work; I wanted it to work; it *had* to work.

Then the bomb fell. Eric's words were low, almost casual. Because what he said was simply incredible to me, they seemed to scatter into things somewhere outside of my immediate consciousness, and at first I couldn't quite be sure that they had really been uttered.

"I have some bad news," he said gravely, eyes locked to a nearby canyon wall. "You can hear it now or you could hear it later, but you would find out about it sooner or later anyway. I have multiple sclerosis; I've had it for over two years. Normally, I function fairly well, but l have periods of fatigue and pain at times. There's some vision loss, loss of some strength in my hand, and — pause — I'm impotent."

The miles rolled by, and piece by piece, he explained the disease. The man of my fantasies still sat behind the wheel, and after some time I brought myself to realize that he was unchanged. Something else, though, had. I ran a gamut of emotions ranging from overwhelming disappointment, to honest pity for the man. At least he had been honest. But — had he? I was deeply troubled that he had waited until he saw me on the brink of love to tell me the facts. He had said nothing to date that was untrue, but — if a man allows a potential mate to falsely believe in his normalcy as a man, doesn't he become unethical? At what point does timing enter in?

I sighed as he waited for my answer. I saw my dreams slipping away and rushed to pull them back, desperately wanting to sit on my cloud of hope once again. If I was a big enough person, surely I could live with the deficits. "I don't want anything to change between us," I finally said. He smiled, and the day worked its way through its own form, its own logic. The night saw us nestle down together like simple, unquestioning children, determined to be bound by blind faith.

━━━ ✠ ━━━

It is now nine months later. The time I spent with Eric, from fall through early spring, taught me much about the perspective of a person with an incurable disease. In the process, the euphoric highs of that October day were replaced by an extended turmoil, a roller coaster that I finally abandoned in spite of the acute pain that my leaving caused us both.

More importantly, the questions I asked myself remained unanswered; did the disease fashion the man, compromising all that he could have been — or did the man allow the disease to direct him onto the path he would have followed regardless? I will never know. I suppose anyone meeting a middle-aged MS victim like Eric must, as I did, wrestle with the same dilemma. I imagine that, for the able-bodied, the bottom line is the same; we must live in the present, and our present intimacies must be consistent with what we know of ourselves.

Perhaps you understand now; probably not. You walk in your own shoes. I am I, and Eric is Eric. But you can remember, perhaps, that a real merging of a man and a woman must begin with an act of respect, and not pity. At the very least, I've learned to stay open to the possibilities of a friendship with others like Eric. I hope that the same will be true for you.

⊷⋅⋅🏿✦🏿⋅⋅⊶

Part II — The Fifth Date

by: Eric

When you're closer to 50 than to 40, when you've been divorced for more than a dozen years, when you live on a farm out in the country, no longer work a regular job and don't get to town all that much — and, when you figure you've been around the proverbial block a time or two with one thing or another (including the single's scene), meeting someone who could be special is just that: *special*. And then some. I'm talking about that difficult/impossible–to–define something — that magic, allure, chemistry, or whatever you'd like or care to call it. I'm talking about a quality that is perhaps as simple as a shared smile or glance, something essentially indefinable that makes your heart sing and makes you glad to be alive.

And so it was with Sarah right from the beginning. Yes, I answered her ad in the paper. Yes, she called me one evening a few days later. And yes, we found it easy to talk on the phone that first time, so we arranged to meet that coming weekend for a bike ride, a bike ride that would be the first of many others, and one I would not soon forget.

I pulled up to her place with my road bike in the back of my pickup, a perhaps somewhat unconventional, but nonetheless utili-tarian means of transport. We loaded her bike side–by–side with mine and headed off down–valley to find a convenient point to stop and unload our bicycles.

As we rode around the almost deserted section–line roads that afternoon in the irrigated farm country of the lower valley, and while we dodged small fast-moving thunderstorms that chased us here and there amongst the ripening fields of corn that first late-summer day of ours, an ever-so-special spark was kindled between us. Now and then as we pedaled along, she would turn sideways to look and smile at me as we rode and talked, and I tried my best to absorb it all as it was happening, so that the memory of seeing her on her bike in her white sweater and white helmet with the funny red stripes on it would always be with me, no matter what happened in the future.

Later, after we had returned to her house, I told her I would like to see her again, and asked would she like to see me again, too? She dug into her little bike bag, found a tiny scrap of paper that she pulled out of somewhere, and wrote her phone number on it. — So it began.

And also so began something very different for me, too, as I started to ponder *when* would I tell her — *how* would I tell her — and *where* would I tell her that I had multiple sclerosis. That no matter how well I looked, I was not the whole and well person that I appeared to be. And, that I was not the person she expected me to be.

How would I explain that although there was nothing to see outwardly, on the inside I was only a shadow of the athletic, highly active person I had been only a few years before. Under what dreadful circumstances might I tell her that at least in the literal sense of the word, I was no longer a man; that among other things, the disease had stolen, was *still stealing* my sexuality, and that I was virtually impotent. *How do you fall in love with somebody, and then break their heart and your's too???*

I didn't have an answer then. I don't have an answer now.

—·— ✠✠ —·—

So it went. And we grew closer each time we were with each other. On her birthday, she took the day off, and we went on an all-day four-wheeling journey that would take us up on Dry Mesa, here, there, and (so it seemed) almost everywhere on the southern half of the Uncompahgre Plateau. We stopped for a picnic lunch under a huge cottonwood tree that was brilliant yellow in full fall color, and which was next to a dry streambed just off the two-track backcountry jeep trail which would lead us up on top of that part of the plateau. Crunchy dry leaves rested on the ground which was our makeshift table, and the day was rapidly turning out to be none less than near-perfect. As we settled down to eat, I surprised her by producing her birthday present from its iced hiding place in the two-gallon Gott jug that also served as my lunch bucket, a single red rose in a tiny vase.

━━◆━━

A few days later I called and asked if she would like to go for a bike ride up the Dolores River valley from Gateway the next weekend, and — would she be willing to spend the rest of the weekend at my place? She said that she would think about it, but I could tell without her actually saying so that when the time came, she would want me as much as I wanted her, and she would say "Yes."

Thus the stage was set, and my so-called, much feared moment of truth finally arrived. Of only one thing was I certain; I was *not* going to wait until the last minute to tell her about the MS and the impotence. I would have to do it sometime while we were out on our date that beautiful autumn day. And I would tell her, come what may, while there would be ample time for us to talk about it, and for her to bail out — even go back home if she felt like it, before we were committed to spending the night together. I would *have* to tell her *before* we were in an intimate situation. It would prove to be one of the most difficult things I have ever had to do.

With virtually no preamble, I blurted it out while we were headed towards Gateway, with the steep granite and contorted schist walls of Unaweep Canyon as a scenic, rugged backdrop. I remember her looking at me incredulously and stunned as she did in that frozen moment in the life's time of two people, as I told her about my disease and the various ways it had damaged, and could further damage me. How could I ever forget that confession? How could she?

So, with my admission of ill-health for a prelude, we went for our 30-mile bike ride that cloudless, warm fall day along the impressively different amber/mauve sandstone canyon country along the river. We rode till we got to the roadside spring I kept telling her was just around the next curve, and around the next one, and the next one too, until it became a joke as we pedaled on, until we eventually, *finally* reached it for a cool and much needed drink, even though we both had brought water in our water bottles.

Later that afternoon when we returned to Gateway, we put our bikes back on the carrier of my old rusty Saab sedan, cinched them up with more than enough bungie cords to keep them secure, and made our way back to my place, after my first having to fiddle around with the starter motor on the car, because it had a loose wire and wouldn't start.

Two hours later we arrived at my home, and I fixed us dinner. In due course, as we had tacitly planned, the time came for us to begin to explore each other, and share the night.

When the inevitable happened (or perhaps I should say *didn't* happen), at least we had talked about it earlier, not that it made things any easier for either of us. Not sleeping well, and with having the novelty of a bed partner, plus the anxiety and stress of the whole situation, I finally awoke in the wee hours, wide-eyed and in a weird state of biological semi-panic, my legs cramping from our long day on the bicycles in new, urgent, and highly unpleasant MS-type ways. Although I tried not to wake her, Sarah awoke from my agitated inability to just keep still. She offered to massage my legs, and did so until her hands grew tired and she couldn't continue. The deep kneading of my leg muscles helped relieve some of my tenseness, agitation, and discomfort, but nonetheless it turned out to be a long night for both of us.

There were other long nights too, during those coming winter months when we spent so much time together, nights with tears, nights with me feeling totally inadequate and the complete fool, as I tried my damndest to please her intimately one way or another, and with me not really giving a good-goddamn about my own satisfaction (or the lack thereof). But she apparently felt guilty and/or frustrated, perhaps because she thought she couldn't please me. Or was it more than that? Perhaps.

Not once — *not even one time* — was I able to have an orgasm with her.

Eventually the sum of all the parts got to be more than either of us, more than both of us could sustain. Over what unexpectedly turned into a disastrous Chinese dinner one early spring evening, the emotional bottom finally fell out of what had begun with such high hopes for both of us, each of us, when she said without any warning that it was coming, just as I had laid my MS on her that fine fall day, on our bike ride to the roadside spring: She said, "I tried." And then, she burst into tears.

❧ ❦❧ ❧

A Year Later

Yes, we are still friends; we see each other every week or two for one thing or another. Sometimes it's dinner and/or a movie; sometimes, a bike ride or a walk. Now and then I "critter-sit" Mali, her cat, when she goes out of town. Or whatever. And yes, as she told you, our friendship is also partly much more. For that I'm thankful, although it often isn't easy for me in any number of ways. Our relationship has evolved into a different sort of merging and sharing than any other I have ever had, and I cherish it, sometimes long for it. I try not to categorize what it is, analyze, or dissect it. I try to stay strictly in present time when I am with her, but often I'm unable to do so, and I know only that I savor the companionship, trust, and friendship of this person deeply. She is a very important, though sometimes paradoxically painful, part of my life.

I'm often surprised at the extent and depth of my feelings for Sarah, and how those feelings surface at unexpected times. This last year I've often wondered: "What is the nature of love when it transcends clichés and youthful beguilement with someone? What is "love" to a person well past the probable mid-point of their life? Is it possible to still have profound emotional feelings for someone, yet not actually be around them very often, let alone not live with them, or be intimate any longer? Is it "right" or "wrong" to have these feelings? As with so many other imponderables, once again, I do not know the answer, and probably never will.

⊷⊷ ⊠✦⊠ ⊶⊷

Epilogue

Over a late night cup of coffee in her kitchen last winter, I finally broke down and told her something that had been heavy on my mind and crosswise with my soul for a long time; something I had never been able to tell her point-blank previously, even when we spent precious time together: "I love you. I always have. I still do, but not in a romantic way." She just looked at me, and for the moment, said nothing. Just like the short days of winter to bring me up short emotionally, and get me to confess my real feelings — the consequences of doing so be damned.

I'm fairly confident that once again, I caught her completely off guard with my unexpected, forthright admissions that evening. However, though I was looking right at her, I didn't see the expression on her face reflect the enormity of what I had just said. I struggled to maintain my own composure, trying to keep my own eyes and appearance poker-faced, blank, and expressionless as we shared a few more leftover, but nonetheless heavy-duty mutual confessions about one thing or the other.

However, Sarah's verbal pièce de résistance that evening was something I felt I had intuitively known all along, but that she had steadfastly denied on many occasions previously: She said that although we probably could have gone on together a lot longer, it was true that a major factor in our breaking up was *indeed* the MS and what went with it.

*— As I sit here writing this, I hope that she will be able to understand that I have not stated my feelings above as a means of retribution, to embellish my story, or to disparage her in any way. Rather, I do so because — right or wrong — true or untrue — that's the way I perceived things to be **when** they happened, **as** they happened. My perception of reality is only just that — **my** perception. Feeling that I know her rather well at this point, I am compelled to add that the ancillary component of my sexual dysfunction and my concomitantly self-perceived botched love-making also played a less than minor role in the failure of our relationship. Readers of my story must keep in mind that there was more than one reason our relationship went under. Issues of some considerable substance that any couple trying to make a go of it might differ on, such as religion, how I came by my income, my generic anger — often times outright hostility towards others which surfaced inappropriately and at seemingly trivial circumstances, a perceived "lack of service to others" on my part, and more —*

Emotionally blindsided by these not unforeseen, but finally verbalized, out-in-the-open revelations, and with my mind reeling, I eventually said good-bye for the evening, and made my way out the door into the January night.

Good grief.

I had the highway virtually to myself on that late mid-week evening/early morning, and it was a good thing too, as I was definitely on autopilot and flying low. A waning half-moon hung oddly close to the horizon and strange in the eastern sky, the morning-to-be's sunrise illuminating its belly, hopefully showing promise of a better day to come with the dawn.

Sometimes a truth half-known but left dormant, only to be abruptly and unexpectedly awakened is a dangerous verbal elixir, and I tried desperately, but ineffectively, to turn off my mind as I stared down the highway towards the limits of my high beams in the distance. My thoughts were as bleak as the snow-covered desert landscape on either side of me, my car's studded snow tires drumming a steady monotone on the pavement as I made my way back towards home, towards my sanctuary, for what seemed like longer than forever.

I thought of good health and disease, of youth and aging, of successes and failures, dreams come true and hopes gone bad, of life and death, and seemingly everything else in-between. I thought too, of love won and love lost, and of all the love-making and love-living that would now very possibly never be a part of my life ever again. I thought of the grim truth of probably never feeling really well again, of all the mountains I would now never climb, the hikes and bike rides that would not be taken, journeys not made, dreams not shared or realized, and all the other things I would not be able to do — my life's experiences put on terminal hold because of multiple sclerosis. I balked at the thought of what could happen to me from the inside out on any given day in the future because of this screwball, crazy disease. I felt my plans and wish-me-so's being yanked straight from the deepest part of me, pulled right out of my soul as I hurtled down the unfolding straight black ribbon of the highway, starkly contrasted against the half-reflected grayish faintly-moonlit snow. Shipwrecked, a castaway in my own mind, I drifted off into a personal boneyard of dead and dying dreams as I drove on into the blackness. Eventually, almost in a trance, I turned off the highway and realized that I was finally home.

Jesus wept.

I tried to, but found that this time, I couldn't.

❖

— Author's Notes —

Although the person who wrote the first segment of this chapter is a real person, the name "Sarah" is fictitious.

This chapter's title, *Pool of Tears*, is taken from the title of a chapter in Lewis Carroll's *The Adventures of Alice in Wonderland.*

❖

Chapter VII — Homeward Bound

The Moving Finger writes; and, having writ,
Moves on: nor all thy Piety nor Wit
  Shall lure it back to cancel half a Line
Nor all thy Tears wash out a Word of it.

from: The Rubáiyát of Omar Khayyám — Verse LI

What's **your** definition of courage? **How** do you measure it?

I have to tell you that I originally had planned a very different ending to my story than the one you'll be reading today in this last segment of my tale. I'll leave to your imagination what that ending might have been, had I not been standing at a country intersection not far from my home one gorgeous fall afternoon not all that long ago.

If you've been wondering, I didn't write the chapters of my story in order. I didn't work on any of the segments one at a time until I was finished with that particular installment. Nor were they worked on randomly. Sometimes the thoughts and words flowed with ease, as did my fingers on the keyboard. Other times they seemed to be trapped, hanging suspended in a mind-world of clarity like a bubble of air in a quartz crystal. Trapped yes, as in the stiff, semi-feeling, yet hypersensitive fingers of my right hand — my MS hand. Sometimes, I had the feeling that my story resembled a stone tossed into a perfectly still pond so large it had unseeable boundaries. Detached from my own self and life, I watched my own tiny personal ripples spreading out into the vastness of time when I was writing —

spreading outwards, but eventually reaching some unknown shore, where they began to return towards the center, moving back and forth, to and fro, forever. Coming full circle. Coming home —

October 6, 1991 — 4:00 P.M. —

"S" has come to visit, and for a day of picking apples in my orchard, a helping of late-season vegetables from my garden, lunch, and perhaps a bicycle ride later in the afternoon, time permitting. It is an exquisite western Colorado fall day, just a week past this year's *Color Sunday* — cloudless, warm, dry — and beautiful. It is a seemingly perfect day. Who could ask for more?

As it turns out, we *do* in fact have time for our bike ride that afternoon before she has to return home, so off we go, here and there around the general area where I live for an hour or so.

On the way back to my place, although I suggested that we return via one of the less travelled secondary roads in the area rather than on the highway, I defer to her choice to just head back up the hill on the main road. We will only be on the highway for half a mile, and I ride on it all the time by myself anyway, so what the hell. It would soon prove to be a fateful decision, indeed.

It's kind of a standing joke between "S" and myself that I can "out-bike" her on any given day, especially uphill, MS or otherwise, so when I arrive at the road on which I live a couple hundred yards ahead of her, I lean my bike against the road sign at the intersection and proceed to putter around with the "apples for sale" signs I have propped up on either side of the road in an effort to attract drive-by customers to my orchard. Finished with fooling around with my signs, I look down the road at "S" slowly but surely approaching, her

10–speed making the amusing *tinkety-ta-klinkety—tinkety-ta-klinkety* sound it makes when she's in the lowest gear. I smile an inward smile thinking of how she and I met the first time for a bike ride on the section line farm roads on the outskirts of Fruita. I remember her white sweater and her white helmet with the funny red stripes on it, and her sweet smile when she turned to look at me that first afternoon, a smile I will never forget. My heart melts when I think of her this way.

My sweet nostalgic daydream is shattered by the sound of a vehicle approaching up the hill on the gravel road to the west. What especially gets my attention is the sound of the engine — the sound of a V–8 with a four–barrel carburetor, a typical Rochester Quadrajet sound when the secondaries are open, foot–on–the–floor wide–open, and still accelerating. In a couple more seconds, it becomes disturbingly apparent that this vehicle is not going to stop, *cannot possibly stop!* for the stop sign at the intersection with the highway. Hearing the driver goose the throttle one last time as he reaches the intersection, I turn around to see what in hell is going on and—find myself standing square in the middle of a kaleidoscopic explosion of glass shards, bits and pieces of different colored plastic, clods of dirt, flying multi–sized pieces of metal, a bursting spray of liquid, and blurry/unknown God–only–knows other things that are coming **right for me!!!** from the collision of a full–size older light blue pickup truck and a dark late–model automobile. There is a simultaneous blast of sound from compressing/tearing steel, breaking glass and plastic, scuffing tires, moving air, and whatever else was interacting with whatever else at that instant. The truck, airborne when it crested the small rise at the intersection with the pavement of the highway, has run the stop sign at about 45–50 mph, and a car going southbound on the highway has hit it broadside, squarely, and at full speed. There was no time for brakes and skidding, or the blowing of horns. No time to think or be afraid. No time to wonder about being hurt or even dying. There is only a realization of what is occurring, and that I am right in the middle of it, being only about 25 or 30 feet away from the collision, and looking directly at it when it happens.

The smaller, higher velocity ejecta from the collision envelop me and pass me by, leaving me untouched as I stand facing this horizontal shotgun blast of fragments. A non-verbal half-thought forms in my mind that—*I'm all right!*, but at virtually the same instant, I see the slower moving airborne truck and other huge pieces of debris coming directly at me. The now–damaged truck is nose down, tail up and about chest-high off the ground, turning slowly — crazily — clockwise as it rolls through the air, passing me about four feet off the ground and at arm's length. I could have reached out and touched it as it goes by, it is so near to me, had I had the time to do so. As it passes, an unknown/unseen *something* smashes me to the ground instantaneously. I never saw what actually hit me. I involuntarily screamed a stentorian bellow of pain and rage from being struck so unexpectedly and forcefully, immediately followed by a breath-long string of expletives, also at the top of my lungs, from the pain that exploded in my left leg simultaneously with the blow. Somebody else close by screamed a moment later, a female voice. It was "S." (Months later I asked her if she remembered what she had yelled at the time. She told me no, she didn't remember. But I did, in my diamond–clear memory of the moment; she screamed: *"Oh NO!!!"*)

In the odd way of a person who has just been seriously injured, I could tell that I hadn't been mortally wounded (outside of the fact that I might bleed to death) and my first thought was a non-verbal: *I'm still alive!* Next, I smelled the blood — my blood — and felt its warm stickiness on the back of my head as it spread in a rapidly growing puddle on the pavement while I writhed involuntarily in agony from what was very obviously a smashed, broken leg, a serious head wound, and a variety of other injuries. Strangely, I heard cooling metal tinkling nearby in the now abrupt, unexpected silence. Then I heard the beginnings of a great deal of commotion and other people shouting incoherent things.

A few seconds later, I see "S" leaning over me, and I am vastly relieved to see she appears to be unscathed.

In short order, some strange character of what must have been a vehicular passer-by appears in my field of vision, and peering at me owlishly, he begins giving me a weird ad lib—ad hoc, holy-roller version of what he apparently thinks are "last rites." Had I not been at that time essentially restrained by "S" and the paramedics who had arrived on the scene, and who obviously thought I had suffered some grievous head or neck injury (among other things) from all the blood that was coming from the back of my head, I would have lunged at and tried to grab this horse's ass by his ears to show him just how "dead" I actually was!

Although it has taken a while for me to describe this scene, and for you to read it, keep in mind that this whole incident "went down" in about three seconds. In the weeks and months that followed, I was to discover (not unexpectedly) that seeing the collision and watching all the debris and that airborne truck coming right at me was to become a permanent part of my life — a short loop of video tape permanently stuck on slow-mo freeze-frame replay, and that it would play back in my mind over and over again, hundreds and hundreds of times. The spectacle of the crash has been diamond-etched in my memory, a tiny fragment of frozen time in a bell jar of perfectly clear glycerine, just like a fossil insect trapped forever in a piece of amber.

Beginning the day after the wreck, I was to re-learn some things about myself that I had almost forgotten over the years. Things especially forgotten since MS became such an important part of my life. I'm talking about, among other things, appreciation for simply existing — *still being alive* — by luck, by fate and chance, or as some of my more religious friends would tell me — by God.

Virtually housebound, on crutches, and in more pain than I had ever known in my entire life from my various injuries (even with medication), with a vast amount of difficulty and hurting, I ventured outside my front door the next day after an almost sleepless night. Just 15 feet away from the house, I eased my bruised and damaged body onto the top of my picnic table where I had eaten lunch just yesterday with "S," and feeling the warmth of the sun on my skin, gave silent thanks to whatever or whomever had let me survive relatively intact what certainly should — *by rights* — have killed me in place where I stood the previous afternoon. Just 75 feet farther away from where I was sitting, but for me that second day it could have been a thousand miles, I could hear the creek that flows through my farm faintly burbling and gurgling in the baseflow period of its own annual cycle of life. Even injured and hurting so much, it felt good to be alive, good to still be able to experience some of the wonders of life. And so yes, I silently gave thanks — and let the warm afternoon sun bathe my skin and soothe my soul.

Next would come the task of finding out what healing of the body and spirit was possible, given the damage from sunny yesterday — *lucky* yesterday. Like Sisyphus pushing his boulder up the mountain for the Nth time, I too would try to recover and go on, once again — *one more time* — starting at the bottom of the proverbial hill with my own burden.

And I found myself drifting back in time as I sat there on the picnic table, back to a time well over 40 years before when a little boy of perhaps three years with white-blond hair wandered off from his (what was in those days) rural home in suburban Maryland, and headed down to the creek a good half mile away, much to the dismay of his young mother when she discovered that he had disappeared from where he had been playing in the yard. He was off exploring his new and wonderful world, being fresh in life himself. So many things to experience — so many things to do and see for a curious child who had never heard of danger, and who had yet to be hurt. The child had yet to learn about failed trust and perfidy, incurable disease, injury, and death. He still had the shine of new, whole life on him.

Some hours later, a passing motorist in a big black automobile found the youngster walking along what was in those days a hardpacked clay dirt road. The man stopped when he saw him, asking the child where he lived, since he thought the boy was wandering and lost. The little blond boy told the man that he wasn't lost — that he had just been out exploring, and now he was on his way back home, which was just down the road a ways.

Of course, the man in the black car didn't take the toddler seriously, picked him up and put him on the front seat of the car, and turning around, drove him the quarter-mile back down the road to his home, much to the great relief of his by that time nearly frantic mother.

I have been exploring ever since, but it took coming within a yard and a heartbeat of dying to refresh my memory of how precious life is. Even when you have multiple sclerosis.

⋅⋅ ⧓⧓ ⋅⋅

I began keeping an activity journal in a pocket-size calendar book, a "micro-diary," if you will, when I started running in earnest the summer after "J" left, the summer of my divorce in 1979. This abbreviated daily account of what I did (or didn't do) athletically every day helped me keep track of my progress in my training, injuries, any unusual experiences that occurred, and just how I felt in general. On days that I felt extra strong and good, days that I had the proverbial tiger by his tail, I would put a small red asterisk in the upper left hand corner of that day's small square in my book.

Several years later, in the summer of 1981, I was living near Norwood in what we locals here call the "West End," on a 1,400 acre ranch. I had a job that I loved — 4-wheeling and hiking about all over the BLM backcountry from the Ismay Trading Post near Yellow Jacket Canyon, Cortez, and Four Corners, to Escalante Canyon, the Uncompahgre Plateau, and beyond. I was putting in 10-mile runs every other day or so on top of everything else, and I was fit and hard, tanned, and as tough as nails. I hadn't thought of optic neuritis, Dr. "T"'s statistical prognosis, or MS in years. It was the furthest thing from my mind.

Outside of working 10-hour days, five days a week, I was training for the ascent portion of the Pikes Peak Marathon that summer, as well as a number of other events such as the Kendall Mountain Run, the Imogene Pass Mountain Marathon, the Mt. Evans Road Race, and a variety of half-marathons, ten-milers, and what-have-you. I was concentrating on a lot of long hills in my workouts, and Norwood Hill was one of my training runs. I was fit enough to be able to run it twice, both up and down — no stopping or walking, no problem, two times — *yes, sir*. For those of you who know that particular stretch of State Highway 145 as it climbs out of the San Miguel River canyon to the Norwood bench, I'm confident you're impressed with what I just said. For those of you who haven't been there, Norwood Hill is a solid two mile upgrade of 6–7%. If I hadn't actually run up and down it twice my very own self, I might think that the character telling me that they had actually done so was just a BS artist, and that he was telling me this screwball story over a few beers at a picnic or at a bar.

It intuitively occurred to me at that point in my life that I was doing something special — was *living* something special — and that physically I might be on the cusp, the apogee, of my life's experience in terms of physical prowess, and I tried to keep a favored, permanent place in my mind for each one of those extra-special days, those red star days. In retrospect, only twelve years hence, I'm glad I had the foresight at the time to do so.

Sometimes, perhaps more often than I should, I recall those long days that summer, days before I became a prisoner within my own body, days when my spirit and my body were free to soar wherever and whenever they pleased — days before disease and injury robbed me of so much of my freedom. Several times each month that year, I would put another one of those red stars in my book for another good day — a very special — an extra-strong day.

Now, once in a very great while, and then only when I am emotionally up to it, I haul out my stack of pocket-size yearly calendars from years past that rest in a clump under "R" in a tattered accordion manila folder, along with some race results and other notable athletic memorabilia. As I said before, in those little books are somewhat cryptically written from day-to-day, a very terse story of my life for the last twelve years — my divorce, my triumphs and failures in the world of running and athletics, notable experiences and adventures with people and places, and for the last three years now, the progression of my MS and my physical decline.

Wistfully (and more often than not also "mistfully"/"missedfully," I am always drawn to one particular red-starred entry of a months-long cluster of others on a particularly good day that summer of 1981.

After a 10-hour day at work, I had gone off on a typical long training run, out and about on the two-track jeep trails and deer and cow paths in the sparse piñon-juniper country that comprised the bulk of the huge ranch, and the BLM backcountry surrounding it. The evening air that day was rich with the smells of that P-J country, the new and slowly growing piñon pine cones with pungent sticky sap droplets glistening on them, ripening juniper berries on the cedars, and fresh sagebrush. I was alone as I ran, except for the nighthawks that were keening from their lofty vantage points so far up in the evening sky as they flew erratically above, surveying the two-legged intruder on the ground who had violated their sanctuary. Now and then, one would dive-bomb me wildly, recklessly, its wings cutting the evening air with an always totally unexpected feathered scream as it pulled up out of its dive, and which would invariably raise the hairs on the back of my neck for a moment every time it happened.

As dusk deepened, I cruised effortlessly on those soft dirt trails with the view of Lone Cone, Wilson Peak and El Diente, and the La Sal Mountains just over the Utah line for a backdrop. My lungs filled full with air easily, sweetly, and I thought that Mercury's winged feet might indeed be my very own. I felt incredibly full of strength, energy and life that long summer evening as I ran and ran. I was so replete with verve that I thought I might be having a wonderful dream, or that even perhaps I was in *other time*, running with some of *The Ancient Ones*, chasing down a wounded buckskin or rabbit — but actually I was running just for the sheer joy of such free and easy movement itself, as I darted here and there amongst the old gnarled trees and clumps of sage, jogged now and then, or sometimes pushed myself flat-out in a sprint for a while up and down the powder-dry hillsides and shallow ravines.

I knew I was having an unusual, possibly unique moment in my life — something that might even be transcendental — and I reached down into myself as deeply as I could to embrace this experience — *this run* — and fix it in my mind and in my very flesh permanently, lest this precious gift of strength and physical freedom be taken from me one day in the future.

And so I ran on —

Returning to my tiny ranch cabin only when it became too dark to see, I wrote the following later that evening in my journal alongside another, and this time very special little red star:

> ~ 10 mi. in 1:21
> felt **V** strong
> — *Could have run forever* —

May all **your** days be good ones, too.

Author

Profiles

Peter C. Andre
Colonel, U. S. Army (ret.)
New Port Richey, Florida

Peter C. Andre was born a premature baby of 2½ lbs. on Valentines Day, 1934, in Brooklyn, New York. Shortly thereafter, his parents moved to Pawtucket, Rhode Island, where he lived until he was midway through high school. His family moved to Manasquan on the New Jersey coast, which was where he spent his high school years. He received a track scholarship to Pennsylvania Military College, and graduated in 1955 with a B.S. in Business Administration, and a regular army commission. He entered the service that same year as a 2nd Lieutenant. Also during that year, he married Virginia (Ginnie) Clauberg and they would in time have two boys — Scott and Colin.

His multiple sclerosis first appeared in 1963. Through a series of lucky events he remained in the service, not to be medically retired until 1984 with the rank of colonel. During most of that period he had over 18 years on parachute status, had several different commands, and three tours in Vietnam. Among his awards and decorations, he treasures most of all the eight different U.S. and foreign parachute wings he was awarded. All his decorations were earned and awarded while silently carrying MS, and he served a total of 29 years in the Armed Forces.

Today his family lives on the west central coast of Florida, with Pete and Ginnie's home near New Port Richey. They are now enjoying the good life of being grandparents.

THE MS AUTOBIOGRAPHY BOOK

Karen G. Stone
Albuquerque, New Mexico

Born and raised in San Francisco, Karen Stone, 45, studied photography and later obtained a B.A. in Communications from Antioch College. She worked as a professional photographer for ten years and then, utilizing both her photography and writing skills, moved into the marketing field for publishers. Upon relocating to Albuquerque, New Mexico, she continued to work in marketing for architectural/engineering firms until MS slowed her down.

This led to Karen's full-time writing efforts. Currently, she writes a biweekly column for the Albuquerque Journal, free-lances other pieces for national magazines, and is in the process of completing a non-fiction photography book on accessible architecture.

Beverly Zajicek
Wonder Lake, Illinois

—— ⌗⬩⌗ ——

Beverly Zajicek is a 45 year-old native of Illinois. She has a bachelor's degree as well as advanced hours in elementary education, with concentrations in music and environmental science. She has taught for 23 years, and continues to teach social studies at the middle school level.

She has been a volunteer in several community-based charitable organizations, and currently serves as secretary for her church's social action committee, where she emphasizes ministry to the handicapped.

Teaching has allowed her to experience a variety of interesting summer jobs. One of which she says was most rewarding, was to supervise the United States Youth Conservation Corps in her county for several summers. Teaching also allows her time for summer travel. Most recently, Ms. Zajicek accompanied her native Russian speaking husband on their fourth trip to Russia where they took 15 teenagers to do street witnessing and school evangelism.

Between teaching, travel, and summer jobs, she finds writing an enjoyable activity, and has done free-lance writing, as well as being the editor of two denominational publications.

Ms. Zajicek's mother was diagnosed with MS when Beverly was 9. It was the chronic-progressive type of the disease, which left her mother a quadriplegic for 19 of the 29 years she lived with it. The family was able to care for Mrs. Zajicek at home, and Beverly became an expert on multiple sclerosis, reading extensively, and acting as facilitator for the MS Patient and Family Support Group in her county. In 1989, Ms. Zajicek herself was diagnosed with multiple sclerosis, but has not experienced any functional handicap.

Lisa A. McCoy
Worcester, Massachusetts

Lisa McCoy, 29, is a native New Englander, and has lived in Worcester her entire life. Lisa became disabled with multiple sclerosis in 1982 while still an undergraduate at Boston University. Despite this illness, she continued her education, and successfully earned a degree in Business Administration/Finance.

Lisa is currently employed in the accounting department of a health-related organization, and uses her free time getting involved in diverse activities, most notably Girl Scouts of the U.S.A., where she has been a leader for the past six years.

She is thankful that she was given many opportunities to travel all her life, and looks upon it as a challenge to still visit parts of the world in her current condition. Lisa still dreams of one day visiting the grand state of Alaska, and hopes one day this dream will come true.

Lee J. Draper
Moorooka, Queensland, Australia

Lee Draper spent her childhood and teenage years in the steel town of Wollongong, not far from Sydney, "down under" in Australia. She moved to sunny Queensland with her baby son and husband, John, in 1964.

She worked as a hairdressing teacher at the Brisbane Technical and Further Education College, which was a job she enjoyed for 20 years.

She resides in the leafy suburb of Moorooka (an aboriginal word for iron bark) with John and their two cats, Pie and Chips. She still has a special place in her heart for the neighborhood possums and leaves cake out for them every night.

A Change of Attitude is her first venture into writing. She is presently working on a novel relating to her experiences with her much loved Possum, "Muscles."

Jeanette Stones
Seattle, Washington

Jeanette Stones is thirty-two years old, and lives in Seattle, Washington with her two precious cats. She was diagnosed with multiple sclerosis when she was twenty-nine. Nothing prior to this diagnosis prepared her for what it would be like to live with MS. Jeanette has always been very creative, and she uses this, plus her irreverent sense of humor, and her strength and spirit in all aspects of her life. In the past three years she began writing and drawing. She likes to think of this work as "healing through art." Living with a chronic illness creates a lot of stress, but her art has become a healthy tool in coping with the daily ups and downs of living with MS.

Heather Lewton
Maidstone, Kent, England

Heather Lewton is 43, and has lived in Kent for 24 years. She works as a Classroom Assistant for the Special Tuition Centre at a local High School.

Heather became "disabled" in 1972 whilst employed as a Radio/ Teleprinter operator for the Kent County Police Force. The diagnosis of MS was not made formally until 1981. Still mobile — albeit with the aid of a stick — she tries to live a "normal" life, although pain and fatigue are constant factors.

In the past she played both flute and clarinet, but has now lost the dexterity to do so. Heather enjoys listening to music, reads a great deal, and loves solving crosswords. A new computer gives her yet another interest, plus coping with the hectic life of a 16 year old son!

Alison D. Kovaleski
Lisle, Illinois

—·—⚏✦⚏—·—

Alison Kovaleski has been writing for eighteen years, starting when she penned her first poem at the age of seven. Now 25, and recently relocated from New England to the Chicago area, she works full-time in the long-range planning department of a major corporation. In addition to her hectic work schedule, she is currently pursuing her bachelor's degree in Business Administration, and her long-term plans include earning an M.B.A.

Ms. Kovaleski was diagnosed with MS at age 22, but refused to let it stop her from living a full life. The essay published in this book was the result of an English assignment in her first year of college at Sacred Heart University in Connecticut, where it garnered the 1990 Rycenga Freshman Essay Award. Encouraged by that honor, as well as the honor of being included in this book, she continues to transform her scribbled notes into essays, and hopes for future publication.

1990 was a "banner" year for her — in addition to being diagnosed with MS, and winning an award for her account of it, she also had her first poem published.

Ms. Kovaleski now lives in the Chicago area, along with her typewriter and two cats, Ambush and Sabotage. When she is not working, studying, or writing, she can usually be found at Wrigley Field, wishing she was in Yankee Stadium.

Yvonne A. Fischer
Juneau, Wisconsin

Yvonne Fischer is 39, and has lived in Wisconsin all of her life. Yvonne is the fifth-born of eight children, and was raised on a dairy farm. She married her high school sweetheart, Jim, at age 20.

Before becoming disabled, she competed in trapshooting several times a week, year-round. The trophies she received while competing are on display in her office. Yvonne was actively involved in writer's groups, and has judged for national writing contests. She has written four novels (none were published), and is just now starting to write again.

Yvonne has been self-employed since 1986, when MS first surfaced. She is a tax preparer and a business consultant. She likes to help people, and in her business, she does so by solving problems her clients face with being in business, or sometimes, just for being. Yvonne feels she has a good balance in her life. Her active business continues to give her challenges, and her northern retreat gives her serenity.

Yvonne loves the outdoors, and for the last 15 years has spent as much time as she can at her vacation home in northern Wisconsin. She uses a hand controlled golf cart to take her walks through the national forest that borders her property. In winter, she drives a snowmobile, modified for easier handling and comfort. She and her husband spend many of their days on the lake fishing and their evenings stargazing.

Barbara Gurman
New York, New York

◆◆◆

Barbara Gurman was born in 1944 in New York City, and has lived in all the boroughs with the exception of Staten Island. She has worked since the age of 18 as a secretary/administrative assistant for several publishing houses, and presently works for United Cerebral Palsy of NYC.

Over the years she has traveled in the U.S. and Europe, both prior to and after her diagnosis of MS, and she has more trips planned for the future.

Eric Smirnow
Cedaredge, Colorado

＊＊＊

Eric Smirnow is 46, and has lived in Colorado most of his adult life, the last 17 years in the western part of the state. He was born and spent his childhood and teen years in suburban Maryland near Washington, D.C., before attending the Univ. of Wisconsin/Madison, and subsequently moving to Colorado in 1969. He has a degree in geography from the Univ. of Colorado/Boulder, and worked as a civilian federal employee in different positions and locations for close to 25 years. Most recently he was employed by the U.S. Dept. of the Interior – Bureau of Land Management, and the U.S. Dept. of Agriculture – Forest Service in western Colorado as a hydrologic technician.

Mr. Smirnow became "invisibly disabled" with MS in 1989, and has been self-employed and semi-retired since then. It is worthy of note that his mother also has had MS for many years, although for a considerable time, it was not "officially" diagnosed as such.

Mr. Smirnow lives alone on his 4½ acre orchard, where he grows certified organic fruit, writes, does custom desktop publishing, and water resource consulting. He still loves being outdoors, as well as pursuing to a lesser degree many of the activities he has always enjoyed, and he tries to stay as active as his present circumstances will permit. He considers himself privileged to have extensively travelled and explored the hinterland of southwest Colorado year-round in various ways while he was employed by government agencies.

He also is grateful, indeed, to have had the privilege and good fortune when in his thirties of being able to train for and compete in many local and regional endurance running events, such as the 14 mile ascent portion of the *Pikes Peak Marathon*, and the 18 mile *Imogene Pass Mountain Marathon* from Ouray to Telluride, Colorado.

Mary S. Martinez
Pullman, Washington

Mary Martinez was born and raised in the shadows of the Rocky Mountains in Helena, Montana. She adapted to, then tolerated, the snow and sub–zero cold fronts that dropped down from the north, not to lift for months at a time, until she reasoned there must be more to life than jumper cables, mud, and snow drifts that seemed to dominate three of the four seasons.

In 1970 she loaded her car and migrated to Seattle, the jewel of the Evergreen State, sandwiched between the Olympic and Cascade Mountain Ranges. She instantly acclimated to exploring abundant mountain trails, lakes, and beaches, as well as the city's rich offering of cultural and social events. It was in Seattle that she met and married her husband, Fredy; it was also in Seattle that her wonderful baby boy was born. In 1976 the family moved across the state to Pullman, where Fredy's job took them. They have lived there ever since, except for a year spent in hot, humid Houston.

Mary is a medical technologist. She received her degree from Carroll College in Helena. She worked for over ten years in clinics, and community and university hospital laboratories in both research and clinical laboratory medicine until she was forced into "early retirement" because of her illness.

Mary has had MS for 23 years. Her symptoms are mainly sensory, but she also has motor involvement. In addition to being a wife and mother, she is involved in school and community activities as her energies and limitations permit. She is continually fascinated with reading and writing, and never gets bored scrutinizing the puzzles and stories of her family history and genealogy. But, more than anything, Mary treasures the time spent with her loyal and supportive friends.

Ruth Greer
Carney, Michigan

—•—¤◆¤—•—

Ruth Greer is 47, and lives near Carney, in the Upper Peninsula of Michigan with her husband Bernie. They have been married 26 years, and have three grown children and three grandchildren.

Ruth lived most of her growing-up years in Indiana. She attended Indiana University. She worked for the telephone company, as well as for various newspapers, and then attended an apprenticeship program in medical records. For most of the past twenty-five years, she has worked as a medical secretary. She is still employed at a medical facility that allows flexible work hours.

Her other interests include drawing, sewing, crocheting, writing, and gardening. She has conducted seminars on overcoming the effects of childhood abuse. She does some volunteer work, and teaches art classes in local grade schools.

A few years ago, when her older children were in college, Ruth went back to school and earned a degree in Communications. That was such a positive experience, she went back to school last year when her younger son was in college, and took additional classes, where she was the first student to use an electric three-wheeler at the college. Now there are three students using the three-wheelers on campus, and the school has obtained one of its own for handicapped students and visitors to use.

In 1980, a car accident began a series of odd physical problems that have made life an adventure that is sometimes painful and bewildering. Relapsing-remitting MS, or "roller coaster living" as Ruth calls it, means that some days she walks and some days she lies in bed. Good humor is the key to keeping life balanced for her, but she is known for losing her keys! She is thankful for her husband, Bernie, whose love has been steady through many ups and downs, and for the beautiful view from her window.

O. Kathleen McCauley
Grand Island, Nebraska

Born in Oak Park, Illinois in the spring of 1952, Kathy lived in Illinois for twenty-seven years before moving to Nebraska in 1980.

After completing high school she spent an intensely full summer at The School of the Art Institute of Chicago, stoking a creative fire that burns to this day.

For many years she worked in nursing homes in social rehabilitation, "adopting" dozens of grandparents in the process. It was a bittersweet experience that served as a catalyst for prolific writing.

She now arranges and frames pressed flowers with antique ephemera for her very small business, Catlin's Garden.

When not working in her studio or caring for a large house, she pursues Victorian studies, writes, and collects antiques.

Kathy lives in Grand Island with her husband Bob and cat Guinness.

Lindy A. Newell
Seattle, Washington

—•—✠✦✠—•—

Lindy Newell was diagnosed with MS in 1973. She received her Masters degree from Whitworth College in 1978, and this enabled her to continue counseling other MS patients and their families through the difficult periods MS inevitably creates. Due to the fatigue MS often causes for her, she can only offer support over the telephone, but she derives great satisfaction doing so.

Writing has been a passion of hers for twenty-five years, and continues to play an important role in her life, as she becomes more disabled.

A native northwesterner, she has lived briefly outside the northwest, but always returns to that part of the country.

Ted–Luke Greene
Cheyenne, Wyoming

—•— ▦✦▤ —•—

Ted-Luke Greene is 49, and has been "wrestling" with MS for a known period of five years. His condition has been slowly deteriorating to the point of walking short periods with and without a cane, with wheelchair use for longer distances.

He has seen his writing as a skill he can sustain through his ups and downs with MS, and it serves as a major balance to the personal losses from the disease. He also feels that his past careers in social work and teaching are useful in his service to others.

He finds the calm life in Cheyenne a great help to his health, and enjoys the city with his wife and daughter.

Cecelia J. McGregor
Goshen, Indiana

Ms. McGregor is 40 years old, and has lived in the Midwest all of her life. Childhood through college years were spent in the state of Iowa, followed by residency in Indiana since her entrance into Notre Dame Law School (University of Notre Dame, South Bend, Indiana). She has been engaged in the practice of law for the past fourteen years. In 1984 she became Judge of the Goshen City Court, a position she has held since that time.

Ms. McGregor was diagnosed with MS in January, 1990 after a lengthy period of significant deterioration in her physical capabilities. She utilizes an electric wheelchair to enable her to maintain employment. She is visibly disabled in her gait and unstable movements, and has come to recognize that it is through this visible disability that she is able to show others that the disabled do have a rightful place in the public arena. She is deeply grateful to public officials who have provided her with facilities which reduce her burden in getting to and from work each day, and it is her desire to advocate for the disabled in whatever ways seem appropriate.

In addition to her work she enjoys conducting legal research projects, writing in areas of the law and otherwise, and engaging in sacred and meaningful experiences with staff and retreatants at a local retreat center. She feels very fortunate to be at this particular point in her life. She has been married for eighteen years, and has a 12 year-old son.

Caroline Paulson
New Paltz, New York

━•━ ✠ ━•━

Caroline Paulson lives quietly and independently accompanied by a menagerie of 6 dogs and cats. Prior to becoming disabled, she worked in Manhattan in the international petroleum business for Shell Oil and the National Oil Company of Venezuela. She suffered her first serious attack of MS while she was completing her studies for her B.A. at Columbia University. Despite this and numerous subsequent disabling attacks, she remained undiagnosed until after she had been declared legally disabled, 25 years after the onset of the disease.

Toni R. Tate
Memphis, Tennessee

—·—≖◆≕—·—

Toni R. Tate has lived in Memphis for all of her 32 years. She has been a registered nurse in the state of Tennessee since 1985. She was diagnosed with MS 2 months after she had received her nursing license, and subsequently to successfully completing the State Board examination. As exacerbations plagued her, she was eventually forced to leave her work in the Elvis Presley Memorial Trauma Center as an operating room nurse. Serving as a floor nurse in medical/surgical areas, she was able to continue to function in this capacity until 1991.

She met and fell in love with a wonderful man, Randy, in 1986 after a failed marriage. Together they are parenting two sons, ages 13 and 4. Toni is proud to say that she and her husband are in the process of buying a new home in the same in the same general area as that of the city's mayor.

She is grateful to have spent nearly seven years in a profession where she was truly needed. She plans to continue her education to receive a higher degree this fall at Memphis State University, and perhaps teach nursing students at a local college.

Glenn Liebensohn
Fairfield, Connecticut

Glenn Liebensohn is 40 years of age. He was diagnosed with MS the summer of 1984, when he was employed as a general manager of a large Connecticut corporation.

He is a self-taught guitarist/pianist and song writer, and has been involved in music since the age of 13. He toured with many well-known musicians in the 1970s, such as John Mayall, Edgar Winter, and REO Speedwagon.

Since his diagnosis with multiple sclerosis, he has used his musical talents to raise thousands of dollars for MS research. He is presently a paraplegic, and lives in a nursing home in Fairfield County, Connecticut.

Denni Evans
London, England

⊷ ⊶ ⊷

Denni Evans was born in 1953, and is a former community worker and founder of several housing cooperatives. In her time as a community worker she was instrumental in the founding and implementation of a number of organisations for and of the disabled, including the Centres for Independent Living in Greater London, Dial-a-Ride in Lewisham, and a local CRACK group (the young persons group of the MS Society.

She gave up full-time employment in order to maintain the level of health that she had achieved through her particular regime of self-management of MS. She is now concentrating on a writing career — as much as bringing up two small children will allow.

She lives in southeast London in a housing co-op house she had rehabilitated to her own specifications with her husband and children. She is presently working on her first novel.

Mary Martin Farrell
Seabeck, Washington

Mary Farrell is 39, and a native of Washington State. She lives on five acres of land with her husband, three dogs, and five cats. Her hobbies include sewing, quilting, camping, and bird watching.

Barbara B. McInturf
Columbus, Ohio

Barbara McInturf was born in Columbus, Ohio 40 years ago, and has lived there most of her life. After graduation from high school, she attended Ohio University in Athens, majoring in elementary education. Upon completion of her degree she taught for four years in the Morgan County school system. She then attended Ohio State University to study school counseling, receiving her Masters degree in 1979. She returned to Morgan County to teach one more year before getting married and moving back to Columbus. Barbara taught for three more years in the Groveport-Madison system before becoming pregnant.

She became "invisibly" disabled with multiple sclerosis while a junior in high school. Her condition has slowly progressed, and she now is confined to a wheelchair, being able to move only above her shoulders.

Mrs. McInturf is a very active member of the Bexley United Methodist Church, where she is a member of the Education Committee, the United Methodist Women, Priscilla Circle, and also Bible and study groups. She additionally volunteers several times a week at her daughter's school, tutoring children in subjects where help is needed. Her family enjoys traveling together, yard work, camping, and spending time with friends and other family members.

Barbara lost her mother August 7, 1992, and she dedicates her story in memory of her friend and mom, Gerry Basil.

Karin Summers
Shorewood, Wisconsin

—•—⊞•⊞—•—

Karin Summers, born in 1945 in Wisconsin, has lived the Midwest all of her life. After graduating from the University of Wisconsin – Oshkosh in 1970, she moved to upper Michigan where she began her professional social work career. In 1985, she began her graduate education, completing her Masters in Social Work in 1989 at the University of Wisconsin – Milwaukee.

She has worked for the last thirteen years in various community agencies and hospital programs, focusing on child welfare, alcoholism, and family treatment. She is now employed full-time by a major health care provider and medical school, working in a special research project committed to improving accessibility of health care services to needy populations.

Ms. Summers began pursuing free-lance writing in 1992, has had several articles published, and hopes to expand her writing efforts to short stories. Writing fills most of her free time, has been a great deal of work, but is also very rewarding.

She was diagnosed with multiple sclerosis in 1988, after living with inexplicable symptoms for eight years. With the exception of one short period of disability, she has remained employed full-time. She says her life is more active now than it has ever been, and in spite of (or perhaps because of) MS, she feels blessed.

J. D. Huxtable
Fairfield, Connecticut

J. D. Huxtable is 56, and has lived in Connecticut for most of her adult life. She was born in Ottawa, Canada, and her family moved to Toronto in 1948. She attended high school there, as well as Ryerson Tech. She has always been interested in textile design. She married in 1957, and she and her husband moved to the States. She studied at Parsons School of Design, and Fashion Institute of Technology, subsequently becoming a textile designer.

She has three daughters, of whom she is very proud. The oldest is married and living in San Juan, Puerto Rico, and is expecting the first grandchild! She and her husband have a very successful graphics design business. The second girl is an architect in Cincinnati, Ohio, having gone to Ohio University on full scholarship. The third girl lives in Cambridge, Massachusetts. She works for Harvard University, and attends Radcliff part-time to become a landscape designer.

In 1973, J. D. remarried a physician. She works on Medicare claims in the office, and on the computer at home by electronic transmission. She goes to the "Y" three times a week for "aquasize" exercise, and has recently started going to a physiotherapist twice a week to strengthen muscles in her leg to take over from the ones that are affected by MS. She is working very hard on that possibility.

She and her husband travelled a great deal before she was diagnosed, in locations such as England, Europe, Egypt, Israel, and Turkey. She is very grateful that they did so while it wasn't so difficult. In 1990 they went to Alaska with friends on a cruise in the Inland Passage from Vancouver to Alaska and back, which was glorious.

After the kids had left home, she, her husband, and their cat moved in early 1985 to a very spacious condominium with lots of room, which enables her to garden. It is a very well designed condominium situated on 40 acres, with lots of trees and not too many other townhouses.

Stacey Thompson
Paisley, Scotland

Stacey Thompson is 19 years old, and was born in Hamilton. She moved to Paisley when she was four, and has lived there since. She attended the University of Paisley, where she graduated with a B.Sc. in Biology in July, 1992.

Miss Thompson's first MS symptoms were noted at 15 years of age, and she was diagnosed at 16.

Even though she was diagnosed at a very young age, this hasn't stopped her living her life to the fullest extent, and she still hopes to travel world–wide.

She has already traveled extensively in Europe with her family, and in 1991 she and a friend backpacked through France. In 1992, she traveled to Corfu. Life continues to have tremendous enjoyment, and she looks forward to a happy and hopefully productive future with a challenging career.

/

The
MS Autobiography
Book

− order form −

The MS Autobiography Book is:
$9.95/copy (United States)
$12.95/copy (Canada)
$14.95/copy (other countries − surface mail)
$29.95/copy (other countries − air mail)

[WE REGRET THE HIGH COST OF AIR MAIL POSTAGE TO
OTHER COUNTRIES, BUT WE CANNOT, OF COURSE,
CONTROL SUCH ELEMENTS OF EXPENSE FOR OUR CUSTOMERS]

*Send orders with check or money order (U.S.A. only − no cash, please),
or an international money order payable in U.S. funds
for Canadian orders and orders for delivery to other countries to:*

Eric Smirnow
P.O. Box 581
Cedaredge, Colorado   81413
U.S.A.

Your Name:_____

Address:_____

City:_____

State:_____   Zip:_____

Country *(other than U.S.A.):* _____

Please send me:_____ book(s) at $_____ each.

Order Total:$_____

—— all orders are shipped postage paid ——